"The Great American Novel ——"

Books by CLYDE BRION DAVIS

THE ANOINTED

"THE GREAT AMERICAN NOVEL——"

"THE GREAT AMERICAN NOVEL——"

BY CLYDE BRION DAVIS

FARRAR & RINEHART
Incorporated
NEW YORK · TORONTO

TO MY MOTHER,

who likes this one better

Contents

"The Great American Novel ——"

1. Buffalo

MAY 12—JUNE 2, 1906. I remember hearing once about a child that was playing in a garden and a butterfly came along and brushed his cheek and how that incident changed the whole course of the boy's life. I forget what the child grew into, but it probably was a great general or poet or something.

I mention it here only to show that small things can change your life, and I suppose when I am 50 or 60 I shall look back at my youth and remember a day with Pete Buchtel and I shall realize that day directed my life into a different channel. That was eight years ago.

Pete Buchtel had a little Flobert rifle and he thought we could shoot some fish in the river. He thought we could go down to the river and shoot the fish when they came mouthing it to the surface and that if we killed a fish it would float to the top on its side and we could get it.

So we rode our bicycles down to the foot of Katharine Street where the Buffalo River makes a wide loop south. It was all weed-grown fields and railroad tracks down there at that time, with no houses or buildings within a quarter of a mile except for the mill and blast towers of the Buffalo Union Furnace Company.

It was about 7 o'clock in the evening when we got down there and everything was quiet, the workmen having gone home from the furnace plant. So we cracked away with the rifle a dozen times or more at bubbles in the sluggish current, but no dead fish came to the surface. Then we began to get discouraged.

After a while Pete looked around and pointed to a pile of wooden boxes in a field belonging to the furnace company. These boxes were a couple of long blocks from the mill itself and at least a hundred yards from us and because there was a little evening mist in the air the boxes looked even farther away, although you could see there was some red printing on their sides. Pete and I didn't think anything about what might be in the boxes. Anybody would have taken them to be empty junk boxes that had been dumped out there to burn or to give to poor people for kindling wood because they were out there so far from everything else with just a sagging old barb-wire fence around the field.

Pete said, "I bet you a nickel I can hit the top box from here."

I didn't think his little Flobert rifle would carry that far and we had been shooting .22 shorts which are cheap but not very accurate. But Pete had a .22 long in his pocket which he slipped into the gun without telling me or I probably never would have made the bet, and I, thinking he was shooting a .22 short, said, "All right, you're on. I'll bet you a nickel you can't."

Pete spread his skinny, long legs apart to get a steady support and pushed his long, blond hair out of his eyes and squinted up his lean, homely face and took careful aim. I looked off at the pile of boxes just as Pete pulled the trigger.

While I was looking the boxes disappeared before my eyes in a quick white flash topped by a billow of cottony smoke. Then Pete and I were struck by something like a man's hand cuffing a couple of small bugs and knocked flat on the ground.

I sat up right away and saw my bicycle wandering in a crazy way off from the sapling where I had rested it and it wobbled about eight feet before it toppled over with a crash

of pedals. The air was full of dust and little green leaves from
the saplings. Blood was running down from my nose.

Pete was sitting up too, and his face was gray with dust
and his overalls were covered with dirt and dead sticks and
grass. He looked very frightened. He said, "Holy Mother,"
and his voice sounded faint and strange because I had been
deafened for a moment by the shock.

"What was it?" I asked.

"We've played h— some way," said Pete. "Let's get away
from here."

I looked over at the furnace plant and where there had
been a row of windows there now was only a row of black
oblongs with the glass entirely gone. From around the side
of the plant an old man came running. One leg was stiff, but
he was running the best he could and he was yelling at us.

"We better jigger," Pete said. "Come on."

I was wiping my bloody nose while we ran for our bicycles.
Pete's rear tire was flat. It was an old tire and probably had
a slow leak that the shock loosened.

Carrying his rifle in one hand, Pete got on his wheel in
spite of the flat tire and tried to ride through the weeds toward
Katharine Street, but he hadn't bumped a hundred feet over
the rough ground before the flat tire came off the rim and
threw him.

All this time the old man was hobbling across the field as
fast as he could, screaming and yelling, and when it became
quite plain that Pete couldn't ride his bicycle I noticed what
the old man was saying. He was yelling, "Stop, in the name
of the law!" Being a night watchman, he had a tin badge on
his vest and he was a special policeman.

"You're under arrest," he shouted when he had crawled
through the wire fence.

"What for?" Pete asked.

"What for? Why, Almighty G—, if it ain't murder you'll
be lucky." The old man grabbed both our arms. "What for?

You've blowed up seven hundred sticks of dynamite. You've wrecked the plant. You've done God knows what all. You've been trespassing where you had no business and it'd been a mercy if you both was blowed to glory for your pains."

"We didn't do any trespassing," I said. "We haven't been inside that fence, ever."

Then he looked down at Pete's Flobert. "Oh," he said, "you shot the dynamite with that gun. You set it off that way."

"How was we to know it was dynamite?" Pete asked. "What you have your old dynamite piled way out there for?"

"Yeah," I put in, "how were we to know? It just looked like a pile of old boxes."

"You come with me while I call the police wagon," said the old man. "You got no business shooting down here at any time. You got no business being down here. You got no business having a gun. And I'll catch h— because I didn't happen to see you before you did it."

He started pulling us toward the plant, but before we got there Katharine Street was full of people tearing down to see what had happened. There were people on bicycles and in buggies and running on foot, and presently there came a fire wagon with bell clanging and horses galloping and then a police patrol wagon full of gray-helmeted policemen and there were six or eight newspaper reporters and a couple of photographers with their big Graflex cameras.

So the regular police took Pete and me into custody and the whole crowd of us went over in the field to see the hole the dynamite made. It measured 8 feet deep and 16 feet across and we found out later that the explosion broke windows for more than half a mile and made the whole city rock like an earthquake.

At the Louisiana Street police station they finally let me go because I wasn't 15 years old yet and because it wasn't my gun and because I hadn't fired the shot. Pete, who was 17, was held on a charge of malicious mischief, but got off finally with a suspended sentence.

But the reason for me writing about this experience is this:

There was an amazing lot of excitement over this explosion because everyone in town had heard it and wondered what had happened. And when the police turned me loose a reporter for the *Morning Journal* cornered me. His name was Hartley.

"Bud," he said, "the *Journal* wants you to write your own story of this explosion. You just tell me about it. Just tell me everything—how it looked and what you thought and all and I'll write it in your own words. It'll be printed under your name and I'll give you two dollars."

So I told him everything and the next morning, along with the main account of the explosion, there was my story with *"By Homer Zigler"* in black type at the top. And Hartley gave me two silver dollars, which made me a clean profit of $1.95 after I paid Pete Buchtel the nickel I bet and lost although there was no way to know for sure Pete hit the top box instead of any box in the pile and besides Pete admitted he used a .22 long cartridge instead of the .22 short I thought he was using.

So a prank which might easily have ruined my life and which might easily have killed a lot of people gave me my first real ambition.

That story with "By Homer Zigler" over it fascinated me. As a matter of fact, the reporter Hartley fascinated me too. He was a handsome, devil-may-care sort of fellow with a loud, checkered cap and a very high linen collar.

And I got to thinking that a newspaper reporter led the most interesting life imaginable. Where anything was happening, there was the reporter as fast as he could go, digging into all interesting phases so he could relay the story to the public at large. It was much better than being a policeman, because the reporter was excused from such disagreeable jobs as dragging drunken men down to jail. Besides, I had no hope of growing large enough to be a policeman. And a reporter was at the front during all celebrations and political meetings. He got to meet all the prominent people that came to town and he was privileged to write how they acted and what they said.

Most important, though, was the fact I had read that many of the most famous novelists had been journalists. For years I had been more or less a bookworm. From the time I was a little boy I had made a practice of walking from our home on Peach Street in the "Fruit Belt" down to the big brownstone library in Lafayette Square after books. And by the time I was 13 or 14 I had a vague ambition to write books and stories myself someday. But this ambition was as secret as it was vague. My father, who was foreman at the Queen City Brass Works, considered storybooks nonsense. He frequently was out of patience with me because I had my "nose buried in a book" so often. My mother also had little use for storybooks. My two sisters and older brother read little and consequently gave little sympathy to my "mooning over some fairy tale."

So it happened that Frances Harbach was the first person in whom I ever confided my aspirations. Frances encouraged me.

I have been in love with Fran since I was 16 years old— the year after the dynamite explosion. I now am 23 and have been a reporter on the *Journal* for more than a year.

My ambition to become a novelist no longer is a vague thing. It is very real. I am directing my thoughts and my reading to the purpose of preparing myself for that career and that is my reason for writing this record.

I shall keep here my thoughts and experiences and impressions and reactions for later use, for, after all, any good novel I think is merely the distillation of the author's own experiences. I have found that when interesting and even exciting

experiences heap themselves upon one, day by day, one is inclined to lose the true flavor of minor incidents stored away
in his memory. Each new adventure and each new impression
tends to lessen the sharpness of earlier memories. Therefore,
I must put incidents down in black and white at their true
value before they become tarnished by time.

I now have a splendid opportunity to study and to learn
life. I have analyzed myself carefully and I know my weaknesses and I know my strengths. I know I have no head for
business, but I feel certain I have a certain facility for writing
which will develop as I grow more experienced with the tools
of my trade and I know I am more observing than most men
and probably more sensitive to impressions. I have a sympathy
for people and an ability for putting myself in the other fellow's shoes and I also believe I sense the dramatic possibilities
of a situation.

At present it doesn't seem possible that I ever could forget
even the smallest item of my association with Frances. It
would seem almost unnecessary to write about Fran, except
that she is so all-important, except that she must play a leading role in anything I may accomplish. As a matter of fact,
it is to Fran's credit that I have traveled as far as I have gone.

We have been sweethearts since our second year in high
school. Since then, I believe I can say truthfully, she never
has been out of my thoughts for more than a few minutes.
Everything I see, everything I do, is important only in that
it may seem important to Fran.

It has been so since that September day in second year
English when she took a seat across the aisle from me. She
was wearing a starchy wash dress of red, orange and brown.
And her lead pencil rolled from her desk as she was adjusting
her books and papers. When I picked up the pencil from the
floor I saw the lead was broken and I resharpened it and
handed it back to her. Then I saw her hair was almost the
same color as the slick, yellow lead pencil. She smiled and

thanked me. It was a warm, friendly smile, but not in the least coquettish. It was more the frank sort of smile one boy might give another. But her eyes were the color of the summer sky down in the Allegheny Mountains, away from the lake, and they made me think of a hilltop with a far vista of the sea and of something that happened so long ago that it well may have been in another existence.

From that moment I have loved Fran. But from that moment, also, I have realized my own unworthiness of her.

Fran is very beautiful. I am not. I am afraid I am slightly below the average in height. I am dark and sallow and thin. My nose is too large. My mouth is too wide and the lips too thick. My chin is not big enough. But in spite of all this I believe Fran really loves me. Since that day after school when she praised a theme I had written and I confessed to her that I hoped someday to become a writer, she has encouraged me in that direction. She had faith in me when I was fired as a bookkeeper. She encouraged me to leave the comparative security of a streetcar conductor job to become a reporter. She reads everything I write in the *Journal*, gives me wise criticism when I need it and praises me when I have praise coming. She tells me she is sure I shall become a novelist of the Irving Bacheller type—which is exactly the goal at which I am aiming.

Fran and I are not formally engaged, but it is tacitly understood we shall get married when I am making $12 a week.

But I must record a little more background on myself for in later years even that might become dim. During two school vacations I worked with my father at the brassworks, but showed little aptitude. It was after this second session that my father told me it was about time I made up my mind what I was going to make of myself. So I told him I should like to go to college and prepare myself to become a journalist and he flew into a rage.

Newspapermen, he declared, were a drunken, shiftless lot of deadbeats. It seems he had known two newspapermen, or former newspapermen, who fitted that description. And college, he swore, ruined young men by filling their heads with impractical nonsense.

My father has a lot of force. He is a good foreman. If I myself had my father's aggressiveness and determination I probably should not have given in to his ideas. I probably should have worked my way through college. I probably should have avoided being swayed into courses I ought not to have taken.

When it became apparent that I had no real talents for mechanical work, there was but one logical alternative—to my father's mind. I must become an office worker, apply myself and become a business executive.

To this end, after I was graduated from high school, my father financed a year at a business college. Then I obtained a job as assistant bookkeeper at the Washburn-Crosby mill. But I had no head for figures, despite my business college training, and I had been working only two months when I made a serious error in simple addition and was fired.

With no reference from my late employer and with my school reference now outlawed, it proved impossible to get further work as a bookkeeper. For months I lived in an acute misery of realized incompetence. I worked at odd jobs when I could find them. I tried selling scented toilet soap from door to door and failed at that also. I think I should have left home and become a tramp had it not been for Fran. My mother was sympathetic, but her sympathy was tempered with, "Goodness knows, I've tried to teach you to be orderly. Don't know what more I could have done than I've already done." And my father grew openly contemptuous of me.

Fran, however, kept assuring me that I was smart in spite of everything, that I should find something soon that suited me better than bookkeeping. She was right. I became a streetcar conductor. And I really liked it. There is something exciting about being a streetcar conductor, about mingling with crowds of people, making change quickly, giving transfers, jerking the bell rope two clicking ding-dings to go ahead, moving, moving, always traveling.

This International Railway job was a fine antidote for the state of mind I had slipped into. Even the cap and uniform were good, for they gave me a sense of belonging to something, of being a part of a mighty system. When a passenger asked some question about operation, I could answer *"we"* do thus and so.

Particularly I liked the owl car job, tearing through the dark residence districts in the small hours of the morning while all the rest of the world slept, picking up passengers at outlying corners coming from unknown missions of intrigue or tragedy. And I heard strange stories from men, mellowed and garrulous after a night of conviviality.

Yes, I might have stayed on that job always except that I realized the time would come soon enough when I should have nothing to show for my life's work but a row of gold stars on my sleeve. It was Frances again who caused me to make the break.

"After all, Homer," she said, "you want to be a writer and you'll never do anything about it as long as you're a streetcar conductor."

I had dropped by her house in the evening on my way to work. We were sitting on her front steps, me with my conductor's cap on the back of my head and my lunch pail between my knees.

"Well, I'm learning something of life," I said.

"Yes," she argued, "but the world from a streetcar isn't such a big place. And you won't learn to write about it when you're working twelve hours a day as a conductor. You won't have a chance."

One important reason why I wished to remain with the

I.R.C. was that I was saving money and I had hopes it might not be long before Fran and I could be married. But I saw she was telling the truth and it made me feel gloomy.

Neither of us said anything for a little while. Then she smiled. Her teeth are very white and there is a little space between her two front teeth which makes her smile distinctive and even more attractive. She took hold of my arm.

"Homer," she said, "why don't you get a newspaper reporter job?"

"For goodness' sake," I said, almost dropping my lunch pail, "you know I'd like to do that. But how can I?"

"How does anybody get a newspaper job?" she asked.

"I don't know. When they haven't had any experience, I suppose they must have friends who—"

"Well, I suppose so . . . But I bet you can write better than most of the beginners."

"It'd be fine if you were the editor, Fran. But you've got to have experience to get a job and you can't get experience without a job."

"It wouldn't hurt to try."

"Well, I know how it'd be. Just some more, 'no openings now, but I'll take your name.' "

"Homer—"

"Yes."

"I've been studying the newspapers. You know they have a pattern for writing?"

"What do you mean by pattern?"

"Well," she said, "I mean if you study the items in a newspaper you'll see they write everything according to a pattern. You read several papers that have written up the same thing and you'll see what I mean. They'll be different in a way, but all the papers will give all the important facts in the very first paragraph or maybe even in the first sentence. Then they just keep elaborating these facts for the rest of the story and telling the particulars."

She went in and got a paper and showed me what she meant by the "pattern" or the formula of newswriting. And she had an idea for me.

"Why don't you," she asked, "take some papers and rewrite some of their news items in your own words, but following their general pattern? I'll bet it wouldn't take you long to be writing better than most of their reporters."

"But it wouldn't mean anything," I objected.

"It'd mean you had learned their pattern," she said.

"Then what?"

"Then you could take some samples of your work and go down to see the editors on afternoons before you go to work. And you could tell them what you'd been doing and I'll bet somebody will give you a job. You'd show you had ambition and enterprise and employers like that in a young man."

Well, I wasn't entirely convinced. But Fran kept after me and I started rewriting news stories from old newspapers and showing the results to Fran. And when she thought I had progressed sufficiently I went down to the *Morning Journal* office one afternoon. I picked the *Journal* primarily because I thought the reporter Hartley might remember me from the day of the dynamite explosion and help me out with the editor.

Hartley, however, had been gone from the *Journal* so long that he was practically forgotten. So I was sent to John Penny, the city editor, with no introduction.

Mr. Penny was busy for a minute or so and I stood beside his desk looking around the room. It amazed me. I had been led to believe that all large offices must be neat and filled with dignified gentlemen working in alpaca jackets such as was the case at the Washburn-Crosby office and other places I visited while looking for employment as a bookkeeper.

But the *Morning Journal* editorial office was the antithesis of any of these. To begin with, it is a ramshackle place that quivers ominously when the presses are running. Along one side was a row of office doors for department editors, separated from the main room by a haphazard partition. There were wastebaskets, but they were little used. The floor was littered with torn newspapers and sheets of copy paper. Mr. Penny, coatless, was wearing black protectors over his striped shirt sleeves and a green eyeshade at a rakish angle on his tousled head. A little way from the city desk a man was sitting with his hat on and his feet comfortably propped on a rickety typewriter table while he smoked a corncob pipe and languidly perused an afternoon paper. Telephones were ringing, men were talking loudly and profanely. There was an air of tenseness, but also an air of immense informality and relaxation.

John Penny is no larger than I and no whit handsomer. I feel that this was a distinct advantage for me. Usually John Penny is pretty bluff and short with strangers, but he treated me with great sympathy and kindness. He listened to my story and he read some of my samples. Then he grinned up at me with tobacco-stained teeth.

"All right, Zigler," he said, "if you're d— fool enough to want to try this crazy business, I'll give you enough rope to hang yourself. If you want to give up a good I.R.C. conductor's job, you can start here Monday at seven dollars a week."

That was more than a year ago, and I never have regretted the change.

Of course Fran was delighted that I got the job, but she was a little disappointed that I hadn't tried one of the afternoon papers first. While I am working nights we can have only one night out together each week.

For myself, while I certainly could wish to see Fran more, I never before dreamed that any work could be so utterly fascinating as this last year has been. In the afternoon when one goes to work, one never knows what new experiences, what new excitements the night may hold. Of course some nights are comparatively dull. But there are others which would stand out as high spots in the average individual's entire life.

I have met and talked with and interviewed many prominent and interesting men, but the outstanding experience in that line came this spring on April 18. It was an experience which I am sure will affect my life profoundly.

Late in the afternoon Mr. Penny called me and said William Jennings Bryan was in town. Mr. Penny was laughing. It seemed that the Great Commoner apparently had dropped off in Buffalo to see Norman Mack, who not only is Democratic national committeeman, but publisher of the *Buffalo Times,* which, of course, is a Democratic newspaper. But Mr. and Mrs. Mack didn't happen to be at home.

"Zig," said Mr. Penny, "Old Silver Tongue is up to no good here. He slipped into town secretly and went right out to Norman Mack's home. Norman and Hattie didn't know he was coming and were over in Utica. Of course they're on a train by now and coming h— for leather back to Buffalo, but we've got a chance to interview Bryan alone before the Macks get back. Cab driver that took Silver Tongue and wife from the Exchange Street station is a friend of mine and gave me the tip."

"Yes, sir," I said, and doubled up some copy paper and put it in my pocket.

"Here, wait a minute," said Mr. Penny. "This is mighty important. Bryan has been awful silent on whether he's going to run again in nineteen-eight. It may be that's what he's here for now. Maybe he's going to talk things over with Mack. Maybe Mack will break the news in tomorrow's *Times* that Bryan will consent to take his third licking. But there's a bare chance that if Silver Tongue has made up his mind he might be anxious to break the glad tidings and will spill the news to us—if it's put up to him right."

"Yes, sir," I said, starting to leave his desk.

"Whoa!" called Mr. Penny, "wait a minute. Listen here, Zig—this is a big opportunity for you. Fleming ordinarily would handle this, but he's sick. It's up to you. Now, skiddoo and get it."

So I scorched out Delaware Avenue on my bicycle to the Mack home and a hired girl answered the door. I have learned that you mustn't be polite to hired girls at houses or they will cause you much trouble. You mustn't even tip your hat to them at the door or they will swell up with importance and play the fine lady on you. So I spoke to this Mack hired girl in a brusque manner: "Tell Mr. Bryan that Mr. Zigler is here to see him."

"Yes, sir," she said. "Won't you step inside?"

I moved into the big dark hall, which was cluttered with furniture and mirrors, while the hired girl hitched up a fold of petticoats in each hand and went up the wide, winding staircase. Presently she came swishing down again and said, "Won't you wait in the parlor, sir? Mr. Bryan will be down in a moment."

So I went into the parlor and sat down in a big, soft leather chair. It was a very fine room with a thick, heavy art square on the floor, for Mr. Mack is a millionaire or close to it, and there were a number of large, dark oil paintings in gilt frames and other large gilt frames with mirrors in them and quite a few heavy leather chairs and some frail gilt chairs and other furniture that I should have made notes on but didn't because I was so busy trying to think of what I should ask Mr. Bryan.

It wasn't long before he came down. It was the first time I had ever seen him. But if I had been a Chinaman and had never even heard of him, I should have known immediately that here was a very great person. There was that about him which stamped him as extraordinary. You would have felt it had he been dressed in farmer's overalls and carrying a manure fork. You would have felt it had you met him in a coal mine. An aura of greatness hangs over Mr. Bryan.

The Commoner is tall and broad-shouldered and he moves with the vigor of youth despite the fact he is nearly fifty years old. His hair is black, his mouth wide and thin and firm. His dark eyes are the keenest and most penetrating eyes I have ever seen. He was wearing a black frock coat with silken lapels. His tie was a black string tie carelessly bowed. But his shirt was just a plain dollar shirt with black stripes.

"What can I do for you, Mr. — Zigler, isn't it?" he asked. He shook hands with the grip of a blacksmith.

"Yes," I said, "Homer Zigler. Mr. Bryan, I want to ask you if you'll be a candidate in nineteen-eight?"

He looked at me in surprise and raised his heavy black eyebrows. Then he laughed, and his deep musical voice filled the house. I felt myself blushing red because I knew I had been very clumsy and undiplomatic and perhaps rude to boot.

"Who sent you to ask that?" he demanded.

"The *Morning Journal*," I said. "I am a reporter."

Mr. Bryan slapped me on the shoulder in a friendly way. "Pray be seated," he said. "How's my old friend Bill Conners?"

"Well," I answered, sitting again in the big leather chair and taking out my pencil and paper, "I think he's quite well. But Mr. Conners is the *Enquirer,* you know."

"Oh, to be sure." Mr. Bryan laughed heartily again. "To be sure. You're with the *Journal.* That's the Buffalo paper which prints cartoons of me as a serpent."

I looked down in embarrassment. I didn't know whether I should tell Mr. Bryan the truth, which was that I personally was not in sympathy with the political policies of my newspaper, or whether that would give the impression of being disloyal to my employer.

The Commoner sensed my discomfit, however, and kindly came to my aid.

"Oh, that's all right, my boy," he said. "All is fair in love, war and politics, I suppose. And you can quote me as saying my visit to Buffalo is quite without political significance. My wife and I are on our way to Europe on a pleasure tour, but I couldn't pass through Buffalo without stopping to pay my compliments to my very dear friend, Norman E. Mack."

I wrote this down on my copy paper. Mr. Bryan watched me. Then he asked, "What's the latest word from San Francisco?"

"We just got a report," I said, "that a fourth of the city is in flames. We hear there are probably more than a thousand dead."

Mr. Bryan shook his head sorrowfully. "Terrible, terrible thing," he said. "There are many wicked people in San Francisco, many dens of deepest iniquity. But it is difficult for us to understand why the innocent must suffer with the guilty."

He matched the tips of his strong, white fingers together and looked at me inquiringly.

"Will you say," I asked, "what man you might favor as the Democratic candidate?"

He smiled broadly and shook his head. "Not a word on politics," he said. "Not a word. Anything else you wanted to ask me?"

For a moment I was at a loss. Here I was, alone with the Great Commoner, to my mind the greatest living American, with a perfect opportunity for an outstanding interview, an interview that might be carried by the press wires to the farthest corner of America—and I couldn't think of anything to ask. I could feel perspiration running down the insides of my arms in shame at my horrible inadequacy.

Finally I blurted out lamely, "Mr. Bryan, have you any advice to offer young men?"

Of course that was a very bad question. With ninety-nine out of a hundred public men the answer would have been something equally trite. For instance, he might have said, "Be honest and industrious and save your money."

But Mr. Bryan's bigness saved me. His cream-smooth voice

took on a soft, intimate tone. "Well," he said, "let us take young Mr. Zigler, for instance. What advice could I offer him? Do you wish to become an editor someday?"

"I'd rather," I told him, "become a great writer—if I have it in me. Of course I'm not certain I have the ability, but my ambitions lie in that direction."

He smiled—not in ridicule, but in friendliness. "I believe," he said, "the mere fact that your ambition takes such a turn is evidence that you have talents in that line. But don't underrate yourself—even in the interests of modesty. Don't underrate yourself to anybody. My father used to say if a man has the big head it can be whittled down. But if he has the little head, there's no hope for him.

"If you don't believe you can do big things, you'll never attempt to do them. A person who lacks faith in himself never attempts anything and therefore cannot possibly succeed. A person with great faith will attempt the seemingly impossible and frequently he will accomplish the seemingly impossible too."

I cannot express the charm of Mr. Bryan's speaking voice. Sometimes it is so soft as to be almost a caressing whisper. Then, without apparent effort, his voice booms in the ears like a full brass band bearing down on a final chord. But always his voice has the quality of being convincing in itself. I mean the mere sound of it is convincing, without thought of the words it conveys or of the keen logic of the mind back of it.

"But, my friend," he went on, leaning slightly forward in his chair, "you can't have faith in your ability unless you are conscious that you are prepared for your work. Prepare yourself for your writing by reading and studying the masters who have gone before you. And probably the most necessary part of your preparation is a high purpose. I might ask just why you wish to become a great writer. Is it for mere self-glorification and the satisfaction of being a success? Or is it

because you believe you have a message which will make this
world of men a better place in which to live?"

"I suppose," I said, "that it's a little of both."

He smiled. "You cannot," he declared, "afford to put a
low purpose in competition with a high one. If you go to
work with a purely selfish standpoint you will be ashamed
to stand in the presence of those who have higher aims and
nobler purposes."

Mr. Bryan rose from his chair. His eyes were glowing as
he turned and sank his fingers into the leather chair back.

"But the faith in yourself is not enough," he said in a
reverberating whisper. "You must have faith in God. If you
have faith in God and the ultimate triumph of the right,
nobody can set a limit to your achievements. Have you faith
in God? Have you faith in the Christ who died on the cross
that you and I should have eternal life?"

I felt oddly warm and dizzy under his burning eyes. I felt
exalted, lifted to the stars on terms of equality with the gods
of the heavens.

Mr. Bryan paused for a moment, caught a glimpse of himself in a gilt-framed mirror and straightened his string tie.
Then he continued, his voice almost a chant, caressing each
single word as it left his lips:

"If the Father deigns to touch with divine power the cold
and pulseless heart of the buried acorn and make it burst
from its prison walls, will he leave neglected in the earth the
soul of man, made in the image of his Creator?

"My young friend, one day last summer I was eating a
piece of watermelon and I was struck by the beauty of it.
I took some of the seeds and dried them and found it would
require five thousand of them to make a pound. Then I
applied mathematics to that forty-pound melon.

"One of those seeds, put into the ground, when warmed
by the sun and moistened by the rain, takes off its coat and
goes to work. From somewhere, it gathers two hundred thou-

sand times its own weight and, forcing the raw material through a tiny stem, it constucts a watermelon.

"It ornaments the outside with a covering of green. Inside the green it puts a layer of white and within the white a core of red and all through the red it scatters seeds, each one capable of continuing the work of reproduction.

"Where does that little seed get its tremendous power? Where does it find its coloring matter? Where does it find its flavoring extract?

"Until you, my friend, can explain a watermelon, do not feel that you can set limits to the power of the Almighty. You and I cannot explain a watermelon, but we can eat it and enjoy it. You and I cannot explain the smallest thing about this wonderful world in which we live. But we can live in it and enjoy it and praise the Creator who made it. We can have faith. We must have faith. There is no other reasonable course open. Prepare yourself for your work and then have faith in your ability, with God's help, to do it. Have faith in your God and there will be no limits to your achievements."

I was still under the spell of the Great Commoner's magic when I got back to the office. I felt that I had an interview more lasting in its effect than if Mr. Bryan had declared himself a candidate for the presidency at this time. But Mr. Penny was swamped with work and lost all interest when I told him Mr. Bryan refused to comment on politics.

I wrote, however, about a column of my interview and turned it in. None of it was printed—only a paragraph to the effect that Mr. and Mrs. William J. Bryan were Buffalo visitors briefly while on their way to Europe and that Mr. Bryan refused to deny or confirm reports that he would be a candidate in 1908.

Of course I was much disappointed at the moment. But I realize the *Journal* is not sympathetic to Mr. Bryan politically. And on that day there was little room in the paper for anything except news of the San Francisco earthquake and fire.

However, there is little doubt in my mind that this interview, which never was printed, has had a more profound influence on me than any other single event in my life.

I may never make use of Mr. Bryan's words in my novel. But the effect of them will last with me always. First, and foremost, I shall make most certain that I am fully prepared before I ever set out on my real lifework.

In my year as a newspaper reporter I have interviewed several other prominent men, but they were as chaff blown in the wind. Probably the most famous of these was Admiral George Dewey, hero of Manila Bay.

Admiral Dewey was here to make a speech and I interviewed him at Hotel Lafayette. He is scarcely taller than I, but quite bulky. He seemed pompous and imperious. I did not like him.

I tried to talk to him about the destruction of the Spanish fleet in the Philippines.

"Everybody knows about that," he blurted. "Happened eight years ago. Every school child knows all about it. Silly to write anything more.

"What the papers need to print is that Admiral Dewey says we need a bigger navy. Write that. Write that Admiral Dewey says we need more ships and more men. We're rich and we can afford it."

I said, "Admiral, don't you think we have a pretty good navy now?"

He twisted one prong of his big white mustache and glared at me. When he is thinking about something else Admiral Dewey is a rather placid and comfortable-looking man. But he fancies himself as a fierce old sea dog. So he looked fierce at me and growled, "Pretty good! Fellow, I'll have you understand the United States has got the best navy in the world."

"Well," I asked, "why, then, do we need a bigger navy?"

He shook his head in disgust. "We've got to have a still bigger navy because we're the richest nation on earth. The whole world is jealous of us. And we've got to keep them afraid. But one of our American ships is equal to two of most nations'. Take our enlisted men. They're all young Americans. You know what that means?"

"Well," I said, "I suppose—"

He interrupted me. He hadn't asked the question to find out what I thought. He wasn't a bit interested in what I thought about anything. He made that quite plain.

"It means," he said, "that if all the officers in the fleet were killed the enlisted men could fight the ships and do it successfully. The United States navy takes only the cream of the nation's youth."

He looked me up and down pointedly. "The navy will take no skinny, undersized men. A man lacking in bodily vigor is usually lacking in mental vigor. The navy wants only those young men who may work up to command. A man has got to be well-nigh perfect physically before he even gets by the recruiting officer."

Of course I was there to meet a great man and to get an interview, but it seemed to me he was making a deliberate attempt to affront me because of my physical limitations. So I looked him up and down pointedly also. And I said, "I presume, Admiral, that must be a rather recent ruling?"

My sarcasm was lost. "Not at all," he said, "not at all. That ruling has been a tradition with the United States navy. It used to be iron men and wooden ships. Now it is steel men and steel ships."

It all seemed somewhat silly. To me it seems that building more and more battleships is like putting a chip on your shoulder and daring somebody to knock it off. The nations of the world are growing to understand one another. Education is dissipating the old fog of international distrust and

jealousy. Christianity is spreading. I am convinced there
never will be another war of consequence.

People are learning how insane war is. I really don't believe the young men of the world could be induced to enlist
for a war in these modern times. And they couldn't have a
war without soldiers.

My greatest success in the newspaper business came early
last month quite by accident. I mean an actual physical accident. I had been off the night before and Fran and I went
roller skating at the Coliseum on Edward and Main streets.
We were skating double pretty fast when one of Fran's skates
came unfastened. I tried to save her, but we both went down
and I struck my knee sharply on her loose skate.

The next day my knee was swollen and it was quite painful to ride my bicycle. So, when Mr. Penny sent me out on
Broadway to get a picture of a prominent Polish woman who
had died, I took the streetcar.

As a result of this chance I received high compliments
from Mr. Penny and my second increase in salary—which
brings me up to $9 a week.

While waiting for the trolley car on the return trip I witnessed a tragedy which proved to be the culmination of a
woman's conscientious efforts to keep herself pure against the
attempts of an unscrupulous man to ruin her.

The woman, Mrs. Francisca Skrocka, was 30 years old and
pretty in a heavy, Slavic way. She had just come from the
Broadway market and was carrying a basket filled with groceries. The man, John Korycinski, was a slim, dark fellow of
about her age. He was following her along the street and
talking earnestly to her in Polish.

They passed me in this manner. And, because the woman
seemed angry, I turned and watched them. When they were
25 or 30 feet up the sidewalk, the woman turned on him.
Her face was flushed and she said loudly in English, "Go
away! Don't want anything to do with you."

Then she started walking rapidly away. For a moment the man stood as if undecided what to do. He pushed his derby hat to the back of his head. Then he reached into his pocket and as he ran after the woman I caught a glint of something in his hand. My first impression was that he had drawn a knife. Then a shot rang out. It didn't sound especially loud, for an outbound streetcar was passing at the moment and the street was noisy otherwise with the clop of truck horse hooves and the chug of automobiles.

Korycinski was quite close to the woman when he fired into her back and as she fell face forward he fired again. The market basket dropped on the sidewalk with a splintering sound. A head of cabbage bounced out and rolled slowly off the sidewalk into the gutter. Again he fired at the prone body before him, but even at that distance the bullet missed, struck the flagstones and, richocheting, crashed through the front window of Z. Z. Kielawa's pharmacy.

People came running from all directions, but stopped short at sight of the tall, dark man with the nickeled revolver in his hand. He stood as if in a trance, gazing down at the woman he had killed. Presently he straightened and looked at the circle of horrified people around him. He said nothing. But he smiled with a flash of white teeth and then for the first time, I noticed he had a toothpick in the corner of his mouth.

He raised the revolver slowly and peered at it as if he had never seen it before. Then with his left hand he very deliberately unbuttoned his coat.

He turned the barrel of the gun against his own chest, fired a bullet into his heart and fell dead at the feet of the woman whose love he had been unable to win. His derby hat rolled into the gutter and lay beside the head of cabbage.

I found out their story from the woman's husband. Stanley Skrocka, while living in Altoona, Pa., had believed Korycinski to be his friend. Not realizing the man's true nature, he had brought him home to dinner. That was a fatal mistake. Kory-cinski immediately had become infatuated with Mrs. Skrocka and, having no moral sensibilities, paid violent court to her at every opportunity. Mrs. Skrocka resisted him to the best of her ability.

Then one day Stanley Skrocka came home unexpectedly and found his supposed friend with his wife. They were not in the living room of their four-room house, nor in the kitchen.

Skrocka drove Korycinski from the house with a shotgun. "I should have shot the —. I should have shot him," he told me, tearfully. And Mrs. Skrocka, nearly hysterical with grief and humiliation, begged her husband to take her away from Altoona where Korycinski could not find them, declaring that, while she had done nothing wrong yet, Korycinski was hypnotizing her, was casting a spell over her.

Skrocka moved his wife to Buffalo, but Korycinski discovered their whereabouts and followed them. He had obtained employment in the Broadway market, feeling that sooner or later she would come there to make purchases. He guessed right. And I witnessed the tragic denouement.

Life often is stark and ugly. I feel, somehow, that there is tremendous drama in a case like this. But, of course, the real story cannot be written. The implication would be left that the woman still would be alive had she given in to the man's importunities. And literature worthy of the name must have a wholesome moral. Its purpose is to make the world better.

Suppose a novelist were acquainted with conditions among the mining people of Altoona, Pa., and with the customs of Polish-Americans. Suppose he set out to write the story of a woman like Mrs. Francisca Skrocka, relating her early child-hood and the minor family climaxes, and her dreams and hopes and finally the love story of Francisca and Stanley Skrocka.

That much would be all right. But I doubt if the novel

would be especially significant or even very interesting. The real drama enters with John Korycinski and it could not be written. If a novelist were so uncouth and possessed of so little moral sense that he should write of illicit love, his book would be barred from the public libraries and he would be ostracized by society.

I admit that I find myself fascinated by the hopelessness, by the inevitability of Mrs. Skrocka's fate. It is as Frances says, I suppose, that I have a morbid streak in my nature which I must conquer. I do realize that experiences such as this are valuable to me only in that they form contrasts. Knowing the shadows, I shall better appreciate the light.

In the last month I have read two new books which I should note here. One was an amusing little story by Ellis Parker Butler called "Pigs Is Pigs." It is a frivolous piece which one may enjoy while reading, but will forget in a week.

The other is "Silas Strong," by Irving Bacheller. And "Silas Strong" will prove, I believe, a valuable addition to the living literature of America. It concerns another quaint character of the Adirondack country, such as "Eben Holden," and it preserves a type of character and the customs of his time for posterity. While I do not feel that Mr. Bacheller reached the high plane of his "Eben Holden" in "Silas Strong, Emperor of the Woods," there must always be a "best" in a man's work.

I don't believe I ever have read a finer book than "Eben Holden." It may not be the "Great American Novel" they talk about, because its scope is not broad enough to take in all of America, but it pictures the people and the customs and the drama of upstate New York in the days preceding and following the Civil War with a simplicity that, to my mind, is true art.

I can only hope that I can make my novel in some measure as good and as truthful as "Eben Holden." It seems to me, however, that with the expansion westward in this new century, I must of necessity make my novel take in more territory. I feel I must not limit my experience to Buffalo and I hope that Fran will not be adverse to moving elsewhere when we are married. When, as Mr. Bryan advised me, I have fully prepared myself for my career and actually start writing, I should like to have worked in several other cities.

Sunday I had dinner with the Harbachs, with Fran and her father and mother and younger sister, Ruth. It was very warm for this time of the year, so we made some ice cream.

Fran and I rode over to the brewery on Broadway and bought a cake of ice. I wrapped the ice in a gunny sack and brought it back in the wire carrier on the front of my wheel.

Mrs. Harbach, who looks as Fran will look twenty years from now, had brought the old freezer up from the basement and had the cream ready for freezing. So Fran and I took everything out on the back porch and I broke up the ice in the gunny sack, whacking it with the flat side of a rusty hand ax. It was pleasant with Fran sitting there on the edge of the green-painted wash bench and the ice crunching and crumbling in the sack when I hit it and the musty smell of the sack coming up when the burlap was wet by the melting ice.

So, when the ice was broken up fine, I put the wood-paddled dasher in the tall tin of cream and fitted the nubbin on the bottom of the can into the socket in the wooden bucket of the freezer and poured a circle of ice around the tin. Then I sprinkled a layer of rock salt and then a layer of ice and packed it all down with the handle of the hand ax until the wooden bucket was full and the salted ice was steaming cold in my nostrils. I hooked one end of the corroded, zinc-topped crank in its place on the bucket and wrangled the other end down so its gears meshed into the cog on top of the can and then clamped it down.

I turned the crank slowly at first, with the ice-cream can

swish-swishing through the ice. Then gradually I turned faster as the freezing cream began to offer some resistance. Sometimes the ice would jam against the sides of the can and I would have to back up on the crank for a revolution or two before I could go ahead again. Then the ice water would dribble from the bung hole and run in a thin stream across the faded red, white and blue American eagle on the side of the freezer.

And the spring sun was bright on the weathered boards of the back porch floor and the trees and the lilac bush in the back yard were freshly leafed out and a robin was singing very energetically close by.

Fran stood up beside me and said, "Homer, you're so dead serious about everything—even making ice cream. If your collar weren't so high I'd kiss you on the back of the neck."

I told her the back of the neck was no proper place to kiss a fellow. So she peeked into the kitchen to make sure neither her mother nor Ruth was watching and kissed me right. Her lips are very red.

Pretty soon I could scarcely turn the freezer crank any more, so I unhooked it and wiped the ice carefully off the top and took up the lid. There it was, the ice cream heaped up in delicious, yellow snowdrifts, as flaky as frost.

Fran and Ruth and I got big spoons and cleaned the dasher in the dishpan. It was wonderful ice cream. Much better than you can buy because store ice cream has a lot of cornstarch or something in it.

June 5, 1906. I have been emotionally upset all night and very depressed. Though I tell myself repeatedly that I am silly to feel as I do, I still seem unable to control my thoughts.

It is ridiculous of me to be jealous of Fran. I know she loves me. I know if she were no more sensible than I, she well could worry herself to death over my being out every night and subjected to she knows not what temptations.

Newspaper reporters have a reputation of being wild. And
many of my associates are wild, in fact. But she is sensible
and has confidence in me. Also, she no doubt realizes that I
am not particularly attractive to women at large. And, while
I have confidence in Fran, I know that almost anyone could
fall in love with her.

As a matter of fact, I am almost certain that Paul Clark
is in love with her now. I am quite conscious, also, that Paul
Clark is much more attractive to women than am I. Just suppose Fran should fall in love with him! That thought plagues
me. It is because she is so very important to me that I worry.
I know life would be impossible without her.

Fran has known Paul for a long time. We all went to high
school together and Paul was one of the most popular boys
in school. He was pitcher of the baseball team and a track
star. He is big and I suppose a woman would call him handsome, although he is too sleek for my taste and I definitely
do not like men with curly hair. I call to mind John Penny's
bon mot to the effect that curly-haired men are usually fiddlers
or sons of—. And I know well that Paul Clark does not
play the fiddle.

Paul is not serious like me. He has a talent for small talk
and has a way of approaching very close to the risqué without giving apparent offense to the ladies. Or at least, they
forgive him readily if they are offended.

His father is a well-to-do real estate dealer. Always, until
lately, he kept a team of fine horses and a rubber-tired car-
riage which he used to take customers out to look at property. But a few months ago he acquired a new red Rambler
automobile which Paul drives in the business and uses for
social purposes in the evenings.

I know he has taken Fran riding in the Rambler on several
occasions and it seems to me he is trying deliberately to dazzle
her. While Fran and I are practically engaged, I cannot object logically, without making it appear that I have no confi-

dence in her. I have only Thursday nights free from my work. I cannot expect her to sit home every other evening with her fancy work or pyrography set for, after all, it may be two years yet before I am making enough to support a wife and have enough money saved to set up housekeeping. A beautiful young girl can't be expected to live the life of a nun.

Tonight Jan Kubelik, the great Bohemian violinist, was at the Teck Theater on his farewell tour. I knew Fran wanted to hear him. She loves music and she said it would be something to remember that you heard Kubelik play. There probably will never be another like him.

I tried to have my night off changed to Tuesday, but it couldn't be done.

So Fran accepted Paul Clark's invitation to go to the concert. I suppose he took her for a ride in his red Rambler afterwards. She has spoken of how thrilling it is to ride in an automobile. I have never ridden in one of the stinking, noisy machines. I hope if he got fresh with her that she slapped his face.

Perhaps I should try to get a job on one of the afternoon newspapers so I could have all my evenings free.

JUNE 12, 1906. The Democratic state conventions of Indiana, Arkansas, South Dakota and Missouri have endorsed William J. Bryan for President in 1908. The Missouri convention adopted a resolution declaring Mr. Bryan was defeated in 1900 only by the corrupt campaign contributions of trusts.

Mr. Bryan, now in Berlin, still is refusing to deny or confirm the persistent reports that he will be a candidate. But almost everyone, both Democrats and Republicans, believe he can be prevailed upon to make the race. The *Buffalo Commercial,* for instance, remarked editorially the other day, "Can a duck's determination to resist the lure of a nice level of water be trusted?"

I believe the people are awakening to Bryan's greatness. While he came close to election in 1896, the nation at large did not really know him then. After all, the people do the voting. It may take time for them to learn their lesson, but when they have learned it all the power of the interests and special privilege cannot say them nay.

Automobiles are becoming a problem in Buffalo. It is estimated there are nearly 10,000 of them in the city and, while they frighten few horses into runaways these days, a certain class of automobilist constitutes a distinct menace to respectable citizens. They have no regard for the rights of people in carriages nor for bicyclists nor for pedestrians. The other day a scorcher, traveling at near express train speed, nearly ran over me at Ellicott and South Division streets when I was crossing Ellicott on my bicycle. Yesterday an electric automobile struck Attorney Leroy Andrus at Franklin and Niagara streets and broke Mr. Andrus' ankle. "I tried to jump on the thing's dashboard, but it knocked me down," Mr. Andrus said. The heavy machine ran over his ankle.

The smug complacency of some of these automobilists is a thing to behold. If you have been slow to pull off the road when they come behind you with a great honk-honking of their horns, they will even yell at you as they pass.

I am trying to interest Mr. Penny in starting a campaign in the *Journal* to force police action against these maniacs. Otherwise they soon will become bold enough to run down women and children and speed away, leaving their victims maimed or dying behind.

Buffalo chauffeurs lately have formed a club to further their own interests. And, to ascertain their attitude toward this lawlessness, I called on the secretary of their board of directors. His name is Dai H. Lewis and he is, I found, partly in sympathy with my own ideas.

At first I asked him if he didn't believe laws should be passed to curb the number of automobiles in any community and forbidding them to roar around the streets at night disturbing the sleep of honest citizens. He was opposed to both of those plans. But he did allow me to quote him to the effect that he and the board of directors favor imposing the supreme penalty of the law on daredevil motorists who scorch more than fifteen miles an hour, especially in Delaware Park.

"The average new motorist," Mr. Lewis said, "seems to think he is driving the fastest car made. When he gets behind the steering lever or wheel, he turns his cap backwards, puts on a grim look and tries to set a speed record. This type of new motorist is giving motoring a black eye in Buffalo. If a few of these speed fiends are given jail sentences, it will make the situation happier for all of us."

I have been unable to raise any great enthusiasm about the campaign from Mr. Penny. Probably that is because a number of rich advertisers own automobiles and he is afraid he might offend them.

June 21, 1906. A week ago tonight Fran and I had the first really serious quarrel since we were 16 years old. But it is settled amicably now. After all, a quarrel now and then may be a good thing for people who are as close as Fran and I. It clears the sky. It makes both parties concerned appreciate the other more when the storm is over.

We went to the Woodmen's dance out on Genesee Street and had a nice time, except that Paul Clark was there with Daisy Mueller and I had to dance with her five or six times while Paul was waltzing with Fran.

Of course Fran is a fine dancer. Of course I, if anything, am below the average, especially with the waltz. And, as might be expected, Paul Clark is one of the smoothest dancers in the "Fruit Belt." He takes care, also, that people notice how good he is.

I know it is ridiculous to resent skill in a man but nevertheless I was feeling none too kindly toward Clark when the dance was over.

And he came up to us, smiling and confident and patronizing and humming the "Blue Danube." He said, "Well, kiddos, shall we do a little red Rambling before I take you home?"

He really addressed himself to Fran and she smilingly looked at me for consent.

I didn't smile. "No, thanks," I said, "we'll take the streetcar and then we'll be sure of getting home."

"Oh, very well," said Clark.

"Thank you just the same, Paul," said Fran, very sweetly.

Out on Genesee Street we had to wait nearly fifteen minutes for a streetcar. Fran wasn't very pleasant about it. "Homer," she said, "there are times when you're downright hateful."

"All right," I blurted, "if you prefer Clark's company in his stinking gasoline buggy, it's fine and dandy with me. I don't want to force my company on anybody who thinks I'm hateful."

"You know I don't think you're hateful—all the time."

"Just got through saying it," I said.

"Well, you certainly are acting hateful now. If you're going to get hateful and jealous just because I dance with another man, why—"

"Why, what? Go ahead and say it."

"Oh, Homer, why do you act that way? Why spoil our evening by being so silly and jealous?"

"You think I'm jealous of that smart aleck?"

"Well, you're acting mighty like it."

"I'm not jealous. I just hate to see a girl like you being dazzled by a show-off whose dad lets him ride around in a red threshing machine. I'd walk twenty miles before I'd ride in that thing."

"I wouldn't."

"I know you wouldn't. That's just what I'm saying. Maybe you like to show off too. I don't know. Like to go chugging down the street in a cloud of smoke and going 'honk-honk-honk' so everybody will look. Maybe some laundry girl with holes in her stockings would see you and say, 'Gee, wouldn't it be fine to be rich like that girl!' "

"You know better than that, Homer Zigler," said Fran. She was getting mad and stamped her foot on the sidewalk.

"Oh, I know what I'm talking about," I declared. "I'm not so loony."

"You quit talking to me like that," she said. "I won't stand for it."

"Maybe you want me to quit talking to you altogether."

"I certainly do—until you can control your moods better."

"Very well," I said.

So we stood there without saying a word until the car came. The car was crowded and we had to stand, hanging to straps. And when we got off it had started to rain, so we had to walk two blocks to Fran's house on Lemon Street in the drizzle and we both were pretty wet by the time we got there. As we passed the street light near her house I looked at her and saw that she was crying. Then I felt very mean and ashamed of myself.

"Listen, honey," I said, "I'm sorry. I'm terribly sorry for the way I acted."

She didn't say anything. Then in a wave it came over me just how much Fran means to me. It came to me that I was jeopardizing everything in life by my jealousy. It was as if I had wakened from a sleep and found myself standing on the brink of a precipice.

I had opened the gate to her yard and we were walking up to the porch.

"Please, Fran, darling," I said, "I know I don't deserve it, but won't you forgive me? I promise I won't ever act that way again—not in a hundred years."

She stood on the porch, looking down, saying nothing. Her broad-brimmed straw hat was drooping from the rain. She pulled out the hatpins and took it off and the street light shone on her yellow hair.

"Please, Fran."

She looked at me with tears on her cheeks. Then suddenly she threw her arms around my neck and I put my arms around her wet shoulders and held her close and kissed her.

"Sweetheart," she whispered, "I do love you, even if you can be perfectly hateful."

So, after I had sworn off from "hatefulness" again, everything was better even than it had been before.

Tonight was my night off again, but Fran had a bad headache and wanted to go to bed early. I bought some June roses from a Genesee Street dealer and took them to her. Then I went over to Julius' bowling alley on Sycamore Street and rolled a few games with some fellows, including Pete Buchtel, the fellow who shot the dynamite. I rolled one 176 game, which is pretty good for me.

2. Cleveland

JULY 18, 1906. I believe I have at last collected my wits sufficiently to record what has happened.

I am in Cleveland. I have left Buffalo forever. For a month I have been a poor, distraught, bewildered wretch. I have been drunk. I have been in jail. I have been utterly miserable. I suppose I should have committed suicide had I possessed sufficient courage.

Now I have a job on the *Cleveland Empire* and am beginning to come to my senses. But I do not believe I shall remain in Cleveland long. I wish to be farther away from Buffalo. Here there is too much danger of running across people I know.

On June 21 I wrote of a quarrel with my beloved Frances and of our reconciliation. The quarrel was caused by my jealousy of Paul Clark. I realized that. I resolved at least to keep my feelings hidden, even if I were unable to conquer them.

But on the following night, Friday, June 22, I finished work earlier than usual. It was only about a quarter to one when I turned my last copy over to the city desk and Mr. Penny said, "Zig, if you're up you may as well go."

So I rode my wheel slowly out Genesee and over to Cherry and as I approached Lemon Street a sudden whim struck me. I would ride past Fran's house before going home. I made the turn and pedaled east on Lemon.

In front of Harbach's house there is a little iron darkey painted red, white and black who holds a ring out in one hand for you to tie your horses to. But what I saw in front of this little iron darkey made me suddenly dizzy and sick. It was Paul Clark's Rambler shining there in the gas street light.

Turning sharply in the street, I rode back almost to Cherry Street. There I rested my wheel against a telephone pole and walked back toward the car, stepping softly in the grass bordering the sidewalk.

I don't know why I did this, what I expected to do. But I was beside myself. Dimly, I could see two figures in the car. I could not be certain of their identity, but they seemed to be sitting very close together.

As I crept forward my pulse was swishing in my temples. I seemed unable to take a full breath—it was as if a broad surcingle were strapped tightly about my chest. The air was heavy with the scent of lilacs from a near-by bush. I was steeped in misery and lilacs.

Then a girl's laugh floated out into the night. It was lilting, liquid, unaffected laughter—as individual and intimate of Frances as her blue eyes or her slim hands.

I found myself running along the grass toward my bicycle, running and sobbing hysterically. I was drunk with grief and humiliation. I nearly fell in trying to mount my wheel.

The night after Frances had broken a standing engagement with me she was spooning with this speenort, this unspeakable Paul Clark, after one o'clock in the morning.

I pedaled madly down Cherry Street, past Orange. It seemed that I had a definite destination and that speed was most important, but the purpose of it all was vague and uncertain. Then, as I approached Peach Street, I realized why

I was scorching. I was going home. I was going to get my father's revolver. I was going back and kill Paul Clark.

Even in this first insane muster of facts and purposes I had no notion of killing Frances. True, I felt she had betrayed me, but I laid the blame entirely on the oily wiles of Clark. He was the agency which was ruining my life. I would destroy him and everything would be all right again.

I leaned my bicycle against the front porch and, with trembling fingers, opened the front door with my latchkey. The hall light was burning dimly and the ghostly white finger of the gas mantle standing sentry duty against my home-coming seemed to be dozing in the murk. In the air there was a stale smell of corn beef and cabbage left over from supper. The gilt cupid clock in the parlor gabbled about the fleetness of time. But now I must not hurry. I must be quiet and careful.

I closed the heavy front door softly and turned to be suddenly impressed by the strange unfamiliarity of familiar things. The hydra-headed hatrack in the corner all at once was alien and unfriendly and even threatening.

Sitting on the bottom step of the red-carpeted stairs, I removed my bicycle pants guards, unbuttoned and took off my shoes. Then I began my careful ascent, stepping cautiously on the extreme right edges of the third and fifth steps because experience had taught me these were "creakers."

I knew my father kept his old revolver wrapped in a flannel cloth in the second drawer of their bureau. I knew also that I must exercise great caution because the drawers did not pull easily and the bureau was wobbly on its legs.

At the head of the stairs I paused and listened. I could hear my parents' heavy breathing and moved on toward their room.

"Homer!" It was only a whisper, but it sounded like a cry of alarm in the night.

For a moment I couldn't reply—my mouth and throat were that dry. Then I managed to say, "Yes, Mama."

"Is everything all right?"

"I—I guess so. Why?"

"I just had a troubled dream about you. It woke me up."

"Yes, I'm all right."

"You're sure you're all right?"

"Yes, I'm all right."

"Don't you want me to fix you something to eat?"

"No, Mama. Not hungry."

"Wouldn't take me but a minute to scramble you some eggs and make a cup of coffee."

"No, I couldn't eat a thing. . . . Thanks."

"Well, good night, then."

"Good night, Mama."

I went into my room and sat on the edge of the bed waiting for her to go to sleep so I could get the revolver. I felt sicker than I had ever felt before in my whole life—sicker even than when I had typhoid. I was so dizzy and my heart pounded so violently that I wondered if perhaps I were dying.

I knew I must wait a long time before trying to get the revolver; I must be sure my mother was asleep. And by that time Paul Clark would be gone. I thought of getting a knife and attacking him with that. But he was so big and strong, I might not be able to kill him with a knife.

Everything was hopeless, hopeless. Perhaps the only solution was to kill myself. But even that did not seem to be a solution. It had been beaten into my brain that there was a special place in Hades reserved for suicides. Then I still should be conscious of Clark and Fran. Then I should suffer my misery through eternity, the misery of seeing them together.

I slipped down the stairs again, and put on and buttoned my shoes, clipped on the pants guards. I turned off the gas light and went outdoors where the night air was cool on my face.

Irresistibly, I was drawn back to Lemon Street. The Rambler was gone. Fran's house was dark. The little iron darkey's face shone in the gas light. He was grinning in a wicked, knowing way.

I turned back and rode and rode, out Genesee, over to Broadway, over to William and out near the stockyards I stopped at a saloon. It was a filthy booze shop with saw-dust on the floor. The bartender was fat and sleepy. At the far end of the bar two stockyards workers were arguing thickly and paid me no attention.

Two big drinks of raw whisky warmed my stomach and steadied my nerves. But they did not soothe the aching void in my soul. I went out and rode for more miles. It was day-light and the birds were chorusing when I got back home and threw myself, exhausted and fully clothed, on my bed. I didn't really sleep. I only drifted in and out of a horrid, comatose condition for an hour.

When I heard the family getting up I rose and closed my door. I didn't want to see my father. The wild hysteria was gone from me and in its place was the lassitude of deep-est melancholia. It was as if the entire world had been snatched out from under me and I was left alone in nothing-ness.

There was no thought in my mind that possibly I had not lost Frances, that possibly there was a good explanation for what I had seen. There was no thought that perhaps I was attaching too great significance to the incident. There was only a realization, deep as the pit, that Frances was gone from me forever.

Downstairs I heard the clatter of breakfast-getting and smelled bacon and coffee. I heard the family at breakfast. Then, at intervals over a half hour, I heard the good-byes of my father and sisters and the slamming of the front door as they departed.

When they had gone I went down to get a cup of coffee.

My mother was surprised to see me down so early. She was sitting at the kitchen table dreaming over her second cup.

"Why, Homer," she said, "up so early?"

"Couldn't sleep," I said.

"Aren't you feeling well?"

"Not especially, Mama. Couldn't sleep. Just want a cup of java."

"No, no," she said, "I'll cook you some breakfast in a jiffy. What would you like?"

"Nothing, Mama. Just a cup of hot java."

"Well, let me warm it up." She took the cup from my hand. "You're not looking well, Homer," she said.

"I'll be all right. Just couldn't sleep."

"Think you'd feel better if you'd eat some breakfast. Let me make you some nice pancakes and bacon."

"Not now, Mama. Maybe I'll be hungry later."

She poured me a thick ironstone cup of black coffee and set out a plate of friedcakes. I drank the coffee and got my cap and pants guards.

"Going someplace, Homer?" my mother asked. "I think you ought to try and get some more sleep."

"I'll be back soon," I said. "Just going out for a little while."

I rode down to Russell's bicycle shop and sold him my bicycle for $12. It was a good Crescent wheel with a carbide lamp and a tire bell and a Morrow coaster brake and carrier, worth anyhow $30, but Russell only offered ten and I was lucky to get twelve out of him.

Then I went to the savings bank and drew out all the money I had been saving toward the time Frances and I should want to buy furniture, the money I had saved as a streetcar conductor and more than a year reporting. It amounted to $171.62.

Home again, I went to my room and packed the old telescope valise with my extra clothing, including my working suit and this old ledger I am keeping my record in. I shaved and put on my new suit with the broad, padded shoulders.

My mother saw me carrying the valise downstairs. She
was in the parlor with a bandanna handkerchief tied around
her gray hair, squeaking the carpet sweeper back and forth.

"Homer," she said. She dropped the handle of the carpet
sweeper and walked into the hall.

"I'm going away, Mama," I told her.

"Going away—where? Why?"

"Cleveland," I said. I actually hadn't thought definitely
where I was going, except that I felt an urge to move westward. I said Cleveland because it's only a couple of hundred
miles from Buffalo and I thought it would be easier.

"Are you going there for the paper? Or—"

"No, Mama. I'm leaving the *Morning Journal*. I'm leaving
Buffalo."

"Homer, is something wrong? Tell Mama what's happened."

I set the valise down. "Mama," I said, "this is strictly
between you and me. Promise me you won't tell Papa or
anybody."

"Yes."

"You promise?"

"Of course. Tell me."

"Well, Frances and I have broken—definitely and finally."

She put her arms about me. "Now, Homer," she soothed,
"that's no reason to be running away from home. This is
your home. You're my baby. Now you don't have to be
running away from me, do you? You just wait a few days
and you'll feel different. Things have a way of mending
themselves."

"This will never mend itself." My voice was shrill and
unnatural.

"Well, even if it don't," she said and laughed shortly,
"they say there's just as good fish in the sea as ever was
caught."

Her treating me like a little boy irritated me. "Mama," I

said, desperately, "there's just no use talking. I can't stand
it here in Buffalo now. I simply can't. I've got to get away
and I'm going."

She began to cry softly.

"Remember, Mama, you promised not to say anything about
this—about Frances, I mean."

She shook her head. "I won't," she said. "But—but what
can I say?"

"Tell 'em I got a job in Cleveland."

"But you haven't."

"I will have. I know a man on *The Empire*. I'll get a job
without any trouble."

"But maybe you'll get sick away from home. You don't
look well. Oh, Homer, I can't stand you going away like
this."

"I'll be all right, Mama. I'm big enough to take care of
myself, you know." I tried to smile.

Tears were rolling down her plump cheeks, but she smiled
at me and patted me on the back.

"Now," she said, "you let Mama fix you a nice breakfast
and we'll talk this all over very cool and then if you insist
I'll let you go. But you've got to promise to come back
soon."

"Really, Mama," I said. "I couldn't eat a thing. And I've
got to hurry and catch a train."

I kissed her and left her crying and urging me to write
the minute I got to Cleveland and to come home the first
week end I could get away and to let them know if I got
into any trouble because "Papa can handle things, you know."

I felt relieved when I finally was on the train and rattling
through the dirty Buffalo yards westward bound. A sense
of freedom lessened the immense ache.

In Cleveland I took a 50-cent room near the Union Depot
until I could get my bearings. I left my valise and then,

because I had eaten nothing since the night before, went to a restaurant and ate a beefsteak and potatoes.

The meal helped, but as I walked around the strange streets and the lights began to come out and the people all seemed to belong except me, I felt lonelier than ever. I saw young fellows and girls on their way to shows and dances and roller rinks and that made me think more about Fran, made me think that I never again would see her until maybe I was rich and famous and she was the wife of a two-bit real estate man and would come up and speak to me after I had delivered a lecture. But the rosy picture of the future was too far distant to give me any happiness. I went into a saloon to forget my miserableness.

Three drinks and my cheeks felt curiously drawn. Never before had I taken three drinks in rapid succession. Never before that morning when I took two down in the stock-yards district had I ever drunk more than one whisky at a time.

I left the saloon and started up the street. I reached the Public Square and turned over on Euclid Avenue. Here the lights were brighter and the crowd more confusing. The jangle of streetcar bells and honking of automobile horns and cries of newsboys seemed louder. I was feeling pleasantly lightheaded, despite my moroseness, and a bit reckless. After all, nothing mattered any more.

The glitter of another saloon, a very fine saloon, attracted me and I pushed through the swinging doors. I stepped up to the long mahogany bar. "Bourbon," I said to the white-coated bartender.

"Yes, sir," he said, putting out the bottle, glass and chaser. "Pleasant weather, isn't it?"

"Yeah," I said. "Give me a good cigar, will you?"

He brought out a cigar box. "Here's something nice and mild at fifteen cents straight," he said.

"Aw, I want a *good* cigar," I said. Heretofore, I had smoked not more than half a dozen cigars in my life. I had no idea of the brands.

"Yes, sir," the bartender bowed politely. "A Romeo and Juliet, perhaps?"

He brought out the box and I saw the sticker reading "25 cents."

"That'll do," I said. I took one, bit off the end and lit it. Then I tossed off the whisky, poured myself another drink and laid down a five-dollar bill.

I looked around the room. At the far end was a huge oil painting of a nude girl lying on a couch of roses. It was an exciting picture.

"Hey," I said to the bartender and nodded at the painting. "That's a d— silly picture you got there."

He raised his eyebrows.

"A jane," I said, "who would lie down in roses like that would find herself stuck full of thorns."

I downed my whisky.

"Mmmm," the bartender breathed, looking at the picture. "You're a stranger around here, aren't you?"

"Yeah," I said. "Why?"

"Thought so," said the bartender. "Cleveland roses don't have thorns."

"You wouldn't kid me?"

"Should say not," said the bartender, moving down the bar to wait on another customer.

Standing near me were two men talking about the Japanese-Russian War.

"Those Japs are smart," one of them said. "They don't make any silly pretense about war. They know war is war and the main thing is to lick the other fellow."

I poured myself another drink and the bartender reached over and pulled fifteen cents from the change of my five-dollar bill.

"That's so," said the other man. "And Richmond Pearson

Hobson is dead right. They've got their eyes on Uncle Sam now. They've got their eyes on the Philippines."

"The Philippines and Hawaii," said the first man.

"And maybe Southern California," said the second.

"Poppycock," I said.

The first man turned and looked at me with an unfriendly eye. Then he swung his broad back toward me and resumed:

"One of these days there will be no more sign of war than there is today," he said. "The next day, boom! The Japs'll have struck. They'll have captured the Philippines and Hawaii simultaneously."

"That's right," said the second man. "The Pacific fleet will be torpedoed. We'll be licked before the war has even started."

"Poppycock," I said, louder this time. Then I downed my whisky.

The first man—he was a portly fellow with an elk's tooth hanging from his watch chain—glared at me. "Anybody ask your opinion?" he demanded.

I chewed my cigar. "Maybe," I said, "you don't know who I am?"

"I know you're a pest," he said. "Now skiddoo."

He turned his back on me again. The other man laughed shortly and lifted a pretzel from a cut-glass bowl. "Hobson is right," he said. "Nobody knows how strong the Japs are, but you can be d— sure they're stronger than they appear on the surface. We owe it to our forefathers to build up our navy to protect what they fought for."

Now I'm not a forward person at all and ordinarily I am mild rather than quarrelsome. Of course I disagreed emphatically with what these men were saying, but I most certainly never would have injected myself into the conversation of strangers if the liquor hadn't robbed me of all sense of caution and reserve.

As it was, I stepped up to these men and touching the

pretzel eater with my finger, said, "You're a jingo. Just a jingo." Then I turned to the fellow with the elk tooth and said, "You're a jingo too. You're both jingoes and trouble-makers. And you both talk like a fish."

At that the elk tooth man suddenly put his broad hand into my face and gave me a violent shove. I sprawled half-way across the saloon, tripped against a chair and fell. A waiter came running to me. I thought he came to assist me to my feet. He did, in fact, help me to my feet, but he seized my right wrist with a firm grip and, holding my arm straight with a hand at my elbow, he propelled me at a trot to the swinging door. There he gave me a terrific push that sent me flying through the doors and halfway across the sidewalk where I caromed off two middle-aged women and fell to my hands and knees. One of the women screamed and before I could scramble to my feet a blue-garbed policeman had hold of me.

"What's the trouble?" he asked the women.

"This drunken man came staggering out of there and nearly knocked us down," said one of the women.

"All right, fellow." The policeman jerked me around until the street swam dizzily in front of me. A grinning newsboy picked up my hat and crushed it down around my ears. By this time the policeman had my coat sleeve twisted tight as a handcuff about my right wrist. "Come along peaceful or I'll feed you the stick," he said. Then he led me to a call box and pretty soon I was in the dark interior of a patrol wagon, feeling somewhat sick to my stomach as I rode through Cleveland streets listening to the rapid clop-clop of the horses' hooves and the lazy clang of the bell.

They searched me at the station and took my money and watch and pocketknife. Then they put me in the bull pen along with a dozen or so tramps, drunks and dope fiends. The place reeked with disinfectant and with the inmates. It reverberated with awful noises. I had slept none the night

before. I was exhausted from emotional strain. But I couldn't
sleep for more than a few minutes at a time before one
wild-haired tramp would wake me bellowing a song:

> *"I lika you, you lika me*
> *We lika both the same,*
> *I lika say this very day*
> *I lika change your name."*

He must have sung that twenty times during the night
despite vehement protests of the other inmates.

They took me with the other human derelicts to court in the
morning. I had given the name "Thomas Taylor," so when
that name was called I stepped forward to the bench.

"Thomas Taylor," said the white-whiskered judge, in a
bored monotone, "you're charged with being drunk and dis-
orderly. You plead guilty or not guilty?"

"Guilty," I said.

"Five dollars. Next case," said the judge.

I told the clerk I would pay the fine as soon as the police
gave back my money. There was no trouble about that, so
pretty soon I was eating bacon and eggs and fried potatoes
in a restaurant. Then I found my way back to my room
and slept most of the day.

On the way to my room I was surprised how quiet the
streets were and it did not occur to me that this was Sunday
until I got up in the evening. Then I got fairly drunk again,
although I managed to keep out of trouble. I did not go back
to that Euclid Avenue saloon although I knew I had more
than four dollars on the bar when they threw me out. I knew
I couldn't get the money. I knew the bartender would swear
he never had seen it.

Monday I thought some of trying to get a job, but was too
apathetic about everything to make the effort. I didn't care
about getting around to see the town. I didn't care about

going to a show. I didn't care about buying newspapers or magazines to read. I spent a good deal of my time in my dark little room either sleeping or lying on the narrow, rickety iron bed with my hands back of my head looking out the single window at the blank brick wall of the building across the alley.

I though a good deal about Frances and was very sad. I blamed myself for taking a night job which left her exposed to the wiles of Paul Clark a possible six evenings a week. I had not believed Frances susceptible to such superficial charms as a comely appearance, a ready wit, dancing ability, plenty of spending money and a red automobile. I saw, now that it was too late, that I had failed to take into account that Frances, after all, was a woman and subject to woman's weaknesses.

There was little doubt in my mind that Paul Clark had supplanted my place in her heart, or that at least she was putting him up as my rival. And I was not disposed to barter and haggle over Frances' love as the Polish women barter and haggle over a fish at the Broadway market.

Lying there on my lumpy bed I reviewed all these things again and again. Then, shaken with melancholia, I would go out and drink myself sodden.

One morning I went to a saloon for an early drink and a trembling, white wretch came in and stood beside me, asking the bartender for whisky.

"Pour it for me, will you?" he asked.

Then he drew a large silk handkerchief from his pocket and draped it around his neck. He gripped a corner of this handkerchief with each shaking hand and, leaning forward on the bar, took the glass of whisky between his right forefinger and thumb while he clutched the handkerchief corner with the rest of his hand. Straightening, he began to pull on the handkerchief with his left hand, sliding the silk across his neck and bringing the right hand, and the whisky, up to his mouth with a minimum of palsy. He repeated this performance and then his nerves were steadied enough so he could take a third drink without the aid of the handkerchief.

This exhibition brought me to my senses, partially. I realized I must have occupation to take my mind off my grief or I should be committing slow suicide with liquor. Far better, I decided, to drown myself in the lake or put a bullet into my brain than to continue as I had been doing.

That afternoon I got a haircut and shave, took a Turkish bath and got my clothes pressed. Then I went to the *Empire* office to see my old acquaintance, Claude Flagg, who had been a copyreader on the *Morning Journal* in Buffalo. Flagg recommended me to the city editor, Joe Stanford, a lean, youngish man with a black shock of hair and very hairy forearms. Stanford hired me at $10 a week, which is a dollar more than I was making in Buffalo.

For two days I was kept in the office pretty close, doing routine work, writing accounts of church suppers and outings and the like which were brought into the office. The office itself is cleaner and quieter than that of the *Morning Journal*. There is an air of greater efficiency and a lighter-hearted attitude toward news in general.

When they put me on the street I found more difficulty in locating places than I expected. I remembered how impatient Mr. Penny would be in Buffalo when a reporter asked how to find an address he had been assigned to go to, so I didn't like to ask Mr. Stanford.

I would take the assignment and go out on the street and ask directions of a policeman. But that didn't help a lot because they changed the names of about half the streets last year and the policemen haven't learned them yet themselves.

The other day I asked a big policeman on Superior Northcast a direction and he said, "Pal, I'm practically a stranger here myself, now." Then he said, "I think that's down next to Doan Street, but it isn't Doan Street even, any more. My name's Doan and I used to say Doan Street was named for me, even though everybody knew it was named for old Nat Doan who was a pioneer builder and blacksmith and preacher and one thing and another. But they couldn't even leave Doan Street. They changed it to 105th Street."

I've finally worked out one little system. About all the streets with names have a Northeast or Southwest or Southeast or Northwest attached to them so you can locate which end the address is on and the numbered streets run from the Cuyahoga River. That helps some.

I have got a room in a rooming house on Wade Park Avenue Northeast, which is on the car line and which isn't too far from the office. It isn't much of a place, but at least it is better and cleaner than my first room down on West Sixth by the Union Depot. The bed is reasonably comfortable and there are two windows and there is a framed picture on the wall. It is a picture of a red-cheeked farm girl wearing a straw hat. She is smiling very prettily and is carrying a basket of red apples.

Today I had my best opportunity in Cleveland and was complimented by Mr. Stanford for the story I wrote.

There is a Russian named Nicolai Kalinsky in town for a lecture tomorrow night. He came to the United States when a child, was reared in New York and graduated from Columbia University. Then he went back to Russia for three years to study in his homeland, was arrested once as a Nihilist and barely escaped with his life.

An ardent republican, Mr. Kalinsky is able to give a striking comparison between the democracy of America and the oppressions and cruelties under the czarist government. And he is free to predict that someday the masses of Russia will rise against the tyranny of autocratic rule.

He is a striking figure of a man—black-bearded, blue-eyed, more than six feet tall and straight, he wears red Russian boots and a sash. He smokes cigarettes as long as a lead pencil.

Particularly interesting was his account of the famine in the valley of the Volga River in Kazan province.

"It is a land of great natural richness," he said. "But there are periodic drouths of long duration in which nothing can be grown. The history of this region shows seasons of plenty alternated with famines such as grip the land today.

"Thousands are starving and dying of disease. They are living on a bread made of acorn flour and grass seed which ruins the stomachs of those children who do not die of malnutrition. And day by day across the stricken area, dust storms blow, darkening the sun until midday is as twilight. The good, rich topsoil of the Volga region is pulverized powder fine. It drifts like snow against the fences and blocks the roads.

"The ignorant peasants," said Mr. Kalinsky, "accept the famine as an act of God in punishment for unknown, unrealized sins. But the real cause of the famine is the incompetent government, the government which has no thought of the governed."

"How could the government prevent drouths?" I asked.

"Rainfall cannot be controlled to any large degree," he said, waving his cigarette at me, "but famines could be prevented were there any wisdom or farsightedness or compassion in the government.

"Much of that rich Volga region could be irrigated scientifically from the river, insuring more abundant crops than they have ever seen. Much of the rest of the area is too rolling to irrigate and should never be plowed and put into wheat. Once in a while they get a wheat crop, yes. But often it is like this summer—the grain burned out, the soil blowing about in frightening black clouds that kill cattle, that give the people consumption.

"Were there a government of the people by the people and for the people in Russia such as we enjoy in America, much of that land would be planted in thick grass for cattle grazing. The grass would retain the snows of winter as plowed fields cannot. Forests would be planted along the margins of irrigated fields to protect the crops from the hot winds. The soils would be prepared by scientific tillage and fertilizing to retain the moisture.

"But the government of St. Petersburg is not interested so long as they get their own luxuries. What matters it to the Czarina that Volga peasant women are selling their little girls for twenty-five dollars to traders? Her own little girls, eating fresh caviar from golden plates, never will suffer.

"The peasants can be excused for their stupid farming, for they have been given no opportunity to learn scientific soil tillage. But the government cannot be excused. The officials have all the opportunity in the world to learn these things. As government officials it is their duty to know them. But they are allowing that potentially rich agricultural region to be ruined. The lives of those starving children are on their heads."

It is too bad that all the Russians—all Europeans, for that matter—can't hear Mr. Kalinsky. And all Americans may rejoice in our wise democratic government that protects its people against such agricultural tragedies as besets the Volga region.

3. Kansas City

JULY 10, 1907. Nearly a year has passed since I last wrote anything in this record. I have been in Kansas City, Mo., for some months since being fired from the *Cleveland Empire*.

My downfall came when Major Tom Johnson opened the three-cent streetcar fares on the West Side line. There was a great celebration in the evening, which I was assigned to help cover. But there was champagne at this celebration, the first I had ever drunk. It went to my head and I lost all track of time. With a couple of other reporters for the afternoon papers, I dropped into a saloon for a drink on my way back to the *Empire*. As a result I was hours late and Mr. Stanford discharged me forthright. He was correct in doing so.

Coming to Kansas City was pure chance. I went to a ticket scalper with no idea where I wanted to go, except that I did wish to move farther west. He had a ticket stub to Kansas City which would expire if not used immediately and he offered it for $7. Thus I am in this boisterous, blatant young city where there is more activity in a day than Buffalo sees in a week. Everyone is in a hurry. Everyone is sure he soon will be rich. That is, everyone except most of the newspapermen. Much of it all is ridiculous, but somehow I like it.

I have a job on the *Kansas City Times*, the morning issue of the *Star*. It is a strange newspaper. One might expect the newspapers here to be boisterous like the city. But the *Star* and *Times* are even more conservative than the *New York Times*.

They are something like the *Boston Transcript* and something like the *London Times*. But mostly these twin papers are like themselves, as molded by their founding genius and publisher, William R. Nelson.

Mr. Nelson's hero is Teddy Roosevelt. And his editors are not above editing any political story to make it enhance the President's glory. If one believes the *Star* and *Times* one must believe that T.R. and his Big Stick are the greatest figures in American history.

The staffs are mostly fellows recruited from Kansas City and vicinity who have been convinced that Nelson is right no matter what he says. They accept any Nelson ukase without question as the gospel.

There are a few others, however, who have worked elsewhere and who sometimes are amused at this amazing loyalty.

Roy Curtis, one of the latter, who came to the *Times* from the *St. Louis Post-Dispatch* a couple of years ago, has a verse which he says expresses Nelson's adulation of Roosevelt. It goes:

> *He's twice as great as Lincoln,*
> *He's twice as great as Grant;*
> *He's twice as great as Bonaparte,*
> *He's twice as great as Kant;*
> *He's twice as great as any man*
> *Above or 'neath the sod;*
> *In fact I'm half inclined to think*
> *He's twice as great as G—.*

So, of course, the *Star* and *Times* are trying to create a demand for Roosevelt to take a third term. No opportunity is ever lost to point out the great works of T.R. and to point out, too, that there is no valid reason why a President should not have a third term if the people so wish. And besides, they explain, it wouldn't be a third term for Roosevelt at all because in his first term he really was only serving out the assassinated McKinley's time from September 1901 to March 1905.

But despite all the shouting of Colonel Nelson, T.R. has indicated pretty plainly that he will not be a candidate. It is also rumored that he will boost his fat friend, Secretary of War Taft, for the presidency. The Foraker-Dick machine in Ohio, however, is a powerful factor in Republican politics and in Cleveland the Ohio gang was said to be bitterly opposed to Taft. Apparently Taft is an honest man—always a great handicap to a Republican. There is talk that Governor Charles E. Hughes of New York is the "most available" man for the Republican nomination.

I personally would like to see T.R. renominated. It is virtually certain now that Mr. Bryan will accept the Democratic nomination and that will mean an overwhelming defeat for the Republicans, no matter whom they pick. Roosevelt certainly would be their strongest candidate and I should like to see him get it where the chicken got the ax.

Just the other day Mr. Bryan said, "Such a high honor as the presidential nomination is something that no American citizen should decline." That seems tantamount to his acceptance.

Kansas City itself amazes me. Of course I expected it to be something in the line of a raw frontier community with cowboys and Indians. But the city itself, while smaller than Buffalo, is more metropolitan than Buffalo—at least in the uptown district.

I shall never, however, forget my first experiences and my first impressions in Kansas City. Weary from the long journey from Cleveland in a day coach, I left the train at the dingy Union Station in the river bottoms. Although it was early afternoon the sky outside was overcast with choking soft-coal smoke. But through the smoke on Union Avenue the air was filled with the pungent odor of roasting coffee, and the wind brought the not-so-pleasant odor of the stockyards and packing houses to mix with the smoke and coffee.

All was bustle along the narrow, brick-paved street—bustle and noise. There was the clatter of draft horses and steel-tired trucks and the roar of the elevated trolley cars above. But the strangest thing was the chorus of "barkers" outside the cheap clothing stores and pawnshops and novelty bazaars and saloons along the street. Every doorway had its barker like those before circus sideshows.

"Right here—biggest beer in K.C. for a nickel!"

"Come on in. Come on in. Come on in! It's a steal, bud. Your gal will love you when she sees you in one of Uncle Ike's seven-ninety-five suits. Pair of suspenders thrown in absolutely free!"

And before a narrow and dilapidated old store front, which had been converted into something faintly resembling a theater, the hard-faced barker wore a rusty stovepipe hat.

"The thrill of a lifetime, men!" he was shouting. "And for men only, for men only! The little girls will show you things you never saw before. They'll show you things you never heard of before. All for ten cents, one thin dime."

Ahead of me a quarter mile away rose a white limestone cliff two or three hundred feet high with something that looked like pictures of a medieval castle on top. Beyond the castle I could see other buildings and sensed the city proper lay atop this mountain.

I spoke to a man standing beside a pile of cheap suitcases outside a store. "How do I get uptown?" I asked.

He took hold of my arm. "Listen, brother," he said, "you don't want to go uptown wearing a hat like that. You come on in and I'll show you something in the shape of a hat you'll like. You never saw such a dollar value as I'm going to show you."

He tried to force me into the store, but I pulled away and stalked back into the Union Station. There I was directed to follow a long wooden runway, which resembled a covered cattle chute, up to the elevated station. And presently I was rattling along in a trolley car over the roofs of factories and railroad tracks and thence through the Eighth Street tunnel and into the hilliest and most hectic city I have ever seen. No Kansas Citian walks along the streets. He travels at a half run. It is easier to skip down the hills than to hold back in a dignified walk. And the momentum helps climb the hill ahead.

They tell a story that when a civil engineer was called to lay out the streets of Westport Landing (which was to become Kansas City, Mo.) he refused the job. He is supposed to have said it would be easier to storm h— with a brigade of scrubwomen than to build a city in such a spot.

There is a crippled pencil salesman around town whose stumps of legs are strapped to a board mounted on roller skates. He usually is shoving himself around the vicinity of Grand Avenue and Walnut Street and Ninth and he negotiates the long, steep hill between Grand and Main with surprising agility. However, last week I saw him tearing down the Ninth Street grade in a patently intoxicated condition. He was quite out of control, whirling round and round like a child coasting down a toboggan slide in a dishpan. As he smoked into Main Street he yelled "Yippee!" and bumped smack into one of the big traffic policemen whom they call "Hogans." The Hogan arrested the cripple—charged him with being drunk and reckless operation of a vehicle.

I was most fortunate in obtaining a job so soon on the *Times*. It is rare indeed for them to employ a reporter who just walks in and asks for work. Usually they hire no one whose pedigree and history is unknown to them. But when I made application it happened the morning paper was shorthanded. Thus they gave me a probationary position.

Immediately I discovered I must throw overboard virtually everything I have learned of the newswriting technique. The *Star* and *Times* use a narrative form in writing. The difference is startling to one not accustomed to these papers. It also is disconcerting to a new reporter.

For instance, suppose a man has been arrested on a charge of beating his wife with a blacksnake whip. A conventional paper would handle the case something like this:

"Joseph R. Blodus, 36, of 2424 Peradventure Avenue, was arrested today on a charge of aggravated assault on his wife, Bessie, 34. Blodus is alleged to have tied up his wife by her hair and to have beaten her with a blacksnake whip, according to Policeman Henry Sullivan, who made the arrest at the Blodus home. Policeman Sullivan, a neighbor of the Blodus family, heard Mrs. Blodus' screams and dashed into the house.

"There, he declared, he found Mrs. Blodus tied to the chandelier by the hair and Blodus lashing her bare back with the muleskinner's whip; etc., etc."

But the *Star* and *Times* would handle the story something like this:

"When Policeman Henry Sullivan left his home at 2420 Peradventure Avenue this morning he was in a particularly happy frame of mind. He looked back at his trim cottage with the red rambler blooming on the porch and waved at his pretty young wife Myrtle and infant son Patrick in the doorway.

"A thrush was singing in the box elder tree and Policeman Sullivan pursed his lips and whistled an accompaniment. It was a wonderful day and a wonderful world, Policeman Sullivan mused as he set out on his two blocks' walk to the Northeast car line. It seemed that there could be no crime, no grief, no hatred anywhere on such a morning.

"But suddenly Policeman Sullivan ceased his whistling. The agonized scream of a woman stopped him short in his tracks. The scream was repeated again and again. It was coming from the home of Joseph R. Blodus, 36, of 2424 Peradventure.

"Not knowing what emergency might confront him, Policeman Sullivan drew his service revolver and dashed into the Blodus home. There in the living room an allegedly horrible sight met his eyes. Mrs. Blodus, according to the policeman, was unclothed to the waist and tied to the chandelier by her golden hair while Blodus, his face scarlet from rage and exertion, it is charged, was lashing her body with a long, vicious whip known as a 'blacksnake,' etc., etc."

I rather like this novel method of writing. But while the *Star* and *Times* and all the executives and most of the reporters are contemptuous of "yellow journalism," they never overlook any sensational possibilities in a story—even if the particulars are buried far down and the whole thing carried under a small, innocent-looking head.

My pay here is $12 a week, which is $2 more than I was making in Cleveland. There is something saddening about drawing $12 each payday, however. Frances and I had decided it would be possible to get married if one were making $12 a week.

It is now a year since I have seen or heard of Frances. But the pain of my loss is not lessened. For my own good I try to keep from thinking about her. But I cannot control my dreams. At least once a week she visits me in my dreams and usually things are as they were before Paul Clark came between us. She is very sweet. I wonder if she and Clark are married? It is probable they are by now.

August 26, 1907. I have been reading "The Virginian" by Owen Wister and in many ways I find it one of the most fascinating novels I ever read. He has captured the spirit of the West in remarkable fashion, I think. He has done for

Wyoming and the plains what Irving Bacheller has done for the Adirondack country.

As yet no author has preserved on paper the drama of this great midwestern country, the hurly-burly energy of the builders who caught the vision of Senator Thomas Hart Benton, the prophet who nearly a century ago stood on a bluff overlooking the confluence of the Kaw and Missouri rivers and predicted that here one of America's greatest industrial and commercial communities would be built.

I can see the possibilities of a novel written alone on the history of this district. There would be the movement of the pioneers westward in wagon trains. There would be the first steamboats chuffing up the broad Missouri and coming to grief on sand bars and snags. There would be the turbulent times before and during the Civil War with John Brown at Osawatomie. There would be the Red Legs and the Jayhawks and the battle of Westport Landing. There would be Jesse and Frank James. There would be the indomitable courage of the city builders, cutting down the hills and filling the valleys. There would be the increasing movement of the long trains across the great plains, bringing cattle and sheep and grain to the growing clearinghouse which must feed a nation. The swelling symphony of all these could be woven into a fine story. But, as I feel now, this is only a part of my story.

I want my novel to be all-inclusive. I want my novel to be America. I want it to hold the high purpose and sufferings of the Pilgrim fathers. I want it to hold the romance of the Spanish conquistadores and of the French padres who plunged through the terrors of an unknown land for king and church.

I want it to picture the pushing westward from the eastern seaboard of the adventurous souls who sought to build an empire in the wilderness. I want it to hold the California gold rush and the bones of pioneers bleaching on the desert. I want in it the building of the railroads. I want to picture the drama of the cattle kings and the cowboy as drawn by Owen

Wister. I want the gold miners and the venturesome farmers and the growth of the iniquitous trusts which threaten destruction of the founding fathers' work. And I want to write of the final dissolution of this last and most potent menace, which, I hope, will come soon with the election of Mr. Bryan next year.

On the surface this all appears to be too ambitious a program for one man. Certainly it would be too broad a canvas for me to paint now. But I remember Mr. Bryan's words to me in Buffalo: "If you don't believe you can do big things, you'll never attempt to do them. . . . Prepare yourself for your work and then have faith in your ability, with God's help, to do it. Have faith in your God and there will be no limits to your achievement."

I know I am not prepared yet for such a monumental work. But I am learning. I am preparing myself.

Right now I am learning something of the railroads and —incidentally—something of the trusts.

For the *Times* I have been doing some research on the subject of the railroads and my findings are shocking. The railroads have grown so rich and powerful that they believe themselves beyond governmental control. The answer, to my own mind, is government ownership.

So craven are the railroad trusts in their lust for more and greater dividends they now are not spending money to keep up their tracks and equipment. The result is one disastrous wreck after another the country over.

Last year there were 9,703 persons killed and 86,008 injured in American railroad accidents. For the 216,973 miles of track in the nation, a headstone could be placed every 22 miles for a person killed last year. And the dangers of rail travel are increasing day by day.

Railway officials have a weird excuse for this black record. They blame the wrecks on the labor unions, which they claim are breeding antagonism and carelessness on the part of employees.

But really what the unions are working for is security and shorter hours for the workers—which in the long run means greater safety. It was shown that the engineer in the Terra Cotta wreck had only eight hours' sleep in the forty-eight preceding the accident.

Figures prove that working as a trainman now is more hazardous than enlisting in a modern war. Last year there were 3,718 trainmen killed and 49,266 injured seriously enough to require hospitalization.

To show how seriously rail accidents are increasing, there were 6,224 collisions in 1905 and 7,194 in 1906—an increase of 970 in the year. In 1905 there were 5,371 derailments and in 1906 there were 6,261—an increase of 890.

Of course one of the principal causes of wrecks is competition between the roads for greater speed. Surely there is no real necessity to run trains at a mile-a-minute clip. A few hours' difference in a journey makes no difference to one person in ten thousand. But advertised speed attracts passengers. The railroad with the shortest running time between two points gets the bulk of the business. This definitely is a point where T.R.'s Big Stick could be put to use—if he really were sincere.

Quite apart from this, I have found a place of great interest to me under the Eighth Street viaduct near Main Street.

In Kansas City the summer sun blazes down with an intensity that I never before imagined possible. The asphalt simmers in the heat and grows so soft that you leave heelprints when you walk. It absorbs the heat and the odors from the saloons and cheap restaurants in the lower part of the city and it throws both violently back into your face as you walk along. A few blocks of this leaves me weak and dizzy.

Well, the Eighth Street viaduct cuts a heavy black span

across sun-drenched Main Street and Delaware and throws an
equally black and cool shadow beneath. A few wagons and
drays plod up the hill beside this shadow, but underneath
the viaduct and around the pillars is a haven for the weary
and heat-stricken. And here is the gathering place for that remarkable clan known as "street fakers."

There is Peters who sells Magic Oil. He demonstrates how
his product will cure headache, earache, burning feet, rheu-
matism and what not, and he will sell you a dollar vial
for a quarter and make you a present of a second vial.

There is Edwards with his straw hat and red, white and
blue hatband and beery breath who is "advertising" Arkansas
diamonds.

Edwards attracts the crowd by opening his valise on a
tripod and fluttering a pack of cards. His voice is a raucous
bellow that can be heard a block above the roar of the city.
Like everyone in the crowd, Edwards' coat is off. His suspenders are a bright purple. He shoots his celluloid cuffs
back and wets his thumb.

"Come on just a little closer, folks—just a little closer!"

Then as the weary and the jobless and the loafers and the
curious and the little boys and the negroes edge closely around
the stand, Edwards pretends to do a card trick, but ends
up by wrapping in his handkerchief the card selected by an
obliging spectator and promising to "make it disappear"
later. He never does. He counts on exciting them all so in-
tensely with his Arkansas diamonds that they never will ask
about the card trick.

"Now, gentlemen," says Edwards, "I am not going to pass
my hat for a collection and I'm not going to insult your
intelligence by telling you I'm out here this hot day for
my health. No, gentlemen, I'm here to advertise and introduce
the Arkansas diamond. You've read about it in the newspapers, no doubt. Now you'll be given opportunity to see it
with your own eyes. And I say there's no man on G—'s

green earth can look at the Arkansas crystal in your shirt front and tell it from a real diamond!"

At this climax Edwards leans forward and slaps his hands sharply for emphasis. And he unwraps glittering studs and tie pins from tissue paper and holds one in each hand for the admiration of his public.

"You go to a jewelry store and ask to see some real diamonds," says Edwards, "and what's the first thing the clerk does? Why, the first thing he does is to reach down and turn on a blaze of electric lights. Of course they glitter in that blaze of electric lights. A piece of glass will glitter under electric lights.

"Now G— knows I ain't got any blaze of electric lights down under this old viaduct, but I think you'll all agree these Arkansas diamonds sparkle with all the fire and brilliancy and luster of any real diamond of the finest water.

"I don't need to tell you gentlemen who own diamonds what will happen when you take something that looks like a diamond down to a jeweler for appraisal. First thing the jeweler will do is to take some forceps and pry up the prongs and take that stone out of its setting."

With a pair of tweezers Edwards does likewise with his Arkansas diamond.

"And why does he do that?" he asks. "Because he wants to see is there any backing, any tinfoil or quicksilver to give that stone its glitter, sparkle and luster. Well, I defy any jeweler on earth to show any foil or quicksilver or backing whatsoever to this Arkansas crystal."

To the interested craning of necks, Edwards holds his gem aloft in the tweezers, turning it this way and that way for all to admire.

"Next what will your jeweler do? Why, he'll give the stone the acid test. You've all heard of the acid test. And you know that full strength sulphuric acid will dissolve the finest paste diamond ever made, will dissolve it in a moment's time.

So let's see what effect full strength sulphuric acid has on the Arkansas crystal."

From his open grip he brings a bottle and dribbles a few drops of smoking acid on his "diamond" with no apparent effect. Then he lights an alcohol burner and holds the Arkansas crystal in the tweezers over the flame. Still it fails to disintegrate. Then he covers it with mud and slime from between the cobblestones and rolls it under his foot. Then he wipes it clean with tissue paper and lo, it is as bright as ever.

"There's no imitation diamond made can stand those tests," says Edwards, emphatically. "And as I said beforrah, there's no man on G—'s green earth can look at the Arkansas crystal in your shirt front and tell it from a real diamond."

He talks so earnestly and with so much vigor that fine froth appears at the corners of his mouth. Sometimes he pauses an instant, pats his lips delicately with his fingers, says "Pardon me," and resumes.

"Now as I told you, I'm out here to advertise and introduce the Arkansas diamond to the public. I'm supposed to give them away and I'm *going* to give them away. But if I was to say, 'Here's one for you and you and you,' some of them would fall in the hands of tinhorns and deadbeats. That would be a clean waste of Arkansas diamonds. We want these diamonds in the hands of worth-while citizens who will wear them and appreciate them—not trade them for a drink of booze.

"Therefore, to the first man what hands me not five dollars nor one dollar nor even fifty cents, but two bits, a quarter of a dollar, I'm going to pass over one of these Arkansas diamond stickpins and I'm going to make him a present of one of the studs free of charge."

Edwards does a fine business. Ragged loafers whom you'd expect to see begging on lower Main Street dig up a quarter

and buy two Arkansas diamonds. There was one such who
said, "Give me two studs—I ain't got a necktie."

And as soon as it becomes apparent that there are no more
quarters forthcoming, Edwards intones, "All done, all supplied, all satisfied," and moves his tripod aside to make room
for the next entertainer.

The crowd remains to see the act of the faker with the
astounding scientific instrument which is a combination of
microscope, binoculars, shaving mirror, laryngoscope for ex-
amining one's own throat, and mariner's compass constructed
of a substance which he terms "vegetable ivory," but which
looks like celluloid. He gives an elaborate and ungrammatical
scientific lecture and sells his product for 35 cents—with less
success, however, than Edwards and his Arkansas crystal.

The scientist gives way to the man with the combination
pocketknife, glass cutter, bottle and can opener and corkscrew,
which moves fairly well at a dime.

There is the street faker with the patent potato peelers
and the one with the revolutionary cleansing cream with
which he removes spots from volunteers' hats, lapels and ties.
There is the one with the world's most remarkable mending
cement and the fellow with the red paper-covered medicine
books which enable the plain fellow in the street to treat himself for almost any disease under the sun and to cure himself
too. It exposes, according to this orator, a gigantic fraud being
perpetrated by the Latin-writing physicians and pharmacists.

"Suppose," says this faker, "you are troubled with indigestion, heartburn and flatulence. You go to a doctor and say,
'Oh, doc, I feel terrible. What can I do?' And the doctor
says, 'Don't worry, my man, I'll give you some medicine
that'll fix you up.' And he writes down on his prescription
blank, 'Sodium bicarbonate et aqua pura' and says 'Two
dollars and a half, please.'

"So you pay his two bucks and a half and go to the druggist who puts you up a bottle of medicine for another

dollar. You take the medicine and feel much better and say to yourself, 'It was worth it all right. That's a fine doctor.'

"But—" The street faker moistens his thumb and flips the pages of his red-covered pamphlet. "Right here on Page 14 it tells you those symptoms and gives you the cure in plain English. Sodium bicarbonate? Just plain baking soda. For five cents you could buy in your grocery store enough baking soda or sodium bicarbonate to cure two hundred cases of indigestion. Aqua pura? Just pure, God-given Missouri River water that runs out of the faucet, that those horses over there are drinking from the watering trough."

Members of the audience exchange delighted smiles at this exposé.

Then in a hushed voice the professor speaks of what he calls "diseases of manhood," and declares his little book shows how to cure these also at a minimum of expense and trouble. He does a fine business, selling the pamphlets at a quarter. But Edwards, the Arkansas diamond man, takes in the most money.

SEPTEMBER 17, 1907. Yesterday, being Monday, was my day off and it was a strange day. It was drowsy and hot as midsummer and in the afternoon I sauntered languidly up Locust Street to the Library.

Not knowing exactly what I wanted to read, I wandered aimlessly through the shelf room, picking out a book here and one there, and finally began to read at a thin volume of Rudyard Kipling called "The Brushwood Boy."

I found it fascinatingly mystic—the story of a youth and a girl who met in their dreams and went through all sorts of fantastic adventures and finally meet and become sweethearts in real life.

I read all of the story while leaning against a window frame in the shelf room while an electric fan droned sleepily somewhere near by. Across Locust Street and upstairs is a music school and from across the way there came the not always harmonious, but dreamy, faraway sound of a piano and of a soprano practicing scales.

It was an oddly pleasant afternoon and somehow it made a profound impression on me, although I cannot explain how, why or what.

At night Bill Shean, a reporter on the *Star* and I went to the Century Burlesque house on Twelfth Street. It was, of course, a cheaply vulgar performance and sometimes downright salacious. But there was one comedian named Edmund Hayes, who played the part of a fat tramp and put on a piano-moving act with his undersized, scrawny partner which was one of the funniest things I have ever seen. Both these men are artists in their line and I am surprised that they are in burlesque.

After the show Bill and I had a couple of beers in the Hotel Edwards bar and he took the Brooklyn car to go home. Then I walked slowly east on Twelfth to Locust and down to my rooming house.

I have a good enough room which has one asset in particular. That is a gas light on the wall right over the head of the bed which is excellent for reading. So I went to bed and resumed reading "The Crossing" by Winston Churchill. The book didn't hold my interest well. My mind kept drifting away to the fantastically real "Brushwood Boy."

Finally I turned out the light and went to sleep.

Now last spring I was witness to a dramatic tragedy during the flood. I was on Scarrett Point, a high, rocky bluff in the northeast section of the city. The Point is a wooded park on the brink of a cliff which drops three hundred feet to the North Bottoms. And these flat bottom lands, from the foot of the cliff to the river, are filled with railroad tracks, factories, small truck gardens and some few tightly built communities of factory laborers' homes, drab and gray and as much alike as rows of weather-beaten old strawberry boxes.

This day the West Bottoms were all flooded. The swollen Missouri had backed up in the Kaw River and put Armourdale and the packing houses under water. Now there was danger of the levees giving way and flooding the North Bottoms. From my vantage point I could see everything. I was supposed to telephone the office if anything happened.

Water had been seeping through and already large areas of this bottom land were inundated. Most of the residents had moved to higher ground and others were moving as fast as they could.

I watched one group loading furniture into a wagon from a truck garden house. They were working frantically. Apparently they had been told they had little time.

Another wagon careened along the road near them and I could see the occupants wave and motion to the truck gardeners to hurry. Two men, one of whom was hatless and white-haired, lashed a rope around the back of the wagon to hold the furniture. Then they helped a woman and a little girl into the wagon, vaulted aboard themselves and whipped the horses into a gallop.

I looked back of them and saw it coming—a wall of water that glistened at its crest. It was six or seven feet high and from my station it did not seem to be traveling fast.

But it gained rapidly on the wagon and its galloping horses. The water did not move regularly. First the north flank would gain and arch in the shape of a sickle which mowed down houses and trees in its path. Then the center would come forward, straightening the blade of destruction, and finally bow forward in the shape of a giant scimitar.

It was a rough road over which the family was fleeing. The racing wagon rocked and bounced and I saw a phonograph fly overboard and strike the road in a little puff of dust while the horn, shaped like a petunia, broke loose and rolled in a circle.

As the wagon reached a slight grade which would lead to

safety, the flood was at their heels. A hundred yards to go and
the deadly blade of the crest began to bend backward into the
sickle shape. There was water to the north of them and
water also to the south of them, but it appeared that the
hand of God was pushing the water west, back from the
center of the flood to save this family as He pushed back the
waters of the Red Sea to save the Children of Israel.

The white-haired man was standing up, lashing at the
horses which already were running with a frenzy born of
terror of that roaring pursuer.

Back, back, the blade of water bent. Then, with almost the
speed of light, it flashed forward. It was as if the hand
bending a rapier double had suddenly released the steel.

The crest engulfed the wagon, swept it into a fence where
I caught one glimpse of a spinning wagon wheel as it over-
turned. I saw a horse kicking as the water foamed over him.
That was all.

Last night in my dream I was on Scarrett Point again, and
I was standing arm in arm with Frances. Together we were
watching the drama of the approaching flood and it was like
a moving picture I had seen before.

"Oh, hurry, hurry!" Frances cried as the men bound the
furniture with a rope.

And as the wagon sped up the road I said, "Now their
phonograph is going to fall from the wagon. See, there it
goes."

And as the flood bent backward, she cried, "They'll make
it now. Now they'll be safe."

And I spoke to her quietly, "No, honey—the water will
lash out like a released bowstring, like the tongue of a serpent,
and they all will perish."

And as this happened, Frances seized me tightly and wept
on my shoulder.

Today the dream is more real to me than memory of the
actual happening.

AUGUST 3, 1908. It has been terribly hot for a long time—mostly too hot to sleep at night. I have an advantage, getting to bed between 2 and 3:30 a.m., when the temperature has dropped a little and being able to sleep a few hours before the sun starts things boiling again.

I have been very lax in keeping this record lately. Again it has been nearly a year since I wrote a word. But I have been living a routinized existence. I am being kept in the office much of late, writing stories that other reporters telephone in and recently have been put to reading copy on the local copy desk. This consists of editing and correcting copy, cutting it to the required space and writing headlines on the story. While interesting, this work doesn't have the activity of regular general assignment reporting. But the *Times* seems to be pleased with my work and my salary has been raised to $16 a week.

If I could have my choice, I believe I should take political reporting, for I find following the current campaign very interesting. I did not have a chance to hear William J. Bryan when he spoke here, but I did hear William Howard Taft. I personally do not believe the Republicans have any hope of winning the election or they never would have nominated such a pitifully weak candidate.

Taft has no personal appeal. He has no platform except the doubtful one to carry out the program of Mr. Nelson's great T.R. And it can be questioned seriously whether Taft has sufficient force to continue even the semblance of good in Roosevelt's platform.

Taft's speech here was no speech at all. It was merely a recitation of poor jokes directed at Mr. Bryan and which were written by George Ade for the Republican party at so much a joke. Compared with Mr. Bryan on the platform Taft was ridiculous.

Leaning far back to support his prodigious stomach, he would recite one of the George Ade jokes and then laugh until he shook. The Republican crowd liked him, it is true, but they would have cheered Harry Thaw had he been the candidate.

I am confident that Taft will be the worst defeated presidential candidate in history. I have decided to back up my convictions with cash too, and make myself some money. There are plenty of Republicans around K.C. who are waiting to be picked. Already I have bet $45 on the outcome at even money.

Lately I have been getting out more on my day off and enjoying life. But I am careful about my drinking. Being fired in Cleveland made an impression on me. I should not care to be fired from the *Times*—especially for that reason.

This spring I moved to a new rooming house, farther out on Locust Street, where my room is bigger and better ventilated—thus cooler in the summer. The house is operated by a widow named Hawkins, who has been very kind to me. She has a daughter named Pearl whom I have taken to shows and to Electric Park several times. Before I met Pearl I had gone with girls in Kansas City very seldom. But I have come to the conclusion I have been making a mistake and missing much of life. I should not make a monk of myself. Certainly I shall never marry, but when a man denies himself all feminine companionship he is likely to warp his cosmos. I cannot afford to do that if I am to portray life truthfully in my novel.

Pearl Hawkins is the ideal girl for me to go with under these circumstances. She is a rather large girl and while she is not especially pretty she has nice blond hair and is extremely good-natured. One almost might say Pearl is frivolous—never a serious thought in her head. For that reason she is a good influence on me. I am inclined to be too serious and brooding.

Pearl perhaps may have her hair puffed out too much and she does wear an astounding array of gold bracelets on her arms and her clothes may be a trifle gaudy now and then, but this is not noticeable because so many girls do the same thing.

She is quite fond of Electric Park, which is an amusement place out South at the end of the Troost Avenue car line. It is an attractive spot, even if somewhat garish—hundreds of thousands of electric lights spangled over the white concession buildings and towers.

We were out there tonight and had a very enjoyable time dancing, riding the scenic railway (of which Pearl is very fond, although she screams terrifically when the car swoops down) and listening to the Banda Rosa—a 100-piece Italian band which is extremely good. The double climax each night is the electric fountain, where colored lights play up through columns of water with a beautiful effect, and the fireworks. Tonight was Napoleon night in fact. The band's closing number was the exciting "1812 Overture" with part of the band shooting revolvers while a full-sized church bell clanged. And the fireworks presented a tableau in fire of "The Burning of Moscow."

Lately I have been reading "Adventures in Contentment" by David Grayson. It is a remarkable book in its simplicity. And it brings home the fact which so few realize that true happiness lies in the little things of life. I have bought the book, for it will bear rereading. I can learn much of style from David Grayson—to say nothing of philosophy.

NOVEMBER 8, 1908. George Tichnor, a copyreader on the *Times* treated me to an oyster supper tonight at Harvey's Oyster saloon on Wyandotte Street. Tichnor is a good fellow, even if he has deluded political sympathies. He won $10 from me on the election Tuesday and he knew I was a little short of ready cash, having dropped more than a hundred on Mr. Bryan's defeat.

Harvey's is a fine place to eat once in a while—a bar

built in a square with stools around it and the kitchen in the middle. One of his fine cream stews with rye bread and relish is a meal in itself. The restaurant is unique in being for men only—although he has no sign out to that effect.

Tonight two women came in the door. They were nice-looking middle-aged women, but George Harvey blurted out at them, "What do *you* want?"

They were a little embarrassed by his bluntness.

"Why," said one, "we—we thought we'd get some oysters."

"No women allowed in here," Harvey growled. "You can't eat in this place."

"Oh, pardon us," said the woman and they beat a hasty retreat while the patrons around the bar clapped their hands and yelled, "Hurray for Harvey."

George was pretty proud and kept muttering to himself about "No G— d— women going to eat at *my* bar. Maybe them suffragettes think they're going to get to vote, but they ain't going to eat at *my* bar."

I personally believe giving votes to the women might help things. Most women are aligned on the side of righteousness. And had they been able to vote this time, I feel certain this astounding rape of the polls never could have happened. There are few women who would sell their votes for a couple of drinks of squirrel whisky and despite the millions spent by the vested interests to keep Republicanism in power, the Taft crew never could have bought the election.

A fair example lies in the Missouri results. Taft polled 347,203 votes to Bryan's 346,574—a majority of only 629. And it is certain that the Republicans bought many times 629 votes in Kansas City alone.

I have sympathy with some of the principles of Eugene Debs, the Socialist. But I have no sympathy with the selfish campaign he waged. Most of Debs' practical principles were originated by Bryan, but Debs attacked the Democrats with virtually the same bitterness that he launched against the

Republicans. There is no doubt he hurt Bryan. Certainly he realized he had no chance of being elected himself. But if he had come out openly in support of Bryan and stumped for him the result might have been different, despite the corrupt activities of the G.O.P. As it was, Bryan was defeated by only a million votes. And Debs polled a half million himself.

DECEMBER 9, 1908. The new Intercity Viaduct stretches for more than a mile between Kansas City, Mo., and Kansas City, Kan., running mostly over the sand flats bordering the Missouri River. To the south of the viaduct there are factories and packing houses. To the north there is nothing but sand and a few railroad switch tracks.

On these sand flats in the last year and a half a community of squatters has grown—or rather several communities. They have built their shacks of driftwood and tin and castoff secondhand lumber which they have picked up here and there.

Some of the shacks really approach the dignity of houses with peaked roofs and brick chimneys and porches. Some of them have gardens, although how they make things grow in the white sand is a mystery to me. The more fortunate have flocks of chickens and milk goats and even cows. The land they occupy belongs variously to the city, to the railroads and, bordering the river, to the federal government.

Last fall there was something of a disturbance down under the viaduct when a railroad decided to extend a switch track over a territory occupied by several of the shacks. The railroad told the squatters they would have to tear their shacks down, move off the land. Some of them did. Others refused.

At that time I went down there to talk to some of the residents and found them a pitiful lot, wearing what clothing they could salvage out of dump heaps or beg or buy at secondhand stores. They lived largely on catfish caught in the river and on the vegetables they were able to raise in the sand.

Some of the men worked at odd jobs when they could find something to do; others were sick or crippled and unable to work.

I witnessed the railroad playing its trump card against those who refused to tear down their homes. Particularly I remember an old man and woman. He was a one-legged man with a crude, homemade wooden peg. She was frail and ragged and was wearing a pair of castoff dancing slippers with the heels run over and her bare toes sticking out of the split and torn patent leather.

Their shack was a poor thing of boards, tin and tar paper. But it had a glass window and a door and it had a roof to keep the rain and snow out. It was their home, their only home, and back of it was a garden plot with the frost-withered tomato vines still standing.

A switch track ran within 75 feet of this shack and over this track a locomotive backed slowly. On its tender was a crew of men. The locomotive stopped and the men clambered down with a big hempen hawser. They stalked over to the shack with the rope.

"All right," the foreman yelled. "Get out of that shack before we pull it down on your heads."

They were looping the hawser loosely around the little home when the little old man stumped out followed by his wife.

"Hey, you, what you doing here?" he demanded.

"Going to pull this shack down," said the foreman, calmly. "They told you to get off railroad land. You didn't do it. Well, you're going out in a heap now."

"Oh, you wouldn't do *that*—you wouldn't pull our *home* down!" cried out the woman.

"Wouldn't, eh? Just you watch our smoke. Tie that loop tight, Joe."

The little old woman began to cry.

"All right." The old man waved his arms in defeat. "We'll

move. We'll move, all right. Just give us a little time to get our stuff out."

"You had time already. You was told to get out a week ago, two weeks ago. But you was too smart. Oh, yes, you was too smart. Railroad couldn't use its property because you were living on it. All right, see how smart you are now. Hey, Smitty! Hook her to the tender."

They hooked the hawser to the tender. Then the locomotive began to move slowly. The slack went out of the hawser. The loop tightened around the house.

Chuff! The switch engine gave a puff and the hawser flicked out of the dust and tightened with a creaking of hemp. The shack groaned and then suddenly collapsed in a splintering of wood and rattling of tin. The smoke pipe broke loose from its wires and came clattering down. The glass window broke. And the whole tangled mass came tumbling and bumping through the sand, dropping out a broken and rusty old stove and a welter of bedding mixed with a crushed homemade bedstead.

They dragged the wreckage nearly a hundred yards before they unhooked the hawser. They had left a trail of rags and potted plants and kitchen utensils and vegetables in the plowed-up sand.

The little old woman, with tears running down her wrinkled face, was picking up some of the kettles and groceries.

"Where'll we go now?" she sobbed. "Where'll we go now?"

The old man with the peg leg didn't say anything. He just looked at the switch engine.

This was the beginning of the "war" between the railroads and the squatters.

Farther west on the sand flats was a shack community over which a man named James Sharp ruled as king. As a matter of fact Sharp was more than king; he was a deity.

He was the head of one of those strange religious cults which always are springing up in blighted regions. He was called "Adam God" by his followers and it was rumored but never proved that he advocated free love as part of their religious ritual.

In any event, when the railroad had given notice to the community to move under threat of having their shacks pulled down by a switch engine, Adam God went to City Hall seeking an injunction to restrain the railroad from interfering with their homes.

Of course, under the law, the railroad could not be restrained from using its own land, even though Adam God made the claim that title to these sand flats had long since reverted to the public because the railroad had made no use of it for many years. He also claimed, but was unable to prove, that the river had changed its course somewhat since the original grant was made to the railroad and that the sand the Adam Godders occupied was new land which belonged only to his community through squatters' rights.

So yesterday morning the switch engine crew went to work with their hawser.

Late in the afternoon I was down at the City Market which is across Fifth Street from City Hall. I had gone down to interview a fish salesman named Alan MacPherson who was supposed to have come into a large inheritance in Scotland.

MacPherson was reluctant to be interviewed and, with some embarrassment, rearranged his reeking display on cracked ice and admitted there was nothing immediate about the inheritance. He didn't want any publicity. It was only that he "might" come into an inheritance in Scotland someday. When "a bit exhilarated from whoosky" he perhaps had made the inheritance seem more certain and more immediate.

About that time the sound of many voices singing mingled with the smell of fish. I left MacPherson and walked over to Main Street to see a column of 25 or 30 men, women and children marching up the west sidewalk from the river in a column of twos. They were singing with more vehemence than sweetness, *"Glory for me, glory for me—yes, there'll be glory, just glory for me."*

They were a ragged lot. Some of the women had tattered shawls and old blankets draped about their shoulders against the chill wind off the river. Some of the boys and little girls actually were barefoot. At the head of the column marched the gaunt figure of Adam God. He carried a hymnbook and used it like a drum major's baton to keep time.

They crossed Fifth Street and then lined up on the Main Street sidewalk opposite City Hall. Adam God stepped off the curb into the street and faced his company and the December sun lighted up his haggard face. The others were in the shadow of the dingy brick buildings.

Adam God tooted on a pitch pipe. Then they began to sing:

*"Onward, Christian soldiers, marching as to war,
With the cross of Jesus going on before."*

There was something portentous in their manner of singing. It seemed to charge the atmosphere like a coming thunderstorm.

Uniformed policemen came tumbling out the headquarters door to see the fun. Passers-by stopped. Clerks and city officials came out of City Hall. They grouped on the east sidewalk, grinning. And the ragged, dispossessed squatters sang on, verse after verse, while their fanatical chief, Adam God, gesticulated wildly in front of them.

When the song was done Adam God knelt in the street. His followers, men, women and children, knelt on the sidewalk.

"Oh, God," the evangel prayed in a raucous voice, "give us strength to follow your wishes this day. Make our eyesight keen that we may see clearly. Make our hands steady to do your bidding. Bless us, your people, in your work. Protect us with your might as you see fit. Amen."

Adam God arose. His flock also rose and stood nervously while Adam God with head bowed walked slowly south to the head of the column. Then he straightened and looked aloft at the smoky sky.

"Now!" he cried, "we shall drive the money changers from the temple!"

At that the women dropped their shawls and blankets. The men reached inside their ragged coats. And in an instant every member of the party held either a shotgun, rifle or revolver.

"Fire!" shouted Adam God.

There was a tremendous, awful, echoing roar and the west side of Main Street was picketed with stabs of flame. It was all so confusedly unbelievable. There was the crash and clinkle of broken glass in City Hall and a mad scramble among the police and passers-by and City Hall workers who a moment ago had been grinning patronizingly at the singers. Men screamed and fell writhing to the sidewalk. Yelling policemen were jammed in the police department door, some trying to get in, others trying to get out.

Methodically, the Adam Godders were reloading and firing, reloading and firing.

At the end of the column nearest me was a skinny little girl with a big nickel-plated revolver. She was holding it out in two hands and pulling the trigger with great effort, squinting up her emaciated face at the exertion. Each time she fired, the recoil would throw her hands clear over her head and jiggle her pigtail of hair like an eel on a hook.

Apparently the Adam Godders were not shooting so much at the people on the sidewalk as at the windows of City Hall. Otherwise they must have killed everyone in sight. And the glass from windows was crashing to the broad sidewalk in a tinkling shower. I know I saw Adam God himself definitely aiming at an upper window with a long-barreled horse pistol.

It could have been only a few seconds, but it seemed minutes before the police overcame their panic and began shooting with their revolvers. By that time the sidewalk was strewn with bodies, some blue-coated officers of the law, others in civilian garb. Some of the policemen lay down voluntarily to present smaller targets and began banging away. The shots were coming so fast then that it was a continuous, stuttering roar.

The skinny little girl suddenly dropped her big revolver in the street and screaming, "Oh, oh, oh, Mama!" seized her middle with both hands. She started to run down the sidewalk toward the river, but took only a few steps before she collapsed and lay twitching in the dirt.

The battle ended almost as suddenly as it began. Adam God dropped his pistol and threw up his hands.

"We surrender!" he shouted. "We're out of ammunition. We surrender and put our trust in the Lord!"

Bang! A wild-looking, tousled little boy of about 10 fired one more shot from a revolver and Adam God cuffed him in the face with the back of his hand. "Obey me," he commanded, and the little boy dropped his gun on the walk and began to cry noisily. Others of the children were crying, but the men and women, dropping their weapons, stood grimfaced and calm as excited policemen swarmed across the street and handcuffed them.

The skinny little girl, whose name was Lulu Pratt, was dead. So was Policeman Albert O. Dalbow on the other side of the street. There were six seriously wounded, including a police sergeant, Patrick Clark; two policemen; A. J. Selsor, a passerby, and Louis Pratt, Adam Godder father of little Lulu.

MARCH 7, 1909. William Howard Taft was inaugurated President of the United States last Thursday. He couldn't even remember the oath of President. He said "maintain" the

Constitution instead of "protect." I hope the people who voted for him will get enough of their bargain.

I have been reading John Fox, Jr. I liked "The Trail of the Lonesome Pine" so well that I got his "Little Shepherd of Kingdom Come" from the library. And I like that even better.

I am saturated with the glamour of the Cumberlands, for Fox is a master of weaving glamour into every chapter. I believe "The Little Shepherd" is the best Civil War story I have ever read. And it doesn't end with the conventional clinch of hero and heroine. I am glad to see that this is not necessary for a successful book. Rudyard Kipling was severely criticized because of the "unhappy ending" of "The Light That Failed," and I had come to feel that it was necessary to end one's book with a kiss and orange blossoms. That is all right once in a while, but I hate to see it inevitable. I mean I hate to know just how a book is coming out before I read it.

The love story, or rather the love stories, in my novel will be only incidental to the theme.

Tentatively, I plan to call it "Restless Dynasty." And, likewise, tentatively, I plan to start it shortly after the War of 1812 in the Lake Champlain region.

There is a young man named Jeremiah Williams who is dissatisfied with farming the rocky ridges of the Adirondacks when he hears of millions of acres of smooth, stoneless land to the West. With his bride, he makes the overland journey co Ohio, surviving many perils en route.

His oldest son, Jeremiah Jr., dissatisfied with the more or less humdrum business of Ohio farming, marries and moves to the near wilderness of Missouri. Jeremiah Jr. has two sons, Jeremiah III and Nathaniel.

Nathaniel marries and takes the ox-team route to the California gold rush. He loses track of his brother, Jeremiah III, who, being of a mechanical turn, has started a small shop for the manufacture of farm wagons. Both brothers have sons whom they name Jeremiah IV. And both have the characteristic Jeremiah Williams thin, hooked noses, deep-set brown eyes and strong chins. They look enough alike to be twin brothers.

When the Civil War comes, the Missouri Jeremiah IV enlists on the Southern side. The California Jeremiah IV comes east to fight for the North. Of course their regiments must be aligned against each other and as both are captains and as both take part in spying operations there are great possibilities for dramatic action. The climax of this situation should come when one Jeremiah Williams IV captures the other Jeremiah Williams IV and, when his true relationship is developed, saves him from hanging.

After the war, the cousins go to Missouri and take over Jeremiah III's wagonworks and, with the money inherited from the gold-digging Nathaniel, build a railroad.

They marry at a double wedding and the Jeremiahs stage a friendly though most serious wrestling match to determine which should have the honor of naming his first son Jeremiah V.

The California Jeremiah wins, but his first child is a girl and the doctor's verdict is that his wife can have no more children. So, the girl is given the name Jeremiah V, despite her sex.

This causes a break with his cousin who declares it illogical and illegal to name a girl Jeremiah besides being an actual affront to the memory of their honored ancestors. So he names his son Jeremiah V, despite the agreement.

The Jeremiah IV's become bitter enemies, split up their holdings and engage in industrial warfare. When the girl, Jeremiah V, comes to maturity she has a keen business sense and at her father's death takes over his gigantic business. So also with the boy, Jeremiah V.

Both have inherited several railroads, mines, steel plants, etc., and both go into the manufacture of automobiles. Finally, when it becomes apparent that their inherited warfare is doing the country no good, the President of the United States calls the second cousins for a conference in an effort to effect peace.

It is their first meeting and they fall in love at first sight. But they continue to fight until some incident I haven't figured out yet brings them to their senses and they combine forces and get married. Jeremiah V, the wife, confesses she'd much rather be a wife than a magnate anyhow. They have a son and name him Jeremiah Williams VI.

Of course I have the conventional happy ending to this novel, but I believe any novel of such broad scope must end on an optimistic note. After all, the world is progressing and one must be optimistic to denote progress.

Last night when I came home from work at 2:30 I was met by Pearl in the hall. She had been to a dance and got home late, so she had waited up for me.

"I thought," she said, "it would be nice for us two to have a little lunch together in the wee hours of the morning. Hungry?"

"You bet," I said, although I had eaten a bowl of chili on the way.

So we went in the dining room and there she had a supper set out with a Welsh rabbit in a chafing dish and a chocolate cake she had made herself and coffee all ready to eat. We had a very pleasant party. Pearl is a mighty thoughtful girl.

JUNE 20, 1909. Tonight when the gambling boat *Neptune* was on the return trip from Cement City a man, who presumably had lost all his money, jumped into the river. When the passengers cried, "Man overboard," the captain is said to have refused to stop or put out a boat. Witnesses said the captain growled, "If he wants to kill himself, why interfere?"

The *Neptune* is a pretty tough boat. Of course there is a

state law against gambling, but the river is federal territory and there are no federal laws pertaining to games of chance.

Last Wednesday, which now is my day off and George Tichnor's also, George and I took the trip just for the ride. It costs only a quarter and the boat runs 25 miles downstream and back.

Most of the time we sat up on the hurricane deck in the moonlight while George talked about Mark Twain. Strangely enough, I never have read any of his books. I must get some from the library. Recently, however, I have discovered a short story writer whose nom de plume is O. Henry. There are a number of volumes of his tales at the library. I have read "Heart of the West" and "Strictly Business" which I found quite interesting and cleverly written.

Finally George and I went down to see what was going on and discovered shocking conditions. On the main deck were roulette wheels, the first I have ever seen, with people grouped around as they are in movies of Monte Carlo. There were crap tables, faro tables, bird cage and Dewey slot machines where one may drop from a nickel to a silver dollar and collect as much as 40 to 1—if he is lucky. The players, men and women, were in various stages of intoxication, very noisy and often quarrelsome. Scarlet women were plying their trade in the cabins on the deck above.

I became interested in the operation of the roulette and it appeared to me that if one had sufficient self-control not to seek the higher returns but to play either red or black he might always be virtually sure of winning. For instance, he could bet a dollar on the red and if the red failed to come, double the bet next time. If the black came again, raise the bet to $4. If the black came again, raise to $8, etc.

Then suppose you had bet $8. You would win $8 and, as you already had invested $7, you would be a dollar winner. Then drop back to the original dollar bet.

The law of averages keeps the red and black coming

approximately the same. Therefore, if one has a little capital, he scarcely can fail to win each evening.

I tried this simple system, but did not have sufficient capital, and lost the $16 I had in my pocket. To be safe, one should have at least a hundred dollars.

George scoffed at my system, saying systems of the customers are what make gambling profitable for the operators. That may be true, but not with a simple system like mine, which is practically foolproof. The only real danger is in getting excited and not dropping back to the original bet. George played hunches and, having a lucky streak, actually won about $10.

I was tempted to go back on my next night off and at least win back my $16, but I hate to be a party to such an iniquitous institution. Since the man's suicide tonight, I imagine something will be done to stop the boat. There certainly should be something done to halt such lawlessness.

JUNE 27, 1909. Got up early today and went to Swope Park on a picnic with Pearl. Took our lunch in a basket and walked way out past the zoo in the woods bordering the Blue River.

Pearl is a very entertaining girl. She isn't interested in literature at all, but she is a great talker and cheerful. She is a fine influence on me. I always am happier after spending a day or even an evening with Pearl.

The *Star* and *Times* have started a campaign to bring navigation back to the Missouri. At present, practically all the boats on the river are sand barges, government snag boats and boats like the reprehensible *Neptune*.

A committee has been formed, headed by Walter S. Dickey, the sewer pipe manufacturer, to raise a million dollars— "The River Million" it is called. The idea is to rehabilitate the old steamer *Chester,* which is a stern-wheeler, and buy some tugs and barges. The steamers will be equipped with propellers, like an ocean or lake ship, but the propellers will be shielded to protect them from snags. They call this sort of boat a "tunnel-type" boat, because the propeller runs in sort of a tunnel.

It is planned eventually to have a whole fleet of tugs and barges running to St. Louis and New Orleans to bring freight into Kansas City at a fraction of the present rail rate. The railroads themselves precipitated this campaign. At present they charge Kansas City firms an additional high rate to shunt their cars of merchandise or raw material around the yards. Some other cities have to pay only a nominal rate. Others have no switching charges at all.

When the railroads were unreasonable to Kansas City men, they reckoned not on the Kansas City spirit. When, in a year or two, the majority of Kansas City freight is coming in on the river, the railroads will have leisure to regret their avarice. They are raising the million dollars by popular subscription. Everybody who contributes is given a red button lettered "The River Million" to wear in his lapel. I contributed the nominal sum of a dollar and am proud to wear the button.

DECEMBER 7, 1909. I now am a married man. Pearl Hawkins and I will have been married a week tomorrow. The ceremony was performed last Thursday, which was Thanksgiving, in Mrs. Hawkins' parlor under an arch of autumn leaves.

I am quite fond of my wife and am convinced getting married is the wisest thing I ever did.

For two years I have been drifting aimlessly, planning with no great enthusiasm to start doing something in the vague future. I had been mooning overmuch about Frances Harbach, whom I should have forgotten long ago. Every man has at least one unfortunate love affair in his youth. And mine, really, was a mere school boy and girl affair.

I realize I am inclined to brood over things and to attach overemphasis where it should not be attached. When things go wrong I'm afraid, also, that I let myself slip into a slough of self-pity.

For a long time I have needed a wife to help me keep my feet on the ground, to keep me practical, to give me something to work for.

Frankly, I had not thought of Pearl in that connection until early last month. As a matter of fact, I had convinced myself pretty well that marriage was not for me at any time.

Of course I was having a good deal of fun with Pearl and I suppose, in my blind way, I thought this platonic relationship could continue indefinitely. I did not realize she was in love with me. I did not realize I was in love with her. Had I put any thought on the matter at all, I imagine I felt Pearl would laugh at a proposal of marriage from me. I considered we were just good pals, and that was all.

Since last spring, however, Pearl has been in the habit of waiting up for me once or twice a week and preparing some little supper which we would eat together when I came home from work. This was most enjoyable from my standpoint and I took to coming home every night immediately after work instead of lingering in some all-night restaurant with other boys from the office. When I found Pearl waiting for me, I was overjoyed. When the house was dark, I was disappointed in spite of myself.

On the night of Friday, November 5, Pearl was waiting for me with a delicious oyster stew. She hardly seemed her cheerful self this night and while, as usual, she asked me what had happened, she seemed rather preoccupied while I related the night's events.

Finally she said, "Homer, there's something I must tell you."

I looked at her across the table and she was staring at me intently. It rather startled me.

"Why, Pearl," I said, laying down my spoon, "what's wrong?"

"Nothing wrong," she said, and half smiled. She looked down at her hands. "A long time ago I had a beau named Frank McLaughlin. We quarreled and he went down to Oklahoma."

"Course of true love never did run smooth," I said.

"I just got a letter from him, Homer," said Pearl.

"He want to make up?" I asked.

"He wrote me he couldn't forget me," she said.

I knew how that was.

"And," she continued, "he says he's made quite a bit of money in oil and wants to start building me a mansion in Tulsa. He wants to come back to K.C. and marry me."

"That's fine," I said, with consummate stupidity. "I'm sure he's a good man if he's an old beau of yours and I'm sure you'll both be very happy."

She continued to look down at her hands, half smiling.

"Only one thing wrong," I observed, lightly. "It's going to be pretty hard on me giving up these little suppers. It's going to be pretty hard on me to let you go after all the fun we've had together."

She bit her lip. And then, all of a sudden, she covered her face with her hands and burst out crying.

"Why, Pearl," I said, "don't you—" Then in a flash realization came to me. I mean I realized Pearl loved me instead of the rich Oklahoman. I realized she would rather marry insignificant me, a shabby newspaper reporter, than to have the riches the oilman could give her.

For a moment I was stunned. I just sat there watching Pearl sobbing. I thought of Frances and knew in my heart that she must have been married to Paul Clark a year or two by now. I thought of all the misery I had gone through in the last three years because of my hopeless and lost love. I thought that here was surcease from my unhappiness. I thought of how very kind Pearl had been to me. Then I realized how very fond of her I actually had become.

I went over to her side of the table and put my arms around her. And before we went to bed we had set the wedding date for Thanksgiving.

Pearl wore a white satin wedding gown with a long veil. I had a new brown suit. Her uncles, aunts, and a horde of cousins from Manhattan, Kan., and Cowgill, Mo., were there. Her cousin, Mabel Wodge of Manhattan, was her maid of honor—a very pretty, brown-haired girl. George Tichnor stood up with me.

It was a double ring ceremony, performed by the Rev. Julian Gault of the South Methodist Church of which Pearl is a member, and very pretty, they say, although I was a little too intent watching my own part to notice much.

Immediately after the ceremony, just as I turned and kissed Pearl, we were struck by a startling shower of rice—pounds of rice—cascading down from the arch of autumn leaves. It had been poised there in a bucket by Budge and Toddy Wodge, hulking cousins of Pearl's, and was released by their yanking a string.

An immense Thanksgiving dinner followed the ceremony. There were so many guests—relatives and friends of the Hawkinses—that they had to be seated at several tables on folding chairs rented from an undertaker.

Both Budge and Toddy Wodge manipulated things to get seats at our table and annoyed Pearl and me with their coarse, bucolic humor.

In many ways a girl's wedding day is the outstanding event in her life. She looks forward to it all her girlhood; she looks back at it through later life. If never again, on this day she is queen supreme, and it is a shame when this great day must be marred by coarseness of guests—especially when those guests are her own relatives who should be more considerate.

I had obtained four days off from the office for my wedding, so after dinner Pearl and I took the Milwaukee to Excelsior Springs for a short honeymoon at the Elms Hotel.

It is a beautiful spot, with the trees flaming their autumnal colors. After registering at the hotel, "Homer Zigler and Wife, K.C.," we walked around the town, sampled various kinds of the spring water which make Excelsior Springs a famous health resort, and finally in the evening went to a picture show which featured an exciting railroad drama in which a girl leaped from a buggy to a speeding train and saved her sweetheart's life.

It was nearly 11 o'clock when we returned to our hotel room and I could see that Pearl was quite nervous. Few men, I'm afraid, appreciate the delicate sensibilities of a decent girl. It is very easy for a man, by unthinking crudeness, to kill the love of his bride on the first night of their marriage.

Taking into account the fact that the modern girl is reared with modesty foremost in her mind at all times, consider the ordeal of a bride in preparing herself for bed in the same room with a man—even though that man is the one she loves!

When Pearl and I entered our hotel room, I already had my plan in mind. I kissed her. Then I said, "Excuse me for a few minutes, dear. I want to go down and get a cigar."

So I went down in the lobby and bought a Cremo cigar, lit it and walked out under the stars to enjoy a good smoke. When the cigar was burned down to a butt I went back.

Pearl was in bed, her light-brown hair in two braids on the pillow. She looked at me strangely. "I was wondering," she said, "if you'd gone out to get drunk on your wedding night."

I laughed reassuringly and leaned over and kissed her. She clung to me fiercely and then I saw she had been crying. I remembered Pearl's mother telling me her "little girl" never had been away from her for a full night before and I could appreciate my bride's feeling of near-terror and loneliness in this hotel room while I was walking with my cigar.

Switching off the electric light, I undressed in the dark and slipped into my new pajamas. Then I got into bed, took Pearl's hand in mine and went to sleep.

We are now living in two furnished rooms on Holmes Street. There is a kitchen with a gas stove and a living room which becomes a bedroom when the duofold (a divan by day) is opened out. It is a very pleasant room with three windows, two of which look down on Holmes Street. It gives Pearl something to do, looking down on the streetcars and other traffic while I am working, although she goes to call on her mother almost every evening. She waits up for me and doesn't get up until I do at about 10 or 10:30 in the morning.

The first article of furniture we bought is a Duplex graphophone with two horns, which makes for a fuller, sweeter tone. We are accumulating some records which Pearl plays over and over and enjoys very much. There is "Silvery Moon" sung by Billy Murray and a new humorous railroad song called "K. C. Jones."

We have "Cherry Intermezzo," "Cheyenne," "Bedelia," a band piece, and a half a dozen others including two humorous dialogues.

JANUARY 12, 1910. Today I received a letter at the *Times* from Frances Harbach—the first word I have heard from her in three years and a half. Fran met my sister, Bessie, on the street and Bessie told her about getting an announcement of my marriage. Fran wrote to congratulate me and wish me happiness.

Fran is not, as I supposed, married to Paul Clark. She is not married to anyone. I cannot but believe she turned down Paul Clark, expecting me to return. I cannot but believe she still loves me. Not that she actually wrote such a thing, but the general tone of her letter gave me that impression.

It is quite like Fran that she did not upbraid me nor demand explanation for my insane flight from Buffalo. I think she understood. I think she may even have sympathized. Nobody ever has understood me and sympathized with me like Fran.

This is not to criticize Pearl. One cannot criticize the morning glory for not being a rose.

Many, many times in the last three years I have been tempted to write to Fran, explain everything and ask for forgiveness. But I have put those thoughts out of mind, believing she had become infatuated with Clark, believing she surely was married to him by that time. I would to God now that I had followed my impulse. It would have been much better for me, much better for Pearl and—perhaps— better for Fran, herself.

Now it is too late to do anything. I cannot desert Pearl, who truly loves me. While I do not, I must admit, and never could love Pearl or any woman with the holy fervor Frances inspired in me, I am fond of my wife and know that I owe her much.

I have made a series of ghastly mistakes. But now I must make the best of it. I must not allow myself to brood on the situation. I must not allow my mistakes to ruin my life and Pearl's.

I must acknowledge Fran's letter, but I do not know what to write. Shall I explain everything? Shall I confess that I still love her and then ask her to forget me?

After all, would Frances want me after all these years and after all my crazy actions? Would she feel she could trust me? Suppose I did what so many people are doing now—went to Reno or some place where divorces are easy and obtained a decree of legal separation. Would Frances marry me then? I do not know, but I doubt it. But if she does not still love me, why did she write me such a sweet letter? Why did she say, "Homer, I know no one whom I wish more happiness than I wish you"?

I don't know what to do. I don't know what to say.

APRIL 18, 1910. After work in the morning several of us *Times* reporters generally go to Miguel's chili parlor up a ways on Grand Avenue for a lunch and a little beer before going home. Usually there is an argument and we have a lot of fun.

This morning George Tichnor, Dick Archer and I were talking about what inventions could be expected in the next half century. George, especially, is quite extravagant in predicting all sorts of Jules Verne developments, but George essentially is a romanticist.

Personally I believe we are living in the final days of the age of invention. I believe Thomas A. Edison marks the peak of American genius and the world must have time properly to assimilate his discoveries and inventions. Perhaps the human race's development now will be along spiritual, cultural and political lines. Attention must be drawn to education of the masses in self-government so America may purge herself of the wasteful and grafting gangs which now infest our seats of government—such as the "Goats" and "Rabbits" who run Kansas City's City Hall. I believe this is an inevitable development in the next few years. I believe that government ownership of the great utilities such as the railroads is coming soon.

Of no less importance is the task of educating the masses of Europe toward throwing off the senseless shackles of their hereditary kings and establishing self-government. When the downtrodden masses of Europe finally are brought to their senses, when the glory-seeking kings and czars and kaisers finally are deposed there will be no more threat of wars.

George believes the aeroplane is destined to play a great part in the development of the world. He visualizes commercial air lines with great airships hurtling through the clouds at 150 miles an hour, making the trip from New York to San Francisco in less than 24 hours.

When I told him he was silly, that the tendency is toward safety instead of greater speed he called me a reactionary and pulled the old saw about the scoffers who called Robert Fulton and the rest of the inventors and visionaries crazy.

Well, a few weeks ago I interviewed a nut out on Prospect Avenue who is working on a perpetual motion machine and this nut also was comforting himself with the thought that they called Robert Fulton crazy.

The *Literary Digest* last January sized up the aeroplane business correctly. I have dug out the copy and will take it down tonight to confound George.

They comment on the death of Léon Delagrange when his flying machine fell at Bordeaux and observe that sooner or later most of the aeronauts meet death. They class the aeroplane with tight-rope walking and looping the loop rather than as a practical means of locomotion. The aeroplane, they say, should be considered as a spectacular sport for adventurers who have money to spend and who enjoy risking their lives. They compare it to tiger hunting.

The *Digest,* in this line, quotes from the *American Engineering Magazine,* which shows proof that the nature of the aeroplane precludes any practical value.

Aviation enthusiasts, the *Engineering Magazine* says, are letting their emotions run away with their reason.

Pointing out that an aeroplane can carry only one passenger and the aeronaut, the technician says the plane still needs as much room for maneuvering as a thousand-ton steamship. He points out that the atmospheric conditions under which an aeroplane can operate occur scarcely oftener than one day in five and that then it is entirely dependent on the expertness of the juggler at the controls.

Flying is paralleled with navigating Niagara rapids in a submarine and the writer, saying he is a sincere admirer of the Wright brothers, observes it is possible that these two bicycle mechanics may yet fly hundreds of miles and thousands of feet in the air, but he still questions the utilitarian value of any present or possible achievement of the aeroplane.

"We do not," says the *Engineering Magazine,* "believe it

will ever be a commercial vehicle at all. We do not believe it will ever find any large place in the world of sport."

This article should silence George Tichnor.

For the last few months I have been corresponding with Frances Harbach. I receive her letters at the office. I write her from the office. There is nothing in our letters to which Pearl could object, but there is a strange streak of jealousy in Pearl. The mere fact that I am corresponding with an old friend of the opposite sex is enough to make her sulky and cross—if she knew it.

I write Frances about Kansas City and my work. She writes me about Buffalo, what our old schoolmates are doing and about her own work. She has learned stenography and is working for an insurance firm. I can see no harm in this innocent correspondence, although I can admit to myself that I still love Fran and always will. Every letter from her is a great thrill.

APRIL 19, 1910. The principal news of the day in Kansas City is the murder trial of Dr. B. Clark Hyde, on charges of killing Colonel Thomas H. Swope, who gave the magnificent Swope Park to the city.

Today Dr. George Twyman, the state's most important witness, died. His death was a blow to Prosecutor James A. Reed, for Dr. Twyman was to testify that he found Miss Margaret Swope on the point of death from cyanide of potassium a few minutes after she took medicine administered by Dr. Hyde. Frank Walsh, attorney for the defense, claims that cyanide was injected into Colonel Swope's dead body in an attempt to build a case against Hyde. The state's case is based on the assumption that Dr. Hyde sought to wipe out the entire Swope family so he could inherit the fortune through his wife. The city is divided into two camps—those who believe Dr. Hyde innocent and those who believe him guilty.

It seems to me there is enough evidence against him to hang him half a dozen times.

I got another letter from Frances today which to my mind offers additional proof of mental telepathy. Several times I have asked her questions which she has answered before she received my letter and I have answered her questions before I got them.

Day before yesterday I wrote Frances and I asked her if she ever had heard what became of Frank X. Woltz who was in our geometry and physical geography classes. I hadn't thought of Frank in years. He wasn't a particular friend to either Frances or me. I don't know why I thought of him or why I asked about him.

Frances must have been writing me at the same time I was writing her. Her letter was dated April 17 the same as mine. And in the letter she said, "Homer, do you remember Frankie Woltz? Frankie became a salesman for the Seneca Brewery and he married a pretty Polish girl named Stella something-or-other that I couldn't begin to spell. Her father had some money and he set Frankie up in a saloon on Sycamore Street and I hear he is doing very well. I hear, though, that his sisters Ruby and Charlotte feel practically disgraced over Frankie marrying a Polish girl and haven't even gone to call on them."

APRIL 22, 1910. George Tichnor's literary hero, Mark Twain, died yesterday in Redding, Conn. The *Star* and *Times* devoted several columns to his life, which was really remarkable. I got his "Innocents Abroad" out of the library and find it rather humorous, but otherwise not particularly exciting. Apparently his fame rests largely on his books for children and I really have no time for children's books now.

Today I interviewed an inventor out on St. John Avenue who quoted with George Tichnor the fact that scoffers laughed at Robert Fulton. This inventor, whose name is George Wash-

ington Mills, is inventing a gyroscopic belt for window wash-
ers. A motor revolves the gyroscope wheel and, he says,
permits the window washer to lean back from the window sill
with no danger of falling.

To make my novel truly representative of America, I must
have an inventor or two among the characters. The inventors
could supply comedy relief. For instance, I know an inventor
out on Troost Avenue who is devising an apparatus to take
electricity from the air. He has a roomful of rheostats, wire
coils and what not and a tower on top of his house. He
claims he can get enough electricity to light an incandescent
bulb when everything is working properly and I guess he does
get juice from someplace because every few weeks he is
knocked cold and they have to take him to the General Hospital in an ambulance. This inventor claims Westinghouse
has offered him $100,000 to suppress his invention, but he has
refused because he wants to be a benefactor of humanity. I
think he's a liar.

Judge Latshaw has deprived Dr. Hyde of his liberty on
bond and had him locked up in jail following testimony of
the bookkeeper for the Hugo Brecklein drugstore. The bookkeeper testified from his records that Dr. Hyde made four
purchases of cyanide of potassium and declared he wanted it
to kill dogs.

JUNE 1, 1910. Decoration Day I had to help cover a great
aeroplane flight at Swope Park and took Pearl along.

Pearl had a fine time for she loves crowds. We estimated
there were at least 75,000 people out lining the smooth lawn
of the golf course to see Barberry Brown, the famous aeronaut,
make his "death-defying ascent to the skies in the first heavier-
than-air flying machine ever to appear in Kansas City."

They had the National Guard out to keep the crowd from
danger and the flying machine was up at the west end of the
links near the shelter house. It was a flimsy-looking contrap-

tion made of bamboo and cloth with a small gasoline engine and propeller mounted to the rear.

The mechanics had a great deal of trouble with this engine, working on it for an hour or so while the great crowd stood in the blazing sun eating popcorn, ice-cream cones and frankfurter sandwiches and drinking soda pop which vendors were selling along the half-mile course.

Finally the mechanics got the little engine popping merrily and Barberry Brown appeared from the shelter house carrying his little daughter on one arm and holding to his pretty young wife with the other. Despite the heat he was wearing a leather coat and leather leggings. Soldiers were hanging to the aeroplane from every corner to keep it from flying away without Brown, so he kissed his wife and little girl and they both were crying for fear he would be killed. But like a soldier plunging into battle Barberry Brown tore himself away from their loving clutches and climbed up into the aeroplane seat while friends led the apprehensive wife and daughter away to safety.

Brown strapped himself securely into the seat, turned his cap around backwards, and slipped a pair of big automobile goggles over his eyes. He yelled at the soldiers to let go, grabbed hold of the control sticks and leaned forward like a jockey. Then the little gasoline engine went sput-sput and the propeller wagged lazily and stopped. The mechanics yanked and spun the propeller for ten minutes but the engine had gone to sleep and wasn't going to be disturbed. So Barberry Brown finally let go of the control sticks and took off his goggles and unstrapped himself from the seat and climbed down off the aeroplane. He took off his leather coat and went to work on the engine himself while the 75,000 people tried to crowd in closer and were kept back by the National Guardsmen and their rifles, and the vendors sold thousands more ice-cream cones and lukewarm soda pop and cool frankfurter sandwiches.

After half an hour of this Barberry Brown got the engine popping away once more and his wife and little girl were allowed to come up to cry and kiss him and cling to him the second time. Then they were led away sobbing again and Barberry Brown put on his leather coat and turned his cap backwards and adjusted his goggles and climbed back into the seat and strapped himself in tightly.

Again he grabbed the control sticks and yelled "Let her go!" to the soldiers. But this time the engine began to roar like a racing motorcycle and the propeller flew around so fast you could only see a glinting circular streak and Barberry Brown leaned forward like a jockey again and the aeroplane actually began to move down the green lawn of the golf course.

It moved faster and faster and the crowd was cheering so loud you could scarcely hear the roaring engine. For perhaps two blocks it sped, then miraculously it lifted from the ground. It actually was in the air. It lifted higher and higher until there could be no question that it was flying. It was as high or higher than the heads of the people lining the course and it remained in the air nearly a hundred yards. Then it settled easily to the grass again and the engine ceased its song.

Soldiers swarmed over the aeroplane and dragged it back to the starting point with Barberry Brown still riding triumphantly strapped in his seat and waving to the enthusiastic crowd. Near the shelter house they stopped and Brown unstrapped himself and climbed down. His wife and little girl rushed up wild with joy that he had been returned safely and smothered him with kisses. Then the mechanics began to take the aeroplane to pieces and the 75,000 people all made a rush for the streetcars that were lined up back of the shelter house.

Pearl became ill from too many frankfurters and ice-cream cones and I had to go with her behind some shrubbery and hold her head. As a result I was late getting back to the office and nearly missed the first edition with my story. Of course I couldn't write the sort of story I have written here of Kan-

sas City's first aeroplane flight. I had to make it all enthusiasm
and hoop-la.

I wish George Tichnor had seen it all, he being so certain
there will be aeroplane lines crisscrossing the nation like railroads in a few years. I think I have flown almost as far on a
toboggan as Barberry Brown did in his great aeroplane.

JULY 6, 1910. It would seem that Providence directs the human
race upward despite the innate stupidity of humanity itself.
We have just lived through a striking and disgusting example
of mankind attempting to descend to the level of the lower
animals and of kind fate taking a hand.

Interest in the prize fight between the negro, Jack Johnson,
and the white man, James J. Jeffries, approached a national
hysteria. The press far and wide painted Jeffries as the savior
of the White Race. By the power of his huge fists he was to
wrest the prize-fighting championship away from the giant
black man and thus prove superiority of Caucasians over
Africans.

For weeks the newspapers of America have been filled with
the opinions of experts declaring "Jeff" to be invincible, holding "Li'l Arthuh" to be afflicted with a "yellow streak a foot
wide up his back." On the streets, in barrooms and other
gathering places one could hear little else than discussion of
the size of Jeffries' biceps, the fact that he never had been
knocked off his feet in a prize fight except once when he
slipped, how he was capable of crushing in any man's ribs
with one blow, how heretofore he never had dared hit any
opponent with all his strength, but how he would show no
mercy for Johnson and, delightedly, how it was most probable that Johnson actually would be killed by the boiler-
maker.

The most respectable *Star* and *Times* have been as reprehensible in handling this affair as the admittedly yellow *Post*.
For days preceding the fight the first pages have carried long

stories about the magnificent condition of the Great Bronzed
Bear-Man of California, what he ate and his every word was
taken down and published as if this hero of heroes were an
oracle.

And the keynote of the whole spectacle, emblazoned in
black type across the nation were Jeffries' words—"I'm going
into this fight for the sole purpose of proving that a white
man is better than a negro."

The *Star* engaged Convention Hall for the Fourth of July
to accommodate the crowd which should wish to hear a blow-
by-blow account of this epoch-making conflict bellowed by
announcers through megaphones. They say the Hall was
jammed to the rafters with nearly 14,000 men, women and
children eager to avail themselves of this boon conferred upon
them by the paternal *Star* and *Times.*

The promoters of this affair and the daily press co-operated
in making a degrading fist fight an actual issue between races.
Is there any wonder that the negro districts such as Eighteenth
and Vine streets and inner Independence Avenue took Johnson's victory as exemplification of black supremacy? Is it any
wonder that they took Jeffries' knockout as the signal for
orgies of celebration? Is it any wonder that race riots followed
all over the United States resulting in eighteen dead and
hundreds injured?

But, as I say, Providence seems to intervene for the benefit
of humanity. Had Jeffries won, as all the experts agreed he
would win, we should witness a tremendous revival of prize
fighting with all its attendant evils. And if there is any more
brutalizing agency than the sight of two hulking men pound-
ing each other to bleeding insensibility, I cannot imagine it.
I actually feel the admittedly uncivilized sport of bullfighting
is to be preferred.

But Johnson's victory has brought the public to its senses
and has spelled the doom of prize fighting in this country.
Even John L. Sullivan, the former champion, realizes this and

said, "It will be the last big fight in this country." The *Christian Endeavor* has started a move to prohibit motion pictures of prize fights being exhibited and from the local reaction it appears they will be successful.

Even the newspapers are remorseful. The *Star,* attempting to place all the onus on the sport editors, said editorially, "The complete seriousness with which the gentlemen of the sport fraternity have spoken of the fight as hinging the supremacy of the white race is a contribution to essential humor not to be lightly prized."

Prize fighting has played its part in the history of America. It would not be out of place for me to work a prize-fight episode into my book if I can think of a method to utilize it logically without detracting from the principal theme.

My family is moving away from the old home on Peach Street in Buffalo, the house where I was born—where all of us Zigler children were born. I got a letter from Mother last week with the news.

Father has taken a new job in Pittsburgh with the Susquehanna Brass Works where he will be superintendent. They have put the house up for sale with a real estate man and are moving right away.

Bessie will go with them, but Ethel probably will stay in Buffalo. Ethel likes her job at William Hengerer's store and besides she is engaged to a jeweler named Arthur Hodge who has a store out in Kenmore.

It will be strange to think of Mother and Father and Bessie away from Buffalo.

JULY 14, 1910. I had a strange dream this morning. I was back in Buffalo and saw a group of young fellows I did not know standing on the corner of Genesee Street at about Hickory. They were lounging back against the store window smoking cigarettes and talking when Frances came in sight. She stopped on the corner waiting for a streetcar. She was carrying a handbag and a paper package which apparently was her lunch.

Presently an inbound Genesee car came in sight and Frances stepped out. The loafers stayed where they were. There was a depression in the street at that point which forced Frances to step up nearly a foot and a half to the car. It drew her skirt up, revealing perhaps four inches of trim stocking above her shoetop. At this the loafers chortled among themselves and one cried out, "Oh, you kid!"

The dream was exceptionally realistic and I awoke quivering with anger. I looked at my watch and it was 6:30. That would have been 7:30 in Buffalo, the time when Frances actually would be going to work. I wonder if I witnessed something in my dream as it really happened. Unfortunately the nature of the dream precludes writing Frances about it. I should give the world to see Frances. Perhaps I should leave Pearl—perhaps that would be the kinder thing. But I'm afraid Pearl never would give me a divorce and I'm also afraid that Frances would not marry me under those conditions. After all, Frances is religious and I fear she could not countenance marrying a divorced man. I wish I could take a vacation back in Buffalo and then talk things over with Fran. But that is out of the question.

AUGUST 3, 1910. I am out of a job—and under circumstances which seem most unjust to me. Also I cannot get a job on either the *Kansas City Journal* or the *Post*. I am writing letters trying to get a place elsewhere.

Ten days ago Wade Tate, the city editor, gave me an out-of-town assignment to investigate a mystery at Olathe, Kan. A correspondent there had given the tip that a horrible murder apparently had been committed in an old mill on the outskirts of town and the circumstances convinced Tate that an experienced newspaperman should look into it.

As it appeared I might be several days on the assignment.

I packed a bag and took one of the red Strang Line inter-
urban cars late in the afternoon. Olathe is a pretty town of
about 2,500, the county seat of Johnson County and something like 30 miles from Kansas City.

I found the mystery even more spectacularly gruesome than
first reports indicated.

The mill had been closed for more than a year and the
door securely fastened with a large padlock. The keys were
in the charge of an elderly man named Knoche who lives
down the dirt road and across a weed-grown field from the
plant.

This morning Knoche noticed the door of the mill unac-
countably was ajar. The padlock had not been opened. Instead
the heavy staple had been pried and twisted off.

Knoche took one look inside the plant and the sunlight
streaming dimly through the dusty windows revealed a sight
that sent him hobbling as fast as he could go to tell his story
to authorities.

Here is what the Olathe police and the Johnson County
sheriff found when they drove out to the mill:

Fifty or sixty feet back from the door was a rusty old anvil.
This anvil was smeared with clotted blood. Blood was spat-
tered over the floor at this point. Near the anvil was a light
sledge also bloody. And mixed with the blood on the anvil
and on the sledge were strands of long blond hair.

From the anvil to the door there was a trail in the dust of
the floor, indicating that something had been dragged out of
the mill. There was virtually a stream of dried blood along
this trail, which continued outside the door through the plan-
tain weeds to the rutty road. The trail ended there, indicating that the gory burden had been loaded into a wagon or
automobile.

Caught into splinters of the floor the police also found more
strands of long blond hair, a yellow horn side comb and one

yellow horn hairpin. And in the dirt outside the door they picked up a cheap brooch.

This is a complete list of the clues in the possession of police that Saturday night. They had made a perfunctory check of Olathe and surrounding country, but could discover no missing woman.

To their mind and to my mind the evidence indicated a young blond woman had been murdered in the mill and her body carried away either to be buried or to be hauled north to the Kaw River, weighted and thrown into the current.

The fact that no woman was missing around Olathe indicated that the victim had been brought there by her assailant probably from Kansas City or Argentine. This would be evidence that the conveyance employed was an automobile rather than a buggy or wagon and such a deduction was borne out by discovery of faint marks of automobile tires in the road.

If the murderer had an automobile it might be deduced that he was fairly well-to-do—at least something more than a laborer or worker in a packing house or one of the factories of Armourdale. But his victim was not well-to-do. The brooch was such a bauble as might be picked up on the jewelry counter at Jones Store for thirty-five cents.

A well-to-do man slaying a poor woman almost inevitably means an illicit love affair. The sheer ferocity of his act in crushing her skull against the anvil with a sledge would tend to show that she had been using her condition to force him either to marry her, if he were a single man, or to pay her a large sum of money if he were married on threat of revealing their relations.

I deduced that the victim was a large woman from the fact that her body was dragged rather than carried. I pointed out that it was true that if the murderer were a small, weak man he might be forced to drag the body of an average-sized woman, but that, on the other hand, the fact that he swung this sledge with such deadly effect was good evidence he probably possessed more than usual muscular strength.

I wrote at least two columns of my deductions along these lines and it made a wonderful Sunday story. The Sunday *Star* played it on the first page.

Al Wiggins of the *Kansas City Journal* also was down on the story. He is tall and cadaverous and lazy and entirely incapable of deductive thought. I don't think he even bothered to go out and look at the mill. Instead he sat in the sheriff's office rolling and smoking one brown-paper cigarette after the other and acting the smart aleck by poking fun at the authorities.

"I can't get much excited about murders until they find the corpus delicti," he said. Then he took his feet down from the sheriff's desk and rose and stretched.

"Well, Zig," he asked, "going to catch the next car back to town?"

"No," I said. "I'm going to stick around awhile."

Wiggins grinned in his smart-aleck way. "Sorry I can't stay and help you," he said, "but I got a date with a redhead tonight and she'll give me hell for being late now." Then he turned to the sheriff. "Give you a tip, Sherlocko," he drawled. "The way to catch this murderer is to go to the public library down the street. Check up on the kids that've been reading 'Huck Finn' lately."

The *Journal* printed two or three paragraphs of Wiggins' flippancy about the mystery which, compared with my two columns of dramatic description and deduction, looked pitiful and in very poor taste.

But one never can tell what weird tricks the Wheel of Fortune will play. Because Sheriff Ocherblatt is a conscientious officer and not inclined to overlook any possible point in an investigation, he actually followed Wiggins' random shot about the library. It seems there is a faked murder in "The

Adventures of Huckleberry Finn," which is a boys' book written by Mark Twain.

The sheriff discovered the book had been taken out two weeks before by a 15-year-old boy named Claude Johnson, the son of a carpenter and contractor. This Claude Johnson and his chum, Harley Sullivan, also 15, had been seen around the mill in the crowd during the investigation, quite apparently enjoying the excitement.

Under close questioning on Monday Claude Johnson confessed he had been inspired by the Huckleberry Finn story to stir up a sensation and that he and young Sullivan supplied the stage settings for the murder mystery. Johnson had swiped some hair from his older sister's switch as well as taking the side comb and hairpin from her bureau. Sullivan had taken the brooch from a box of old trinkets at home.

Together they stole a rooster from a chicken yard and killed it. It was the rooster's blood which was smeared so liberally over the anvil and sledge, which was dribbled along the dusty floor after they had made a trail with a sack of bricks. Both lads were arrested on charges of malicious mischief, breaking and entering and petit larceny. Their fathers, however, paid for the rooster, repaired the mill door, and finally the boys were discharged after a severe lecture.

Meanwhile, I had followed my Sunday story with an equally long and equally dramatic story of the investigation—which the evidence most certainly warranted—coupled with a list of women missing from the Kansas City district under the caption, "Is One of These Women the Victim?"

The blow fell Tuesday morning when the *Journal* carried a burlesque of my stories on Page One with a two column cut of a crowing rooster which was labeled, "The *Star's* Murder Victim." They made unmerciful sport of the *Star* and *Times* and Colonel Nelson was apoplectic with rage. He ordered my immediate discharge, which I consider a monstrous injustice. Colonel Nelson has the reputation of being a just man and often a kindly man. But he fired me without cause. Had I been drunk on the job it would have been different. If I could have been accused of laxity or laziness or incompetence it would have been different. But my only fault was excess of zeal. I hold that my reasoning on the evidence at hand was exceptional. I hold that my stories were exceptional. If the *Star* and *Times* did not hold with me, why did they play the stories on Page One? It simply did not occur to me that the Olathe Mill case might be a hoax. Neither did it occur to the Olathe authorities. Neither did it occur to City Editor Wade Tate. Neither did it occur to Colonel Nelson himself or the Monday story never would have been printed. And all the evidence was in my stories for them to scan just as it was for me at Olathe.

It was only that the *Journal's* Wiggins, too lazy to make deductions himself, too intent on keeping a date with a red-headed woman to bother about writing a story himself, by the sheer chance of having read the book which inspired the Johnson boy to the hoax, jumped at a conclusion that there might not be any murder at all.

Ninety-nine times out of a hundred Wiggins would have been wrong in following such a course. Nine hundred and ninety-nine times out of a thousand I should have been correct in following my course of hard work and deductions. But this happened to be the exception. Consequently, I suppose Wiggins is a hero at the *Journal* office. And I am out of a job.

I would not go to the *Journal* asking for a job. But I did go to the *Post* in its cluttered-up little office on Main Street.

As I approached the city desk some reporters in the rear of the room recognized me. They broke into a chorus of "Cock-a-doodle-doo!" which confused me terribly as I asked the city editor, a man named Smith, for a job. Smith grinned broadly at the rooster crowing and said he was sorry, but he didn't believe there was an opening on the *Post* for me.

Pearl herself has been far from sympathetic at this turn of fate. Because we have so little money it will be necessary for us to move back with her mother until I can find another job, which will be almost unbearable for me.

At a time like this I cannot help comparing Pearl to Frances. I know Fran would be understanding. I know Fran would see that this misfortune was no fault of mine. I know she would encourage me rather than nag at me and call me loony for being hoaxed by a couple of boys.

I hope I can find a job far away from Kansas City. I never want to see this place again. And when I get away I have made up my mind I shall never send for Pearl. Perhaps that is the course of a cad, but I don't think so. Pearl and I have nothing in common. I know I do not love her. I don't believe she ever loved me. It was only that she wanted to get married and I happened to be an available man. I know now that Pearl doesn't always adhere strictly to the truth when it is to her advantage to lean the other way. Now I doubt very much the story she told me about the Oklahoma oilman. I fear that may have been only a bait to lure me into marriage.

It seems to me that it will be better for all concerned if Pearl and I separate. Then, perhaps—and I pray that this may be so—it may not be too late for Frances and me to be reunited.

4. San Francisco

OCTOBER 5, 1910. I am reading copy of the *San Francisco Tribune*. I like the job, I like the paper and I am entranced with San Francisco. I have been here a month now and have been assured my work is satisfactory. They are paying me $32.50 a week, which is more than I could have made in years in Kansas City.

I have been living at the Dalt Hotel on Turk Street and saving my money to send for Pearl. If everything goes right I shall be able to mail her transportation inside of another two weeks.

I have definitely cut away from Frances, for I realize now that correspondence with her was doing me no good. I have not written her of leaving the *Kansas City Times* and the *Times* had no forwarding address. I owed her a letter when I left Kansas City. She will write one more letter and when that is returned to her she will realize I have gone.

Before I left Kansas City last month Pearl told me she is going to have a baby. It will be born sometime in April.

I now have a great responsibility to provide a comfortable home for my family. I must also save every possible cent toward doctor bills, as well as for Pearl's transportation out here. And she, in her condition, cannot travel two-thirds across the continent in a day coach the way I did. She must have the best of care.

I am working harder than I ever did before at the office, hoping against hope for promotion. I am grooming myself for an executive job.

Because I am more than willing to put in a little overtime reading time copy, which they call "grape" or "bulldog," Hugh Murphy, the head of the copy desk feels kindly toward me. He has made a point of complimenting me on my good heads and being very gentle and helpful in correcting me when I violate some rule. This is in direct contrast to the heavy sarcasm he turns at some other copy readers.

There is a feud on between Murphy and Fred Waldron, the telegraph editor. Waldron is friendly with Jimmy Albertson, the news editor, while Murphy is a confidant of Mr. Rothstein, the managing editor.

It is quite plain that Waldron wants to get the copy desk slot job and that Murphy considers Waldron dangerous and would get rid of him if he could.

I personally should like to be telegraph editor. The job probably pays $45 a week, which is practically all the money anyone could want. It seems to me that things are bound to come to a head between Murphy and Waldron soon, and I want to be prepared.

I want to impress Murphy with my work so he might recommend me, should he succeed in ousting Waldron. Also I want to keep on friendly terms with Waldron because the telegraph job would be open also should Waldron become head of the copy desk.

There is a great difference between reading copy here and in Kansas City. In the first place this is what they call a "universal desk," where all copy readers handle local or state or telegraph copy indiscriminately. It is much more difficult writing the headlines than on the *Times* in Kansas City. There you wrote only one top line reading, "Ghastly Crime," or something like that. Here you must try to tell the story in the top of the head in two or three lines of type which must count exactly and which must conform to the *Tribune's* style. Each line of the head must contain as nearly a complete statement as possible. There is a set rule that the top line of the head must not end in a preposition or adverb or anything except a noun or a verb.

The lines are counted by "units"—that is, each letter or character is a single unit except that "I" is half a unit, "M's" and "W's" are a unit and a half, and commas and other punctuation are a half unit. Spaces between words are counted as a half.

I go to work at 4 o'clock in the afternoon and am off at about 12:30.

OCTOBER 10, 1910. I did not work tonight, having a severely wrenched back and a chill from a ducking in San Francisco Bay.

The Hotel Dalt where I am living is frequented by theatrical people, mostly vaudeville actors and actresses. They are a very interesting, happy-go-lucky crew and frequently when I come home from work they are making merry in the rear lobby.

After their performances many of them gather in this back lobby where there is a piano and have midnight lunches, beer and frolic. The musicians and dancers enjoy showing their new acts to brother and sister performers on the theory they will receive expert criticism and be able "to smooth out any rough spots." But it doesn't work out that way. It is all very odd.

For instance, there is a pretty little English girl who is a vaudeville singer and for the gang she gets up and sings a song about, "Any little girl who's a nice little girl is the right little girl for me," and when she has finished everybody is wild with enthusiasm. They applaud and cheer and pound their beer mugs on the table.

And a couple of other actresses rush up to the singer and

they cry, "Darling, you're *marvelous*. Just the right intonations at the right places. Just the right cute little gestures. Why, darling, it must have taken you an *age* to work it all out so perfectly. Don't see how you do it."

And the singer, flushed and pleased, says, "Oh, thank you, dear, you're so kind. But I *am* conscious there are some rough spots that should be smoothed out. Couldn't you suggest something? It's so difficult for me to judge my own work."

And the others clasp their hands and flutter their eyelids and say, "Why, darling, how *can* you feel there are any rough spots? Any change at all would be a perfect *crime*. You're just perfect now, really."

And then they move back to their divan next to me and pick up their beer mugs and one of them says, "My, don't she flat terrible? Never heard anything like it. Maybe she can get by on the Pantages with that stuff, but she wouldn't last a night on the Orpheum."

And the other says, "Isn't all that baby-baby stuff too sickening for words? Say, I've seen *amateur* shows where that gal would get the hook."

Then these two girls, who should know something about the way friendly criticism goes, get up and put on their sister dance act and hear the others say it's one of the finest things of the ages and the little English singer and an acrobat come back to the divan from their enthusiastic eulogy and talk in low tones about how awkward the "sisters" are and how they fake their steps.

That's the way it goes, but they are mostly nice people and quite interesting to me, for I never before knew any actors and actresses. I really prefer the actresses, however, for they aren't as pompous as the actors. And I remember something that George Tichnor said once in Kansas City that actresses and newspapermen were fine people, but heaven save him from actors and newspaperwomen. There may be something to that.

Last night I met a pretty little actress in the Dalt whose name is Flora McDonald. I asked her what theater she was at and she told me she was a moving-picture actress and was working then on a sea picture on a ship in the Bay.

Pretty soon a man came up and spoke to Miss McDonald and he was John Boswell, one of the directors. Mr. Boswell asked me what I did and when I told him I was reading copy on the *Tribune* he said, "You work nights, don't you?"

When I said I did he asked me how I'd like to make $6 a day extra for a few hours in the morning.

"We need extras," he said, "and you might fit in fine. Why don't you come along with us at ten o'clock in the morning? You could get off by one."

Needing money as I do, that sounded splendid. And I'll admit that the glamour of having a part in a motion picture, no matter how small a part, had its attractions also.

So this morning I went down to the water front with Mr. Boswell and some of the other men and we were taken out in a motor launch to a freighter anchored in the Bay.

Aboard the ship there was a great deal of confusion and several other extras and I were herded around a good deal like convicts. Finally I was given a black sweater somewhat too large for me and a seaman's cap and told to put them on right away, which I did and then walked out on deck to see what was going on. Seeing Miss McDonald who also was wearing a sweater, I approached her and said, "Good morning, Miss McDonald, do I look seagoing enough?"

The haughty look she gave me would have frozen a polar bear. She turned her back on me without a word. Then I saw that my status had changed entirely since the night before. Now I was a mere extra and less than the dust beneath this star's feet. And I had, apparently, committed a cardinal sin by daring to speak to her.

Then a blaring voice called all us extras forward, and we were a tough-looking crew indeed, dressed in ragged jerseys and shapeless trousers. Most of the men wore two or three days' beard and their faces bore testimony of recent brawls. But I was to learn more of that later.

One of the directors, wearing leather leggings and a cap, bawled out, "Who's Zigler?"

"I am," I said, stepping forward. He looked me over closely and then grunted, "Guess you'll do—if they slap some grease paint on your face. Listen, you can swim, can't you?"

That last question should have been a hint to me, but I was so excited that it did not register.

"Yes," I said, "I'm no Captain Webb, but I can swim."

"All right, that's enough. There's a mutiny on this ship and there's been a battle. Hans Petersen, the Grizzly of the Deep, is master of this vessel and he's standing off the fo'c'sle single-handed. You're to sneak around the side of the galley with this knife and attack Petersen from the rear. Get it?"

"Yes," I said, "but—"

"Here, take this knife."

He handed me a murderous dagger with a blade eight inches long.

"Now let's see how you'd sneak along here."

So I crouched low with the knife in my hand and tiptoed along the side of the cabin.

"Don't bend over so far," he commanded. "We got to see your face. And don't look so d—— innocent. Look mean. You're going to try to kill a man, not serve him with an ice-cream soda. All right. Now listen, Zigler, when you get to the corner of the galley Petersen will be there. You rush at him, but for G—'s sake be careful with that knife. Pull it back this way like you were going to slash at him and he'll grab your wrist and shake the knife out of your hand. Now we'll try it."

So they had me sneak along the side of the galley and there sure enough was Petersen, a giant of a man muscled like George Hackenschmidt and naked to the waist. I rushed at him when the director yelled and Petersen caught my wrist easily and shook the knife from my hand. He grinned good-naturedly as he did it, but he whispered in my ear, "Listen, shrimp, you be careful of that blade when the cameras are grinding or I'll break your G— d—— neck—understand?"

"I'll be careful," I promised.

Then they sent me back to my station around the galley and somebody yelled "Camera!" and the director shouted at me to start. I crouched over a little and with as fiendish an expression as I could summon to my face, crept along the wall, clutching the knife prominently in front of me.

At the corner I peeked around and then rushed ferociously at the Grizzly of the Deep with the knife pulled back ready to strike.

Petersen grabbed my wrist, but he didn't grab it easily as he did before. His huge hand seemed to be crushing the bones of my arm as he shook the knife clattering to the deck.

Then he seized me bodily, swung me around so his own face was toward the camera and lifted me above his head with his two hands. For a moment he held me there so the cameras could register his tremendously swelling muscles. Then he threw me sprawling like a cat clear over the rail of the ship.

It was not a large ship, but it must have been at least 15 feet to the water. I tried to turn in the air to hit the water in a dive, but was only partly successful. I struck mostly on my back, which knocked the wind from me, but when I came strangling and struggling to the surface there was a motor-boat near by which came to my rescue. The crew was in paroxysms of laughter, but they finally managed to drag me aboard and transport me back to the deck of the ship.

My back was wrenched so badly that I could scarcely stand straight, but the director came up laughing and patted me on the shoulder. "You did fine, Zigler," he said. "You did just fine. You can go for today on the strength of that per-

formance, but be back sure tomorrow." Then he gave me
my $6.

I had been wearing my own trousers, so I had to go ashore
and take the streetcar back to Turk Street in dripping wet
pants. As a consequence I took a chill which with my lame
back, made me feel quite ill.

This afternoon I telephoned Murphy and told him I was
sick and unable to come to work. Naturally I did not tell him
what made me sick. I can tell anyone else who asks, however,
that my career as a moving-picture actor is closed, finally and
definitely.

OCTOBER 25, 1910. I have sent Pearl $70 to pay her way to
San Francisco and she will be here next week. Have looked
around some for apartments but decided to wait until she
gets here and let her do the selecting.

Tuesday is my day off on the *Tribune* so this evening I
wandered alone around the old Barbary Coast which they
say is pretty tame now compared to the days before the fire.

I went into a picturesque place near Broadway which apparently aims to provide every type of entertainment which a
wandering man might desire.

There is a saloon in the front. Off to one side is a penny
arcade with many penny-in-the-slot motion-picture machines
where one may turn a crank and see "High Jinks in the
Dressing Room," "Why Girls Go Wrong," "The Gans-Nelson
Prize Fight," "In Room 202," and other rather salacious kin-
etographs; punching bags which register the power of one's
blow with charts showing the scores of James J. Jeffries,
Robert Fitzsimmons, James J. Corbett and other pugilists;
electric shocking machines; weight-lifting machines; hand-
grip machines; and a device into which the customer wishing
to prove his virility may blow and reveal the strength of his
lungs.

On the other side and to the rear is a dining room circled

with booths where one may pull red velvet curtains and dine or drink in privacy with one of the shopworn nymphs who are part of the establishment's staff.

I dropped a few pennies in the slot machines, but did not find the motion pictures particularly exciting. I tried the punching bag and surprised myself by delivering a blow slightly harder than the one credited to Corbett although not quite so powerful as Jeffries' record. This is particularly surprising because I never have been athletically inclined and weigh only 128 in a moderately heavy suit and several silver dollars in my pocket.

From the penny arcade I went forward again to the saloon and bought a stein of beer at the bar. There were perhaps eight or ten men sitting at tables, mostly unsavory-looking characters, and I noticed casually that the group at one table was talking rather loudly. I was paying them no attention, however, while I sipped at my beer. Rather I was noticing the bartender who was middle-aged, bald, tight-lipped and bland. He was busy polishing beer glasses and I thought he had an interesting face, the face of a man who might be someone of importance instead of a bartender in such a place. I was thinking that I wished I knew his history, that he well might make a character in my book when a light chair sailed perilously close to my left ear and crashed terrifically into the glasses and bottles back of the bar.

Immediately the loud talkers at the one table were engaged in a desperate, bottle-swinging fight and men rushed in from another table to take part. They were yelling, cursing, kicking, swinging fists and throwing everything in sight.

Above the uproar the bartender said to me in an even, slightly bored voice, "Young fellow, maybe you'd better leave before things get rough."

I thanked him, laid down my nickel and walked out. I don't know what caused the free-for-all. I don't know how it came out. I am only glad that I did not become involved, despite the fact that the punching machine shows that I can hit harder than Corbett and almost as hard as Jeffries.

Because of the dynamiting of the *Los Angeles Times,* the *San Francisco Tribune* which hasn't been very friendly to Labor has put armed guards in and around the plant. At night nobody can enter the building without a pass. They issued cards to all the employees.

Last night Phil Blackburn, one of the copyreaders, couldn't get back to work after he'd gone to lunch at 11 o'clock because he had misplaced his card.

JANUARY 10, 1911. This was my night off and I took Pearl to the movies. It was J. Warren Kerrigan, who Pearl thinks is great, in another Civil War picture. I'm afraid the movies are running the Civil War theme into the ground and I believe I had better omit the Civil War as a major point in my novel.

Considering her condition, Pearl is feeling very well, but she doesn't like San Francisco and is lonesome for her mother and old friends in Kansas City.

We are living in a three-room apartment on O'Farrell Street. It is a four-story building built of redwood and painted gray of the type common in San Francisco. Of course it isn't very fine, but we have a front apartment with a bay window and it is quite comfortable.

Pearl complains of the cold, for she isn't used to the chill fog and rain and the radiators in the apartment have only two segments to them. I try to tell her how fortunate she is to be in California and read her accounts of blizzards in the East and of the zero weather in Kansas City.

"Well," she says, "maybe it gets cold in Kansas City, but you can have a fire and keep warm." She keeps the gas oven going a lot in the kitchen. I know I have to make allowances for her irritability now and try to cheer her up all I can. It is most important that she keep in a happy frame of mind, not only for herself, but for my son. I feel certain, somehow, that the baby will be a boy.

I want him named John or Thomas or William or some other good honest, unassuming name and I mean that he shall have all the opportunities a boy should have. I shall devote all the time I can to training him from babyhood up and he shall have a college education and postgraduate courses if necessary, even if I have to go without lunches from now on to pay for it.

Pearl says she can tell the baby will be a girl and she is going to name her Gretchen Marguerite because her widowed Aunt Gretchen has money and would be flattered into making a bequest and because she, Pearl, always thought Marguerite was the prettiest of all names and the girl could drop the Gretchen when the elderly aunt is no more and be just Marguerite Zigler.

At the office Fred Waldron, the old telegraph editor, has been shifted to the Sunday department and the bald-headed Oliver McClelland, a copyreader, was made telegraph editor.

It was plain for a long time that some shift would be necessary because of the antagonism between Waldron and Murphy, the tall, slim head of the copy desk. Murphy has been quite friendly to me and I had hoped he would recommend me for telegraph editor. I guess they figured that Ollie McClelland deserved the job more than I did, though. He has been on the *Tribune* copy desk for about three years. I really think I could do a better job of telegraph editing than Ollie, but it seems they have to consider seniority when making promotions. With the baby coming and all I could certainly use more money, but they have been pretty good to me on the *Tribune* and I don't feel like asking for a raise.

The fellows in Kansas City would be surprised to hear of me making as much as I am reading copy. So, I think, would Colonel Nelson, who ordered me fired as incompetent.

I have been trying to get Pearl interested in reading, but

so far it has been unsuccessful. Once in a while she will read a story in the *Ladies' Home Journal* if it is written by Grace S. Richmond. But she won't read the *Saturday Evening Post,* which I believe is printing the best stuff written today.

Just before Christmas I read Pearl a story in the *Post* which I cannot forget. It was called "The Exit of Anse Dugmore" and was by a new writer named Irvin S. Cobb who has the faculty of describing details more vividly than any writer I have ever read, and that includes such old masters as Dickens and modern masters as Irving Bacheller. The story concerned a Kentucky feud and the hero dies tragically before he accomplishes his purpose; *i.e.,* killing his enemy. I was so enthusiastic over this tale that I had to read it aloud to Pearl. But I am sorry to say the marvelous color and delicate shadings of Cobb's writing were lost on her.

Her comment was, "Why write such gloomy things? Isn't there enough sorrow and trouble in the world without making it up? Why don't they write things to make people feel better? That story makes me feel unhappy and it isn't good for me to feel unhappy in my condition. You ought to have thought of that before you read me that awful thing."

There undoubtedly is a great deal to what Pearl says, but nevertheless my own naturally gloomy nature makes me revel in stories like that. I hope this Irvin S. Cobb will write a lot more.

FEBRUARY 1, 1911. I have been reading Rex Beach's "Silver Horde" which I was lucky enough to get from the library. It is a story of salmon fishing in Alaska. It is a very exciting tale and well done. Also it gives a new picture of the Northland. From Jack London we see Alaska only as a place of extreme cold and super-human heroism under the northern lights. Beach reveals that summer does come to the subarctic and while he does not rob the land of its romance, he makes it seem slightly more real.

My dreams of Frances have started again. It is very strange.
I have made a strong effort to shut her from my mind. I
know my duty lies with Pearl and her baby and with them
alone. I have sternly closed the book of Frances Harbach in
my thoughts, knowing I shall never see her or hear from
her again. Yet in my dreams she is as she was before I left
Buffalo and our relations are those of sweethearts. I say they
are the same, but there is a difference.

The difference is that I seem to be looking at her life today.
There is a strange sense of the thing actually happening just
as I dream it.

For instance, last night was my night off. It was a bad,
rainy night and as Pearl wasn't feeling very well we did not
go out. About 7 o'clock in the evening I was sitting in my
chair reading "The Silver Horde" when I suddenly became
very drowsy. That is no reflection on the book, for I have
been working quite hard and have to get up fairly early in
the morning to take Pearl for a walk or streetcar ride when
the weather permits.

I was not conscious that I had gone to sleep in the chair
until I awoke and I could not have slept more than five minutes. But in that brief period I had this oddly realistic dream.

I saw Fran in her bedroom. I saw every article of furniture,
plainly, including her dresser with my picture in a frame.

Fran was in her nightgown and was sitting before the
mirror combing her beautiful yellow hair. I seemed to be
looking over her shoulder and could see her face reflected in
the mirror. She seemed very sad.

When she had finished with her hair she walked to her
bed and knelt in prayer and I heard her sweet voice say very
plainly, "Oh, God, please take care of Homer, wherever he
may be, and make him as happy as I am sad."

Then I awoke and it seemed that I could smell the faint
unidentifiable perfume that was characteristic of Frances.

I say it was a little after 7 o'clock. Well, in Buffalo it then was a little after 10. I have a feeling that Fran actually was going to bed at that time. While of course I never have seen her room, I have a feeling that it is arranged as I saw it. And I have a feeling which amounts to a conviction that the scene I visioned, that the prayer I heard, occurred at that moment just as it was in the dream.

My first inclination when swept away by emotion was to sit down immediately and write her a letter. But calm reason came to my rescue. I knew that would be foolhardy. I knew that would start everything over again and I who am to be a father soon certainly cannot play false to my child's mother.

And calm reason tells me there cannot be anything to this dream. Calm reason tells me that Frances certainly is too sensible to ruin her life mourning over me. Perhaps even now she has married Paul Clark or some other worthy man. While I dislike Clark extremely, I must admit he is worthy in the eyes of the world. He probably could make Frances happy and I do want her to be happy. For, after all, what right have I to hold jealous feelings in that direction? I have long ago forfeited all claims on Frances.

While to some extent dreams are uncontrollable, I must not allow myself to be upset by them. I must wipe this senti-mental foolishness from my mind if I am ever to be happy.

MARCH 2, 1911. The great news in San Francisco today is the sentencing of Abe Ruef to 14 years in San Quentin.

For a great many years Abe Ruef was political boss of the city and was nominal head of a most corrupt machine. He was in league with the notorious Mayor Schmitz who is sup-posed to have made away with money contributed for relief following the 1906 disaster.

More than three years ago Ruef was indicted on 129 counts on charges of bribery, extortion and what not. In the battle over these charges a prosecuting attorney was shot. Finally the Supreme Court has ruled that Ruef must serve his sentence and he has been taken to prison.

All the San Francisco papers express jubilation over Ruef's punishment. The *Tribune,* however, says, "It is only unfortunate that the worst villain of the gang escaped. Ruef was boss, but at least he had some human qualities."

The *Chronicle* came right out and named names, saying, "Schmitz is a villain pure and simple, utterly sordid, faithless to every trust, with no qualities to attach any man to him in the bonds of friendship, selling himself in cold blood to any buyer."

There is a general feeling that there are a number of rich men up on Nob Hill who used both Schmitz and Ruef to debauch the city government and who should be imprisoned along with Ruef. But they have even more power than Ruef to escape prosecution and also have the added protection of not being so conspicuous.

Ruef was sentenced specifically on a charge of bribing a supervisor named Furey. And he showed himself to be a game fellow by the interview he gave at San Quentin.

He declared he expected to find his stay at San Quentin very interesting and nowhere as unpleasant as some people might think.

"As a matter of fact," he said, "I expect to find San Quentin something of a Utopia. Every one here is on the same level. Here everyone must do his allotted share of the work—which is part of the dream of every advanced Socialist."

Referring to his badly fitting striped suit, he remarked: "It's merely the association of the fact with the idea that causes people to think of a prison uniform with horror. But there actually is nothing wrong with this suit.

"The zebra is no less beautiful than the horse, for instance. With the zebra the stripes are an adornment. They increase his value.

"Now if a company of soldiers marched down Market

Street clothed in the uniform I am wearing they would be admired and thought fine looking and the uniform would be praised. I feel no shame in wearing it because my conscience is easy."

If Ruef is glad to be in prison that makes it practically unanimous.

MARCH 26, 1911. For some time American and Canadian officials have been working toward establishment of tariff reciprocity. Being a native of Buffalo, that has interested me much more than the San Franciscans. I can appreciate the great importance this would hold to American business.

But it appears now that the chances of reciprocity have been ruined by a childish act on the part of a man who has been boomed as a great American leader.

Champ Clark, congressman from Missouri, has been selected by the Democratic majority in the House as next Speaker. There is talk that he will be the Democratic nominee for the presidency next year.

In the House last week, during the debate on Canadian reciprocity, Clark gained the floor and spoke strongly and with great feeling in favor of the measure. He closed with the most asinine utterance of any public man (not even excluding Taft and Theodore Roosevelt) in the last twenty years.

"Reciprocity," said Clark, "will be a long step toward realization of America's great dream. It will be a move toward realization of my hope to see the day when the American flag will float over every square foot of the British North American possessions north of the American possessions clear to the North Pole."

And there were certain congressmen ignorant enough of Canadian sentiment to cheer him.

Of course the inevitable has happened. The Canadians have shied away from the reciprocity plan. Great Britain is incensed and the whole project is collapsing. Anyone who knows anything about Canadians knows they do not want to be Americans. They want to retain their identity rather than to be swallowed up by their mastodonic neighbor. They are proud of being a part of a great empire and any man with brains enough to be Speaker of the House should have known this and guarded his tongue. I should say now that the political career of Champ Clark has been killed by his own undisciplined oratory. And I can just imagine what the Buffalo papers are saying—especially the Republican *Morning Journal*.

APRIL 9, 1911. At 5 o'clock this Sunday morning I became the father of a seven-pound boy. He was born at the Hahnemann Hospital and the doctor says he is perfect in every respect.

Pearl is in good condition, and, according to the doctor, had an exceptionally easy time. She doesn't agree with the doctor, which I suppose is natural enough.

I got home shortly before 3 o'clock this morning, bringing her a frankfurter sandwich. Lately she has been wanting savory things to eat early in the morning and I have been bringing her cartons of chili or hamburger sandwiches or hot dogs from an all-night joint on the way home.

When I got in this morning, however, she was awake and in her bathrobe. She was crying when I entered the bedroom.

"You're late," she accused, "where have you been?"

"Why, I'm not late, Pearl," I said. "I just stopped to get you this nice hot dog."

"I don't want any hot dog. I want to go to the hospital right now." She doubled up with pain.

I dropped the sandwich on the table and ran downstairs to the phone in the hall and called a taxicab. Then I started to call the doctor to arrange things at Hahnemann Hospital, but didn't have another nickel nor even a dime and had to drop a quarter in the phone in order to get Central. I was too excited even to try to get the operator to return the change.

It seemed hours before the taxi arrived. Pearl was in agony and I was afraid the baby would be born there in the apartment without medical attention. I kept looking out the front window at the street, glistening from wet fog in the dim lights and finally I heard the screech of brakes outside and there was the yellow cab parking outside the apartment.

Pearl didn't think she could walk so I tried to carry her. I was staggering when I got to the landing and the taxi driver, a big burly fellow, met us there.

"Here, pal, let me take her," he said, and carried Pearl quite easily to the cab.

We sailed up to the hospital quickly with Pearl complaining I had forgotten the suitcase she had packed and me telling her not to worry, that I'd go right back to the apartment and get it. All she had on was her nightgown and bathrobe and slippers and she had a right to complain. I was so excited I didn't even notice the suitcase standing ready in the bedroom.

I really am delighted that the baby is a boy. I know I'm going to have some great times when he is big enough to play with. And I am going to give him all the opportunities that I missed. I shall not attempt to warp him out of his own orbit, but I shall try to interest him in developing himself along worth-while lines while he is a youngster. If he should show ability in either respect I shall try to interest him in becoming a scientist or political leader, for the world's progress depends on those lines. Just as soon as the doctor's bill is paid I am going to start saving money diligently for the little fellow's education. An ordinary college education will not be enough. He shall go to one of the best universities in the country—Harvard or Yale or Princeton or perhaps the Massachusetts Institute of Technology, if he would be an engineer. And I shall see that he also gets a postgraduate degree. I shall see that he gets all the training it is humanly possible to give a boy. Perhaps he may have no reason to be proud of his dad when he grows up, but at least he shall know his father gave him a chance.

Pearl wants him named Byron. I don't care particularly for that name as it seems somewhat pretentious. But after all she is the mother and she wanted a girl. So who is a mere father to offer objections? And at any rate Byron can be shortened effectively to By.

I am rather tired, having been up all day, but it is time to go to work.

On the copy desk these days I am handling the Mexican situation. Serious trouble is threatening because of the battles near the border between Mexican federals and rebels. And day before yesterday 20,000 American troops were ordered to the Texas border.

If some of these Americans should get killed war would be inevitable.

MAY 16, 1911. This was my night off so I got up early today and went shopping in the secondhand stores to get a baby buggy for little Byron. I found a dandy for $5 that would pass practically for new.

Then this afternoon Pearl and I took him for a ride up to California Street and clear over to Laurel Hill Cemetery and back. It is nicer up on California and we are going to try to find an apartment up there.

Byron is beginning to get cute, but he cries a lot. The doctor has recommended changing him to condensed milk which we are doing. About the time I get home in the morning he wakes up and begins to howl so I change him and heat him a bottle of milk. Then, like as not he develops the colic and I have to walk the floor with him an hour or so. One thing I am certain of—he has fine lungs. I believe he is going to look like Pearl, but it is too early to be sure. I certainly hope he doesn't look like his daddy—I wouldn't want that to happen to any child.

A new danger is developing from aeroplanes. Ordinarily they only kill the aeronaut and whoever is foolish enough to go for a ride in the sky. But in Paris an aviator crashed into a crowd, killing Minister of War Berteaux and seriously injuring Premier Monis.

There is one bright spot at least in the news. At last the government has got next to the Standard Oil Company— and during a Republican administration at that. The United States Supreme Court has ordered the greatest of all trusts to be dissolved within six months. The average man in the street does not realize what important news this is to the common people. It foreshadows the death of all great American monopolies which have been growing bigger and bigger and gaining actual control of the government. This Supreme Court order actually means the death of special privilege and returning of the government to the people.

JUNE 4, 1911. I have been guilty of a very foolish thing and as a consequence Pearl will scarcely speak to me.

We found a much nicer apartment on California Street near Devisadero for only $37.50 and we are paying $35 for our present place where some of the neighbors have said unkind things about the baby crying.

We had decided to take the California place and were going to make a deposit today, yesterday being payday.

Things are always slow on Sunday morning after midnight and somebody pulled out a deck of cards on the copy desk about 12:30. We started playing penny-ante poker, and somehow the limit worked up to 50 cents and when the game broke up at 4 o'clock I was $30 loser.

Perhaps it would have been wiser for me to follow the usual course and to have told Pearl some cock-and-bull story about losing the money or being held up. Or perhaps it would have been better to borrow the money and say nothing at all, paying it back out of my lunch money.

It seemed, however, better to come out frankly and confess, which I did. I had no idea Pearl's anger could reach such heights. She called me things which I never before have been called in my life. She called me names that I did not know she had ever heard. And I couldn't reply in kind for I had to admit her tirade was largely justified.

Now we have to stay here on O'Farrell Street where we can put the landlord off a week or so and let the California Street place go. Well, at least I have learned my lesson even if I did have to pay dearly for it.

NOVEMBER 7, 1911. The baby is sick with a cold so I shall use part of this night off in catching up with this record.

Byron now is nearly seven months old. He has two teeth and can sit up alone. He also does a lot of talking in his own language and is so cute women notice him and smile at him when I am pushing him up and down the hills in his buggy.

Since summer we have been living in a better apartment we found on Devisadero near California. The neighbors are much better here and there is a nice young woman named Castro on the second floor who is glad to take care of the baby for 50 cents when we want to go out on my night off.

I am still working on the rim of the copy desk, but my pay has been raised to $35. That is a great help and I am making an effort to save a little against a rainy day. I have managed to pay off the doctor and hospital bill for Byron and now have a savings account with a nest egg of $15, to which I intend to add at least a dollar or two a week.

I also have a very private hoard of $12. Two weeks ago I was lured into a draw poker game on Sunday morning. I resolved firmly to pull out and go home if I lost as much as $2. But luck was with me and I came out of the game $13.15 winner. I have spent $1.15 for beer—a luxury I have had to deny myself since before the baby came. The $12 I am saving for emergencies. For instance it could stake me in another poker game, but I shall insist on any game I enter being held to a dime limit.

My conscience does not hurt me in keeping these things from Pearl. Living in such close quarters, a man can have little enough privacy from his wife.

It is so with the old ledger in which I have been keeping these notes. While Pearl has shown little or no curiosity about my plans to write, I feel constrained to keep this big old book locked in my trunk. Invariably I have written this record while she is in bed—usually late on my night off. However, if I did not keep it locked Pearl might come across it someday and her curiosity might prompt her to dig into this intimate record. I know that would cause friction.

The most astounding and happiest news of years is the proclamation of the Chinese Republic. The ancient sleeping giant has awakened and set a fine example to some of the supposedly more enlightened nations of Europe.

Now the downtrodden millions of China will come to their own. Now the immensely rich resources of that great country at last will be tapped. Now the increasing menace of Japan in the Pacific will be dampened, for as a republic China will take her place among the most powerful nations in the world, let alone in Asia.

Many people do not understand the Chinese and consider them stupid. I believe that is true even in San Francisco where 30,000 Orientals live. But the Chinese are not stupid as a general thing.

Whenever I have opportunity I go down Grant Avenue into Chinatown and walk by the exotic bazaars and try to talk to some of the Chinamen. I have found them stoically uncommunicative for the most part, but now and then I run across a genial yellow man who displays surprising intelligence and a fine grasp of the affairs of the world.

Soon after we came here I took Pearl into Chinatown but because of her condition the strange odors of the place nauseated her and she has refused steadfastly to accompany me there again.

Beyond Chinatown are the Spanish and Italian colonies which are most colorful, but Pearl has little use for "Dagos" and will not eat in any of these Latin cafés where one may dine so cheaply.

"American restaurants are good enough for me," she says, "and I want to know I'm eating clean food."

I believe she'd rather starve then eat in a Chinese restaurant. And, although it is one of the best places in town, she balked flatfooted against entering the famous Flytrap Café just because of the name.

The original Flytrap was destroyed by the fire and it may have justified the implication, but its successor is as clean as any restaurant I ever saw.

Marks of the fire and earthquake still are plain in many sections of the city and I don't suppose they ever will be entirely wiped out. There are vacant lots hidden by billboards here and there, and if you peek behind the billboards you see heaps of brick and charred timber that have been untouched since 1906. Talk to any native for an hour or so and he is almost certain to bring the conversation around to "the fire" and tell about his own experiences.

Everything is dated as "Before the fire" or "After the fire." And when you have heard a number of stories, you don't wonder. Really it is amazing that there are so few signs of the disaster after only five and a half years.

I have read a number of books recently, three of which were outstanding. First I should list Jeffrey Farnol's "The Broad Highway." Next is "The Winning of Barbara Worth" by Harold Bell Wright; and "Queed" by H. S. Harrison.

"The Broad Highway" really is a marvelous work. It has everything—glamour, adventure, romance and characters that are no wooden puppets, but real living persons. I really should hold it to be a great book and one that will live. It made a profound impression on me. The sense of movement and atmosphere that Farnol imprisoned in his pages is something for me to study. I shall get it from the library again and read it more slowly and try to analyze his methods.

"The Winning of Barbara Worth" is more of a love story than the conquering of the desert. But Wright also has written a glamorous story. I found myself displeased that Willard Holmes, the slick engineer, finally won Barbara rather than Abe Lee, the rough-and-ready, honest young man of the desert. Perhaps that prejudiced me against the novel, but I must admit the author did a competent job. I do not think Harold Bell Wright has the artistry of Farnol, however.

"Queed" is a newspaper story. It is most interesting, but the characters do not ring true with me.

I wish Irvin S. Cobb would write a novel.

APRIL 16, 1912. It doesn't seem that I have much time these days for anything but work and entertaining the family.

Usually I take Pearl to a picture show on my night off while we leave Byron with Mrs. Castro.

Byron was a year old on the 9th and is really a cute, smart baby. He crawls all over the apartment and can stand up by hanging to a chair. Also he jabbers something which Pearl says is "mama." He is blue-eyed like his mother and has curly, yellow hair.

We didn't go to a show tonight because Mrs. Castro is sick with a bad cold and we didn't have any other place to leave the baby. That is why I have time to review things.

One of the most terrible tragedies in history occurred Sunday night.

The new White Star liner *Titanic* making her maiden voyage from Liverpool to New York struck an iceberg and sank, carrying almost 1,600 souls to watery graves. The

Titanic had been advertised as absolutely unsinkable because of her watertight compartments. For that reason, apparently, there were not enough lifeboats for 2,202 passengers and crew. There will be an investigation of that point and also as to why such a ship should sink so quickly after striking an iceberg. John Jacob Astor was one of those who died. Harrowing stories have been coming over the wires from survivors who were picked up by the steamer *Carpathia* ever since the disaster. The *Carpathia* was brought to the scene by wireless CQD's from the *Titanic* after the great liner had struck the berg. This alone marks wireless telegraphy as probably the greatest invention of this age. The world should honor the Italian Marconi, who invented it.

There was one ludicrous angle to the *Titanic* in the *Tribune* office. It was a very dull night for news and Jimmy Albertson, the news editor, was holding a conference with Pete Van Camp, the city editor, and Phil Blackburn, the new telegraph editor, over what story he could play. Pete didn't have anything except a cheap murder in a Kearny Street rooming house and Blackburn said he didn't have anything much.

Then Blackburn looked over his copy again and squinted through his glasses at a bulletin and said, "Well, Jimmy, if you haven't got anything else—you know this new liner, the *Titanic,* biggest ship afloat?"

Albertson was just getting out a new cigarette. "Yeah," he said.

"Well," went on Blackburn, "it's on its maiden voyage from Liverpool to New York."

"Yeah," said Albertson, lighting a match.

"I got a bulletin about the *Titanic* here that says she wirelessed she'd struck an iceberg and was in danger of sinking."

Albertson dropped both the match and cigarette.

"Great G—!" he shouted loud enough to be heard clear out on Market Street. He leaped from his chair, yelling for a boy to get pictures of the liner from the morgue. And late as it was we had an extra on the street in 15 minutes.

There was a certain satisfaction to me in that little drama. Albertson knew I wanted the telegraph job, but when Ollie McClelland went to Los Angeles a month ago, he selected Blackburn for the job. I hope he's satisfied with his selection now. I hope he likes Blackburn's news judgment. The biggest story in years laid in his lap and he thought it might do for an eight-column line if they didn't have "anything else."

I have been strangely depressed all day over another of my dreams about Frances.

Today, I feel certain, was her wedding day. I saw her as plainly as I have ever seen anybody while awake and she was dressed as a bride.

The dream had little continuity, but was a mere series of very sharp pictures. But the pictures told the story. First she was in her room, the room I have seen several times in my dreams. I know this room almost as well as I know our own apartment. I know her bureau and commode and the two chairs and the appearance of her bed and the flowered rug and the lace curtains on the two windows and the pictures on the wall and my own framed photograph, which heretofore has been resting on the bureau beside the mirror.

In the first picture I noticed particularly that my photograph was missing from its accustomed place. Frances was sitting before the mirror combing her hair.

Then she was garbed in a white satin gown with trailing veil and was being fussed over by two girls whom I could not recognize.

The next picture was a shifting confusion of music and crowds and flowers, but in it I caught one glimpse of Frances looking very beautiful and carrying a huge bouquet of hothouse roses.

So far I had seen nothing of the bridegroom nor had any hint of his identity. But the next picture was of the Exchange

Street railway station. There was a crowd of people in the old building. It seemed that I could recognize some of them, but they were all slightly out of focus and I identified no one. Then there was Frances dressed in a gray suit and by her side was Paul Clark. There was much laughter and raillery. Clark looked much the same as he did six years ago, but was about twenty pounds heavier. He seemed to have grown thicker in the neck and waist.

Then the train was in and there was the traditional shower of rice and Frances and Clark entered the car. I have no idea where they were going.

Of course this all could be merely the workings of my perfervid imagination. It may be final proof that I am silly and in a class with the women who go to fortunetellers, but I cannot but believe Frances actually has married Clark.

Certainly I never have wished anything to happen to Pearl, but heretofore I have held hope in the back of my head that someway, somehow, sometime Frances and I should be brought together again. I have not dared actually to think that thought. It merely has been an unexpressed hope in the inner recesses of my being.

Now that unthought thought is shattered. I feel certain that tonight Frances is on her honeymoon with Clark. I don't dare even think of it. I can't bear to think of it.

I know it is ridiculous for me to feel this way. I'm afraid my emotional nature is not as sane as it should be.

APRIL 18, 1912. I am now telegraph editor of the *San Francisco Tribune*.

Phil Blackburn was given a terrible bawling out on the *Titanic* story by Albertson and Rothstein and when Blackburn declared he was "just kidding" Rothstein got mad and put me on the telegraph desk and fired Blackburn.

I have the job officially enough—as long as it lasts—but

nothing has been said about raising my pay. I am willing to let things stand as they are until they see I can make good.

There is really something thrilling about the job. There is a greater sense of doing something important than any other work I have ever done.

We have the complete service of the Associated Press and World-Wide Press which means practically that wires stretch out from my desk to every state in the Union and to every nation in the world.

For instance, should a disastrous fire break out in Singapore or an anarchist assassinate a Balkan prince, word would be brought me with the speed of lightning. I probably should know of the assassination before the newspapers were out in the prince's home city. I probably should know about it before members of the prince's own family were told.

When you stop to consider it, there is a grave responsibility connected with having the whole world laid in your lap every night. For the telegraph editor must decide the relative worth of all these thousands and thousands of words. What will interest San Francisco most? That is the thing I must keep uppermost in my mind. What are the possible repercussions here in San Francisco of a Supreme Court decision in Washington on sugar? A coal mine strike in Colorado is of great interest some places. But little coal is used here. Therefore a coal mine strike would not be a candidate for Page One unless there was a great deal of violence.

The way we work is this: I come on at 2 o'clock in the afternoon and have a stack of flimsy carbon copies of the day reports. I go through these and separate all copy on the main stories and put it in copy paper folders which I label "Congress," "Strike," "Balkans," and whatever else is happening. I keep these carbon copies of the day reports to augment the night wire, if necessary, for quite often there are important angles in the day reports which are not repeated in the night reports. For instance, when the President delivers a message to Congress or any other important speech is made, the text will be carried on one wire and not repeated. Also from the day report I will select quite a number of "shorts"—little freak features, deaths and the like, which I will mark up for two line 14-point heads or one line 6-point black heads as fillers, especially for the first edition. It is always difficult to find enough good "shorts" for the first edition and it would be practically impossible without the day reports.

From this mass of carbon copies I take all sports news and stick it on the sport editor's spindle. The same with financial news for the financial editor.

It takes me about an hour to get this mass straightened out and at 3 o'clock the night wires open and copy boys begin to bring me "hard copy" or the original typescript from the telegraph operators' typewriters.

I not only keep track of all that is going on in the world and pick out possible stories for Page One, which are weeded out each edition by the news editor together with the possible Page One material selected by the city editor from local news, but I judge the merits of all telegraph matter to appear on the inside pages, designate the length to be used and mark the type of head—although I sometimes confer with Jimmy Albertson over this. Also I edit and trim down a good bit of this copy myself and write heads on a certain amount of it, together with writing "dash matter" or background stuff on some stories which will follow the main story after a dash.

It is a real job and I am very excited over it.

Heretofore I have been regarding my newspaper work more or less as a steppingstone to something else. I have considered it preparation for my real lifework of writing truly important novels. Now I am wondering if I have not made a mistake. Nothing could be more important than being a really competent newspaper executive. It is the daily press, after all, which influences public thought. A paper like the *Tribune,* for instance, with nearly 200,000 circulation may be read by half a million people daily. How many novelists can hope for an audience like that?

Besides, the newspaperman is dealing with living things, with reality. And the novelist usually is dealing with mere figments of his imagination and not burning questions of the day.

Someday in the distant future I shall write a book or several books. But now I shall devote my energies to making myself the best possible newspaperman. I shall endeavor to be the best telegraph editor the *Tribune* ever had. I shall set my immediate goal at the news editor's desk. Then I shall hope to become managing editor and finally publisher.

High newspaper executives make fine money. I know I have it in me to become a high executive. I shall be able to save a good deal of money, live comfortably, give Byron a good college education. Then, by investing my savings judiciously in first mortgages and gilt-edge securities, I shall be able to retire when I am in my early fifties and devote myself to literature.

Pearl approves this plan heartily and, after all, I must admit Pearl has a pretty level head. Sometimes I have regarded her as overmaterial in her thoughts. But that is woman's way. And it is nothing more than good, common sense.

She was happy over my promotion, but thought I should demand a raise in salary immediately. I convinced her, however, that I should lose nothing by failing to appear anxious on that score.

I shall, however, continue keeping notes on my experiences and thoughts, which I know will prove most valuable to me when I finally have time to write.

I got a letter from Mother today. She is in Kenmore helping my sister Ethel have a baby. Ethel came through all right and has a little girl they have named Harriet. Ethel is married to a Kenmore jeweler named Arthur Hodge. I have never seen him.

Mother has been out in the "Fruit Belt" of Buffalo visiting some of the old neighbors, but she didn't mention the Harbachs. As a matter of fact, she only knew Mrs. Harbach casually, but it seems she is rather going out of her way not to mention Frances.

Mother likes Buffalo better than Pittsburgh, but Father doesn't. He likes his job there and is making much more money than he could have got from the Queen City Brass Works in Buffalo.

OCTOBER 17, 1912. Thursday is my night off now, but Pearl and I did not go out tonight. Mrs. Castro, with whom we leave Byron, is quite ill with a cold and Pearl knows nobody else she would trust with the baby.

A great many things have been happening and I usually am too tired when I get home from work to write anything in this record.

The last big story was the attempt of a crank in Milwaukee to assassinate Theodore Roosevelt.

The man, John Schrank of New York, perhaps had good intentions for the country at large but was most ill-advised. Also, the Roosevelt luck held. Schrank was only six or seven feet distant when he fired at T.R. with a heavy revolver. The bullet struck Roosevelt in the chest. It passed through a bulky manuscript of a speech, through the Colonel's glasses case and into his chest. It inflicted only a flesh wound and Roosevelt, with a great display of fortitude, was able to deliver his speech. Then he was taken to Chicago and placed in a hospital.

The whole incident was made to order for Roosevelt and should bring him many votes.

Many things have happened politically this summer.

To begin with, the Republican national convention repudiated the great T.R. by ignoring his attacks on his former bosom pal, President Taft, and renominated the President. No doubt that was poor political strategy, for Taft is amazingly unpopular. But Roosevelt showed himself to be something less than the good sport he claims to be by bolting from the convention and holding a convention of his own. He formed what he calls the Progressive Party, which has been nicknamed the "Bull Moose Party."

The Bull Moose platform sounds rather good, calling as it does for the recall and referendum—even to the recall of judicial decisions and recall of the judiciary. One cannot, however, fail to be suspicious.

Senator Hiram Johnson was nominated as T.R.'s running mate on the Bull Moose ticket and he should bring the party many votes in California, for Johnson is immensely popular here.

The Democratic convention in Baltimore, thanks to William Jennings Bryan, nominated Governor Woodrow Wilson of New Jersey—a capable and high-minded gentleman.

Mr. Bryan was a delegate from Nebraska and instructed for Speaker of the House Champ Clark. At the outset it appeared that Clark probably would be the nominee, which distressed me greatly.

With the Republican Party hopelessly split and with Taft's bad record to work on, the Democrats have the best chance of electing a President they have held since Grover Cleveland. No doubt Champ Clark could be elected. But I personally, remembering his terrible blunder on Canadian reciprocity, was afraid he lacked proper judgment to sit in the White House. Who could know when he might make a similar blunder which might precipitate serious international complications?

It was such a blunder that turned the tide against him. In the midst of the convention battle, Clark made concessions to Tammany in order to gain the strong New York support. And Bryan, long a foe of the Tammany Tiger, rose to his feet. This, to his mind—and properly too—was sufficient cause for him as a delegate to repudiate his instructions.

The Great Commoner launched into an extemporaneous speech which was scarcely second to his "Cross of Gold" speech of 1896 and swept the convention into roars of enthusiasm. Bryan switched his support from Clark to Wilson and stampeded the convention.

Thus Bryan, who failed three times to reach the White House himself, at least can be credited with making a Democratic President, who I predict will prove one of the finest and greatest ever to be elected. I say this because I believe Wilson's election is practically a foregone conclusion. I do not believe Taft has a chance. And I actually believe Roosevelt will run ahead of the Republican ticket.

We have seen the death of Republicanism, of special privilege and national boodle.

I am now making $40 a week and they seem well pleased with my work as telegraph editor. We have bought a new phonograph, a Victor, which is vastly superior to our old two-horned Duplex. I bought a number of Sousa band records while Pearl selected some popular music such as "Raggy Rag," "You Great Big Beautiful Doll," "Mysterious Rag," and "Alexander's Ragtime Band." That last is one of the catchiest pieces I ever heard. The newsboys on the streets are whistling it and when lulls come on the copy desk late at night somebody will start, "Come on and hear—" in a tenor voice. Then big-chested Tom Rogers will bear down with a bass, "Come on and hear—" Then four or five will chime in on "—Alex-an-der's Ragtime Band."

They'll repeat the "Come on and hears" and then chorus, "It's the best band in the land."

Freddie Simpson will tenor, "They can play a bugle call like you never heard before," and Rogers will bass it, "So natur-al that you want to go to war," and so on until Mr. Rothstein sticks his head out his office door, scowling.

That quiets things for then, but after the next edition it starts all over again.

Speaking of Tom Rogers, he and I had an odd experience the other night after work.

Frequently he and I will go up to Tait's or Kyne's for a lunch after work. He is a fine conversationalist and has had 20 years' experience working on newspapers from New York and New Orleans to the Hawaiian Islands. He probably would be a managing editor or publisher some place if it weren't for his wanderlust and love for liquor. He has lost many jobs because of drunken escapades, but as he is about 40 now he is becoming more steady.

Rogers and I were walking up Ellis Street at about 2 o'clock in the morning. The street was quiet and a block off Market nobody was in sight except a young girl who was leaning disconsolately against a lamppost. She was not more than 19 or 20, but while her clothing was of good quality, she seemed somewhat disheveled.

She looked at us with a bewildered expression as we approached and Rogers said, "Hi, Sis—out kind of late, aren't you?"

The girl straightened. "Gentlemen," she said, "time is only relative. And isn't it safe to be up while you're still out?"

"My young friend," said Rogers, "it's our business to be out at this hour. We're like the owls and the bats and the burglars. We circulate only when honest folk sleep."

"Ah," said the girl, rolling her large eyes upward, "just denizens of the shadows. Well, it's my business to be here, there, everywhere at all times. You don't know it, of course, but I'm royalty. You don't know me, but I know you. You're Mutt and Jeff. And where in h— are you going at this hour?"

"Up to Kyne's," I told her, "after a bite to eat before bed."

The girl shook her head. "I couldn't possibly accompany you to bed," she drawled dreamily, "but I might honor you with my company as far as the restaurant—if I could have a waffle with sausage and coffee."

"You can have a waffle and sausage and coffee and also maple syrup," Rogers promised.

So the girl pushed herself away from the lamppost, seized Rogers' arm and mine and walked between us the block to the restaurant. We took a booth and the girl sat with Rogers on one side of the table. I faced them.

"What's this royalty talk?" I asked her. I thought she was drunk, which was not entirely correct. But there was something unusual about her. And she spoke like an educated person.

She smiled enigmatically into my eyes.

"One never knows, does one?" she drawled. "F'r instance you never dreamed this morning that you should dine with royalty tonight."

"Nope," I said. "One never knows. And what royal house do you happen to represent?"

"Did you ever," she asked, "hear of Betty Butzer?"

"Not *the* Betty Butzer?" said Rogers with simulated awe in his voice.

She smiled and put a long forefinger coyly to the tip of her chin. The fingernail was dirty. "The one and only daughter of the Sawdust King," she proclaimed.

"So *you're* the Sawdust Princess," said Rogers. "My, my."

"The one and only," she said, "and might I ask the identity of my charming hosts?"

"You'd never think it," said Rogers, "but we're twin brothers." He pointed at me with a stubby thumb. "His name is Philander Chase Knox and my name is Philander Chase Knox. You can call us both Philly for short."

"I bet you were cute babies," observed the girl. "But you'd never guess where I have been tonight."

"The sewers of Paris," hazarded Rogers.

"Not even close," said she. "At one o'clock this afternoon I was conferring with His Holiness, the Pope."

"You made a quick trip back."

"At four o'clock this afternoon," she continued, "I was having tea with His Royal Highness, the Prince of Wales." She shook her head dreamily. "Charming fellow, *very* charming."

The waiter came to our booth. The Sawdust Princess turned on him. "Garçon," she said, "bring me filet mignon et green onions et two dishes of fresh strawberries and a demitasse."

"Bring her," boomed Rogers, "a waffle and sausage and a mug of java. What you want, Philander Chase?"

"That'll do for me," I said.

"Make it three and make it snappy," ordered Rogers. "Now what about the Prince of Wales?"

"You'd never believe it," observed the girl, "if I told you how many chests of diamonds and rubies and pearls and emeralds I own."

"That's right," said Rogers, "to say nothing of your sapphires and opals and amethysts and topazes."

She laughed and rested her elbows on the table. "It's such a responsibility. Sometimes I'm so weary I could cry. Do you know I often do cry? Can you imagine Betty Butzer crying? Suppose the world knew Betty Butzer cried. What would happen on the Bourse? What would happen on the Bund? Suppose you told. Suppose the word was flashed around the world. Suppose in the streets of Christiania and Constantinople it was whispered through the shadows—Betty Butzer is a weak, human woman after all. At first the incredible thought would be rejected. 'Preposterous, preposterous,' they'd say. Then they would wonder and perhaps believe, and it would mean death to thousands, perhaps millions. It would mean death to *you* in all probability. But no, it must never be known—never, never, never."

Her eyes were blazing at me. "Do you know who my husband is?" she demanded.

I shook my head. "I couldn't guess."

"Not Cardinal Gibbons?" hazarded Rogers.

"I have no husband," she murmured. "No husband, no husband. His name *was* Michelangelo. He thought he was an artist and could paint God, but he wanted babies, babies, babies. So I shot him there in our hovel on the left bank of the Seine. I killed him and left him surrounded by tubes of paint and brushes and paintings of God. God is *sacred*. No paint-daubed artist has a right to ask God to climb on his model's stand. He'd paint me in the nude, but it was wrong to ask *God* to take off his clothes. It was wrong because he would call God bow-legged, too. I know. And besides, he wanted babies. So I shot him and it was God's work. Works of God oft remind us Life is but a hollow dream. But Jesus knows where he can find us, pulling hard against the stream. That's poetry. I made it up coming here from London tonight. Ah, me! London today, Frisco tonight, Tokio tomorrow."

"On the level, Betty," I said, "what do you do for a living? Do your folks live here?"

She straightened and stared at me haughtily. "I," she said, "am the daughter of the Sawdust King."

"On the level, Betty," said Rogers, "do you sniff it or shoot it?"

"You've never heard of my aeroplane, have you?" she asked. "Of course you haven't. It's quite a secret. Naturally, His Royal Highness, the Prince of Wales, knows I have an aeroplane, but he hasn't an idea how good it is. Took him for a ride once or twice but I had my chauffeur slow it down to about a hundred miles a hour. You know—Davy is a very dear friend, but after all he is the heir to the British throne —it wouldn't do for him to realize my plane will do more than a thousand miles an hour. You can see that, can't you? As it was, some spy cabled my old pal Bill Taft that I'd been taking Davy up and Bill cabled me in code to quit it. Wonder if I have that code message with me? It was cute."

While she was fumbling in her purse for President Taft's message the waiter brought our waffles.

"Where do you keep your plane in San Francisco?" I asked.

The girl looked up from her purse. "You'd just like to know, wouldn't you? I remember now, I burned that message of course. I'm supposed to burn all messages I get from Bill. It isn't on account of his wife—she's not a bit jealous. Just a matter of international diplomacy."

"Of course," said Rogers. "You eat your waffle before it gets cold. You'll feel better after you get some food into you."

She drenched her waffle with syrup and took a bite. "No," she said, "not food, but music. You should hear me play the piano."

"I'm sure we'd love to," said Rogers, "but Philander Chase and I are material. We need groceries now and then."

"Never had but one music lesson in my life, but I could play like Paderewski."

"Must have had a pretty good teacher," I suggested.

"*Pretty* good! Listen, I'll tell you about it. One Sunday afternoon I was alone in the living room and all at once I looked at the piano and wished my mother had made me take lessons when I was a kid. I hadn't any more than wished that than who was standing beside me but St. Cecilia.

"She was looking down at me with a kind smile and she said to me, 'You wish to pay the piano, my child?'

"I said, 'Yes, St. Cecilia, but I'm afraid it's too late now.'

"And she said, 'Not at all, my child. Come sit at the piano and I will teach you.'

"So I went to the piano and St. Cecilia said, 'Put your hands on the keyboard, so. Now what do you want to play?'

"I said, 'Well, if you don't mind, St. Cecilia, I'd like to start with "Everybody's Doin' It."'

" 'Go ahead and play it,' she said, so I started playing and Paderewski couldn't have done better.

" 'That's all right,' said St. Cecilia, 'but you need a little more pedal on the *doin'*. You want to emphasize that.' So I played it again and St. Cecilia said it was very good. Then I played 'Over the Waves' and 'The Mosquito Parade' and everything. And sometimes I could play so fast the piano couldn't deliver as fast as I was hitting the keys. I'd get the keys stacked up way ahead and I could take my hands off and the piano would keep right on playing for five seconds or so until it could catch up with me. And pretty soon when I turned around to see how St. Cecilia liked it she was gone."

The girl took a drink of coffee. "I've been able to play like that ever since. You'd think with anybody playing as fast as I do the keys would stick like typewriter keys, but they don't."

"Oh," said Rogers, "you were a stenographer before you got to be a snowbird, weren't you? Who'd you work for?"

The girl's mouth opened and she turned and stared long at Rogers. Then she began to cry.

"You've insulted me," she blubbered. "You know I'm royalty. You know I'm practically engaged to His Highness, the Prince of Wales. Yet you ask me if I'm a stenographer. Well, that's what one gets for being democratic. Let me out of here this instant."

She rose and tried to push by Rogers.

"Wait a minute, wait a minute," he commanded. "You quiet down and eat your waffle and coffee."

At that she turned and picked up her cup and she threw hot coffee full into Rogers' face. Rogers let out a bellow but before he could wipe the coffee from his eyes the girl had climbed right over his lap and out of the booth. I made a grab for her, but she slapped me in the face with her purse and fled from the restaurant.

Rogers wasn't really burnt by the coffee and our waiter came and sympathetically helped wipe the coffee from his face and coat. Then we went ahead and ate our waffles and sausage.

"That," Rogers said, "is what you get for fooling with a sleigh-rider. Coke-heads are funny, but you can't tell what they'll do. They'd slit your throat and think it was a joke."

Two weeks ago the *Saturday Evening Post* carried another story by Irvin S. Cobb which I believe is the greatest short story I ever read. It was called "The Belled Buzzard" and tells simply of how a man's own imagination convicted him of murder. But it is atmosphere he creates through close attention to minute detail which makes the story remarkable.

I have learned from Cobb that I am far from ready to begin writing seriously yet. Not only must I study means of expression, but I must study life more. When Cobb writes of anything you can be certain he knows even the smallest angle of his subject. So many writers have only a superficial knowledge of their subject and their work shows it.

Before Cobb puts pen to paper he has gone over his locale with a fine-tooth comb. He has dissected every plant in the district, he has studied the life habits of every animal and bird in the vicinity. He knows the manners of speech of the people and their business and recreations.

"Riders of the Purple Sage" by Zane Grey, a new book I have just read aloud to Pearl, is very popular now. It is a very fine book in some ways and Grey seems to know his subject almost as well as Cobb knows his. I find myself unable to analyze the difference, but somehow Cobb's characters and situations seem more real to me than do Grey's. And I have a feeling that Cobb's work will live when Grey's is forgotten. In this, however, I may be mistaken. Pearl much preferred "Riders of the Purple Sage" to "The Belled Buzzard" and said it seemed much more real to her than Cobb's story. And I must remember that I have little taste for the classics. For instance, I remember I hated Thackeray's "Henry Esmond" when we read it in high school.

November 14, 1912. It is cold and foggy and rainy tonight so we stayed in. Mr. and Mrs. Castro came up and we played hearts. Mrs. Castro, who is quite vivacious despite her thinness, is teaching Pearl to play bridge whist and Pearl wants me to learn. But it seems a waste of time to me. I should rather read than play cards, but I get very little opportunity to read these days.

Byron is 19 months old now and is walking all over the place. He fell down the front steps the other day and got a nasty bump on his head. He calls me "poppy" and he loves to climb on my lap and pull my hair. It is amazing how much that child means to me now. I catch myself talking too much about him at the office and I know what bores proud fathers can become.

The fifth was election day and, of course, Woodrow Wilson was elected President by the greatest majority ever recorded. Taft carried only two states, Vermont and Utah, and got a total of 8 electoral votes.

Roosevelt got 88 electoral votes and Wilson 435.

Now we shall see some legislation to help the common people, for Wilson has a Democratic Congress to back him up.

I bet $10 against $7 on the election and won the $7. But I lost $5 on California, which cut my winning to $2. Hiram Johnson carried California for Roosevelt, but by the narrow margin of 174 votes.

Election time is a terrible grind in a newspaper office, especially for the telegraph editor. I went to work at 11 o'clock Tuesday morning and worked straight through until 9 o'clock Wednesday. Then I went home, shaved, took a bath and slept an hour and a half before coming back to the office.

My old bookkeeping training comes in very handy in compiling election returns. I was complimented on my job.

I had another dream of Frances the other night. She was working in her kitchen and wearing a large red and blue apron. I could see a diamond ring and a plain gold band on her left ring finger as she started to wash the dishes in the sink.

She had placed the dishes, apparently from breakfast, in an oval dishpan and took the teakettle off the stove. The water was steaming from the spout as she started to pour it in the dishpan. Then the top fell off the teakettle and steam rushed up over her right hand. She almost dropped the kettle, but managed to set it down quickly on the draining board. Her fingers were scalded from the steam. I saw her get some lard from the refrigerator and smear it on her fingers. Then I saw her sit down, holding her right wrist with her left hand and heard her sobbing softly from the pain. I awoke almost crying myself in sympathy. It was 5:30 a.m., which would have been 8:30 in Buffalo—about the time she would be washing breakfast dishes.

The other day I read of an Austrian scientist named Sigmund Freud who has written a book about the interpretation of dreams. I am going to get that book from the library, if possible, and see if he has any solution for my strange dreams of Frances. I wonder if there are any authenticated cases of people dreaming of occurrences while they actually are happening?

JANUARY 4, 1913. "I should worry" is the current slang rage. To every comment the smart slang reply is, "I should worry" —which means just the opposite; *i.e.,* complete indifference. When I was walking to work this afternoon I saw a little

girl about 8 years old on California Street who was chanting
this commentary on the age:

"I should worry, I should care,
* I should marry a millionaire:*
If he should die, I should cry
* And I should marry another guy."*

The newspaper humorists and cartoonists are having a lot
of fun over this being a "jinx" year. And a good many
superstitious people are willing to concur seriously. That
goes particularly with the Republicans who can see nothing
but disaster in a Democratic administration. I have heard
people point to the armament race in Europe (people who
should know better) and quote how Germany is increasing
her army and how France is increasing her army and Russia
and the other countries and predict that the greatest war in
history is in the offing. They refer to the Agadir, Morocco,
incident of 1911 when Germany and her allies and France
and her allies were snarling at each other. They say war was
narrowly averted then and that next time it will be more difficult to avoid.

Big-voiced Tom Rogers is one of the leading jingoes in
the *Tribune*. Germany, he says, is lusting for more power
and wants territorial expansion. He believes Kaiser Wilhelm
is building up his military force for conquest. Great Britain,
he says, is jealous of Germany's growing foreign trade because Germany, being efficient, can manufacture goods and
undersell England. He sees France as living in terror of
Germany and preparing for a war which is considered inevitable.

I point out to Rogers that wars were the natural thing in
the Dark Ages because the people of every nation were
ignorant of the neighboring peoples and that ignorance
breeds distrust, fear and hatred. Now, however, the peoples

of every land know the nature of their neighbors because they are able to read and because there are daily papers and magazines which show the Frenchman that the German is no different from himself, wishing only a chance to make a living and support his family. Why, then, should he wish to shoot Germans? The Germans are proud of their scientists who are working to conquer disease and physical forces and make the world a better place in which to live. The French scientists are doing the same thing and they are working largely together with the Germans.

It is unthinkable, then, that mere business rivalries could cause a war. True, the nations of the world are building many big cannons and battleships, but those could act as well for preservation of peace as for waging war. Even if some ruler were mad enough to start a major war, it is certain that enlightened twentieth century citizens should refuse to fight and that the ruler would be overthrown.

I was amused at a cartoon I saw the other day, entitled "The Calamity Chorus." It depicted a group of farmers dancing woefully arm in arm and singing:

> *"Frost'll get the peach crop, peach crop, peach crop;*
> *Frost'll get the peach crop, ain't that mean?*
> *Frost'll get the peach crop, for it's nineteen thirteen."*

That, I think, is just as sensible as Tom Rogers' arguments about war.

The government's new venture into business also is causing a lot of comment in the papers—mostly unfavorable. That is parcels post. There are a lot of jokes about the farmer shipping a dozen eggs by parcels post and the recipient getting some chickens, and there are cartoons of poor mail carriers loaded down with cookstoves and calves and sacks of potatoes and there are stories of tests made between parcels post and express companies wherein the express package

arrived far ahead. Express companies are crying it is uncon-
stitutional for the government to go into competition with
private industry.

Nevertheless I believe in government ownership of the
utilities and I believe parcels post can be made to work—if
they give it time. At present you have to go to the post office
to mail a parcels post package and you have to buy special
parcels post stamps. I think they'll have to straighten that
out if they're going to compete with the express companies.
They'll have to fix it so one can phone the post office and
they'll send out a wagon to pick up the parcel and they'll
have to fix it so you can use ordinary postage stamps instead
of the special parcels post stamps.

We had a mighty fine Christmas this year. Pearl got a
little tree and trimmed it. Byron was delighted. He would
toddle around and around, smiling all over his face and saying, "Tee, tee." He tried desperately to eat the ornaments
and we had to move them all out of his reach. We got him
quite a lot of toys, but the thing he likes best is a Teddy
bear. He calls it something that sounds like "Buzz." What he
means or where he gets it, we have no idea.

JANUARY 25, 1913. I really am saving some money now. I am
putting away an average of $5 a week in the savings bank and
now have $149. If I can continue that average, it will make
$260 a year. And it would seem that I can count on getting
advancement in position and salary. I expect to have $1,000
salted away two years from this summer. Then I can invest
that in building and loan or some good, safe stocks. The way
to make money is to have money working for you. I am
carrying $3,000 worth of life insurance, which isn't so very
much, but enough for emergencies. And I believe there are
better ways of saving money than life insurance.

My goal is twofold. First I want to assure Byron of a
college education. And second I am building toward that day

when I shall retire from the newspaper business and start writing for myself.

Morning before last I had a dream of Frances which indicates she is going to have a baby. I saw her sewing in her parlor, and presently she held up the garment and it was a baby's dress.

Now that is very much like the moving pictures. That is always the means by which the young wife of the movies reveals she is to present her young husband with an heir. Thus it is possible my dream mind manufactured this motion picture out of whole cloth. But I do not believe it.

There is talk that William J. Bryan may be made ambassador to England by President Wilson when he is inaugurated. Of course that is an honorable post, but as Wilson owes his very nomination to Bryan, I believe the Great Commoner should be given an even bigger place. It seems to me that Bryan would make an ideal Secretary of State.

Things are being cleared up in preparation for a government of the people by the people and for the people.

Congress has just impeached and convicted U. S. District Judge Robert W. Archbald of Scranton, Pa. It is the first time a federal judge has been ousted in 50 years. Archbald was convicted of corrupt collusion with railroad and mine operators.

President Wilson, as Governor of New Jersey, is waging violent warfare against the trusts, planning seven antitrust bills in the state. That bodes ill for the trusts when he enters the White House. And the Pujo committee investigating the Money Trust has the malefactors of great wealth on the run. As a matter of fact the Money Trust surrendered when George F. Baker, chairman of the First National Bank in New York, admitted that he believed the concentration of wealth has gone about far enough. Baker, who is said to be next to J. P. Morgan in financial power, admitted that if this power "got into bad hands" it would wreck the country.

He didn't believe, however, that it would ever get into "bad hands." Probably he considers "bad hands" are those who would do something to help the common people.

Morgan, himself, said he was unaware that he possessed any unusual power. He must not read the newspapers.

We shall see great things happening in the next four years.

FEBRUARY 13, 1913. Both Pearl and Byron are under the weather with bad colds. So Pearl stayed in bed today on my day off and I have been doing the housework and cooking the meals. I am learning to be a pretty fair cook.

Medical science is moving in leaps and bounds to conquer the ills of the human race. Soon they will perfect a serum which will immunize people against colds and La Grippe such as Pearl and the baby now have.

Smallpox has been practically wiped out by vaccination. Diphtheria, which used to kill thousands of children, has been robbed of its terrors by toxin antitoxin. And now two scourges of the ages are being whipped.

From Biblical times epilepsy has been a terrible affliction that falls upon thousands. Heretofore medical science has regarded this terrible malady as incurable. Now, it is announced, Dr. Ralph H. Spangler of Chicago has discovered a treatment which has cured 110 patients. The treatment consists of injections of rattlesnake venom.

Dr. Spangler has found that epileptic fits are caused by too quick coagulation or clotting of the blood. The rattlesnake poison, diluted of course, lengthens the period of coagulation.

The amazing discovery was made quite by accident. An epileptic in Texas was bitten by a rattlesnake and was cured of his fits.

The second discovery is even more important because it appears to be a sure cure for tuberculosis, and millions more people are afflicted with the White Plague than with epilepsy.

This benefactor of humanity is Dr. Friedrich Friedmann of Berlin. For years Dr. Friedmann has been experimenting with tuberculosis serums, trying to obtain an effective type from every animal imaginable. Finally he tried the turtle and the turtle serum works.

Dr. Friedmann has shown proof that his vaccine is entirely harmless and that he has treated 1,182 cases of tuberculosis in Germany, all of which were completely cured except those far advanced. He now is working on a method to immunize children against the disease and is coming to the United States to open a clinic in New York.

Men like Dr. Spangler and Dr. Friedmann should be honored far above war lords such as Napoleon, General Grant and Bismarck. Scientists are the real heroes. My fondest hope is that Byron may become such a man as Dr. Friedmann or Dr. Spangler.

MARCH 6, 1913. President Woodrow Wilson made one of the greatest speeches on record at his inauguration. He has won the whole nation, the whole world, as a matter of fact.

Even Taft, at the close of the address, put out his hand and said, "Mr. President, we're all behind you."

The press of London, impressed with Wilson's high ideals, declared the spirit of this address would spread over Europe, working for peace and good will among all nations.

The President showed the good judgment to appoint Mr. Bryan Secretary of State, which will strengthen his administration greatly. There also is a new cabinet post, one which has long been needed in America—that of Secretary of Labor.

It will have the effect of bringing justice to the laboring man and prevent wasteful and dangerous strikes. Wilson's Secretary of Labor also is a good choice. He is William B. Wilson, who formerly was secretary of the Miners' Union and who as congressman fathered the bill creating his post.

APRIL 3, 1913. I put Pearl and Byron on the train this afternoon, bound for Kansas City. Pearl has been away from home two years and a half and Mrs. Hawkins never has seen her grandson.

Naturally the trip is expensive. It takes practically all of our savings for the ticket and berth and for clothes for Pearl and the baby, but Pearl was very anxious to go and it was no more than right that she should. Of course now was the time, before it gets so hot in K.C. She plans to come back along the first of May. Well, the change will be good for her.

There have been terrible floods in Ohio, Indiana and Texas. Dayton, Ohio, has been virtually destroyed with nearly a thousand dead in the Ohio Valley. Hundreds also have been drowned around Brazos, Texas. I hope the Missouri and Kaw rivers don't go on a rampage.

APRIL 10, 1913. Fran has had her baby and strangely enough it was born on little Byron's second birthday—yesterday—unless it was born early this morning.

I dreamed of her being in a hospital bed this morning and beside her was the child. It is a girl, I know, because I heard her say to a nurse, "We're going to name her Carol—Carol Clark."

Fran looked pretty pale and wan, but I guess she came through the ordeal all right. I felt almost as excited about it all this morning as if it had been my own child.

I have received a postcard from Pearl showing the Commerce Trust Company building and saying they arrived in K.C. all right and that her mother is crazy about Byron.

While they are gone I have started writing a short story to sell to a magazine. Magazines pay good money for short stories and I may as well make some of it in my spare time.

This is the story of a newspaper reporter in San Francisco who falls in love with a rich girl. The girl's family oppose him as a suitor, but the girl loves him and they have many things in common, including convictions that the world could be run without war, poverty and crime if it were impossible for people to accumulate great wealth and if everyone was sure of an ample living.

The girl has some money of her own and a yacht, so they make up a crew of several young men and girls whom they have convinced of the truth of their ideas and they sail off to the South Seas.

There on an island they found a Utopia and are getting along fine despite a typhoon which wrecks the yacht and the menace of savage natives, whom they finally convert to their way of thinking.

The millionaire father, however, has hired many detectives to trace his daughter and finally they discover "Paradise Island." The father goes down there to get the girl and takes federal officers to arrest the reporter on charges of abduction and stealing the yacht. But after he gets there and looks over the peace and beauty of the island, he falls in love with the place himself, builds a grass hut and joins the colony.

When I rewrite it I am going to send the story to the *Saturday Evening Post,* which pays handsomely for stories they like. "Paradise Island," as I have titled it, should be unusual enough to attract the *Post's* attention.

I should be tempted to send Fran's baby a present if I knew her address. Also there is a possibility that there is nothing to my dreams at all. Perhaps she has no baby, perhaps she isn't even married.

APRIL 14, 1913. Last night after work Tom Rogers, Jack Cullen and I went down around North Beach for a little recreation.

First we went to an Italian place and had some Italian spaghetti and wine. Then we went to another Italian place and had some special kind of wine that Cullen wanted us to try.

There was a rather pretty Italian girl there who served us with the wine and with bread sticks and a Cockney seaman who seemed to be paying court to the Italian girl. He was a wiry fellow of about medium height and very pleasant. Cullen, feeling his wine, invited this sailor to have a glass with us and he accepted. He was shipping on the morrow, he said, around the Horn for Liverpool. When he smiled, which was often, he showed that one of his front teeth had been broken off—probably in a fight. A pivot tooth had been put in, but that also was gone, leaving only the wire core sticking down like a slender steel fang.

He told us his name was Freddie Cutler and in a strong Cockney accent described his life at sea which, he attested, was a veritable h—.

Scarcely a long voyage could he remember where there had not been at least one murder aboard the freighters on which he ships. And in his 15 years at sea he has lived through nearly a dozen mutinies.

"The officers of a freighter," Cutler said, "get their jobs because they are hard men and without conscience. They are always armed with revolvers and the men have little chance in case of a mutiny. More times than I'd care to tell you gentlemen I've seen shipmates bloody well murdered and thrown overboard because they suffered some injury that might cripple them for the rest of the voyage."

"But," I asked, "how can they account for the missing men when the ship reaches a port?"

Cutler smiled. "Blimy," he said, "they write it down in the log that he died of pneumonia or inflammation of the bowels and was buried at sea—God rest his soul."

"Can't the men make a true report?"

"And be black-listed for life? Or murdered themselves when they put to sea again? And what admiralty court would believe a common seaman against an officer?" He laughed bitterly.

"I'd think you'd get away from the sea and find a job on a farm or something," said Cullen.

Cutler shook his head. "The sea," he said, "is something like opium smoking. Once you get the habit you can't get away from it, even when you bloody well know it's going to be the death of you. And what *else* could a sailor man do? I couldn't plow potatoes if I tried. You just have to keep on and on once you're in it.

"I never knew but one skipper to get his deserts and that was a bloody b—— named Plumb on the *Marble Cross* out of Plymouth for Cape Town. There was a cabin boy, a jolly little nipper named Alf Bennett who spilled a bottle of brandy in the skipper's cabin and this Plumb shot him dead in a rage. Well, poor little Alf was a great favorite with the crew and we mutinied proper. First I watches my chance off the Gold Coast and I slips behind this Captain Plumb and I bashes in his skull with a capstan bar. Killed him dead, I did."

"You killed him?" asked Rogers.

"Killed him dead. Then before the first mate and the second mate knew what was happening I had the skipper's revolver and shot *him* dead. And a Yankee named Three-Finger Gotch grabbed the first mate's revolver and shot the second mate dead. The third mate, he see what's up so he joined with us. Then we pipes all hands aft, dumps the bodies over the side and holds an election. Some was in favor of turning pirates, because if we sailed the *Marble Cross* in without officers there'd be a lot of questioning and without doubt a bit of hanging to boot. So we vote to scuttle her and we turn her shorewards toward Dakar. We sight land, wait for night and then open her bottom. When we hit Dakar in the boats we tell of an explosion and of how the officers went down like heroes. That was one time when a skipper got his bloody deserts."

While he was talking Cutler seemed a little embarrassed and self-conscious. He had taken a pair of dice from his pocket and shook them absent-mindedly in his hand. As he finished his tale he rolled the dice on the tablecloth and they came up double one.

Cullen picked them up. "Snake eyes," he said.

"Wasn't there any investigation?" Rogers asked.

"Oh, yes," said Cutler. "But we told 'em there was a sudden explosion in the for'ard coal bunkers and all at once the ship was in flames and she went to the bottom like her hull was bloody well blowed out. They did think it was quite odd the black hole crew all got out while the officers went down, but they couldn't prove anything."

Cullen rolled the dice on the table and a seven came up.

"Shoot you a nickel," said Cullen and Rogers faded him. Before we knew it there was a crap game on, which was joined by a navy sailor and a young civilian who were sitting at a table across the room and pretty soon by the Italian who ran the place.

I lost $5.40. Cullen lost $16, which was all he had. Rogers dropped $9 and the Italian had to visit his cash drawer several times. I don't know how the navy sailor and his civilian friend came out, but I think they lost also. I think the Englishman, Cutler, won about all the money that was won. We shot craps there until 5:30 and then the Italian got us some coffee. Rogers says he thinks the Cockney sailor is entitled to be classed with Baron Munchausen as a liar. But we agreed that his dice couldn't have been crooked. At one time I was about $5 ahead of the game and that couldn't have been if the dice were loaded. The sailor may have been unlucky in his occupation, but he is very lucky at gambling—at least he was last night.

APRIL 25, 1913. I got "Paradise Island" back from the *Saturday Evening Post* today. A short letter accompanying the manuscript did not explain why they could not use it other than the statement, "Rejection of a manuscript does not necessarily imply the manuscript is lacking in merit, but only that it is unsuited for the present needs of the *Saturday Evening Post.*"

I infer from that it might be well to save the story and resubmit it in about a year as necessarily the needs of a magazine must change from time to time. I shall put it by for some time at least. It may be that the theme is too broad to be dealt with adequately in a short story. Perhaps it will take a book-length novel or serial to do it justice.

MAY 1, 1913. I got a letter from Pearl today saying she needed $30 before she could start home. I had to borrow $5 from Tom Rogers and pawn my watch for another five to make up the thirty.

Sunday morning there was a poker game on the copy desk that got turned into table stakes. We played until 6 a.m. and I lost more than $50, mostly in IOU's which I paid off Monday.

I am definitely through with playing poker—even penny ante. Here I need a new suit and a new pair of shoes badly, but Heaven only knows when I can get them. Ten dollars and a quarter of this week's pay must go to pay off Rogers and get my watch out of hock. And I must keep this misfortune from Pearl. I should never hear the last of it if she found out I lost $50 gambling. That is more than I can save in a month under the best of conditions.

A couple of months ago I was feeling so satisfied with the growing bank account. Now I am broke, and not only broke but in debt.

MAY 12, 1913. Pearl and Byron got back yesterday and I almost missed them in the crowd at the Ferry Building.

Passengers come off the ferries on two ramps—from the upper
and lower decks. I stood between the two streams, not knowing which ramp they would be on. I was looking for Pearl
to be wearing her red suit and hat and to be carrying or
leading Byron. But she was wearing a gray suit and hat
she had bought in Kansas City and a man who had taken
a fancy to Byron on the train was carrying him. Pearl looks
very nice in her new clothes.

The first thing Byron said when he saw me was, "Oh,
Poppy, By got choo-choo."

I said, "Yes, you came on a choo-choo."

"No," he said, "By *got* choo-choo."

And sure enough, he did have an engine—a small glass
one that had been full of candy and that his grandmother had
bought for him in the Kansas City Union Station.

Anti-Japanese sentiment has been growing in California
for a long time and it has just reached a climax with passage
of a law which prohibits ownership of land by aliens. It was
signed by Governor Johnson.

Japanese are even more efficient truck gardeners than the
Portuguese. Because they are willing to work such long hours
and because they invariably hire other Orientals to work in
their truck gardens and orchards at wages that no American
could subsist on, they have been making competition most
difficult. There have been a number of demonstrations against
the Japanese over the state.

When the antialien land law was introduced in the legis-
lature, it was aimed directly at the Japanese. Japan was incensed and the ambassador in Washington registered an
official protest.

With bitterness in California at a point where a serious
international incident seemed almost inevitable, Secretary of
State Bryan took a flying trip out here to pour oil on the
troubled waters. To an extent he succeeded. While the bill
was passed and signed into a law, Mr. Bryan has convinced

the Japanese government that the law is not discriminatory, that it is not aimed directly at Japanese nationals, but at all aliens.

Of course it is discriminatory, for other aliens can acquire land merely by taking out naturalization papers. And Orientals are excluded from American citizenship.

JUNE 14, 1913. Yesterday being Friday, the 13th of 1913 should have been the "jinx day" of all time. But nothing untoward occurred, except that I had a quarrel with Pearl.

When I got up a little before 11 o'clock Pearl and Byron weren't in the house. I took it for granted they had gone to the store so I shaved and dressed.

About noon when they hadn't showed up, I got my own combination breakfast and lunch and ate it. Then I played a couple of phonograph records. Then I read some of "Stover at Yale," by Owen Johnson, which is rather humorous, but pretty light.

About 1:30, shortly before I had to go to work, Pearl came home with Byron. I probably wasn't very pleasant when I asked her where they had been. She said they had been riding the cable cars. Byron is crazy about riding the cross-town cable cars, getting quite excited about the way the gripman clangs his bell as the car races up and down the hills and he squeals with delight when they lurch around corners.

I said, "Well, it seems pretty silly putting in all day riding up and down hills on grip cars."

"Yes," said Pearl, "it's just like you to begrudge your family a little entertainment."

"All right," I said, "if that's your idea of entertainment, go on out and spend all the grocery money riding the grip cars. I don't care. I can get my own meals, I guess. But if you've got to ride cable cars it would seem you could do it after I've gone to work. I don't get to see much of Byron anyhow. It would seem you could leave him home in the little time I'm here. It would seem you could go grip car riding enough after two o'clock."

"Yes," said Pearl. "That's just what I'd expect of you. You think it's a pretty fine life for us being cooped up in this dirty old apartment all day while you're in there snoring. You think, I suppose, that I ought to put a gag on the baby so I won't have to be hushing him every minute with, 'Now keep quiet, dear, darling Papa needs his sleep.' "

"All right, all right," I cut in.

"I thought," she went on, "that I was being kind, taking the baby out so he wouldn't disturb you. But I suppose it practically killed you having to get your own breakfast for once."

"Go grip-car riding every day. It's all right with me. I can get my meals. I did it while you were in K.C. and I can do it now."

"If," said Pearl, "you would get a job where you worked days like a white man we could live like white folks, too."

"Yes, I should throw up my job on the *Tribune* where I'm getting ahead and where I'm making good money and get a job reading copy or reporting on one of the little afternoon sheets so it would be better for you to go bouncing around town in a cable car."

"Yeah, you're making swell money. If you were making good money we wouldn't have to ride cable cars. If you were making good money we could have an automobile. And if you were working days we could go out on Sunday down the peninsula for outings and give this child the country air he needs. And furthermore if you think I'm going to stay cooped up in this dump of an apartment like a white slave all day, you're going to get left. And see how you like that."

So I put on my hat and went to work. She'll be all right today. That's one thing about Pearl: if I find fault with her she gets terribly mad, but she's always over it the next day.

AUGUST 7, 1913. We took a ferry over to Neptune Beach today and Byron had a great time paddling in the water. I went swimming and the water was delightful. Pearl, who doesn't swim, played in the sand and ate frankfurter sandwiches and ice-cream cones. Byron's stomach was upset on the way home.

Over there we got weighed on a penny-in-the-slot machine. Pearl weighed 139. I weighed 131 and Byron, as near as we could see, 31, but he wriggled so much the scale hand wouldn't stand still.

Last Thursday we saw a fine movie, "The Spoilers." It is a story of Alaska and in it is the most terrific fist fight imaginable.

I read that this fight really was not acting, but that the principals actually fought for all they were worth to make it convincing. They certainly succeeded. It takes place in a law office and they virtually wreck the place throwing each other around. The hero, William Farnum, is supposed to have broken several of his opponent's ribs in the battle and I don't wonder.

It has been an uneventful summer so far as news is concerned. But they are giving me a week's vacation with pay next week. Because we have little money I would be satisfied to stay home and rest and catch up on my reading, but Pearl wants to get away from the city so we are going over to Sausalito and spend several days in the hotel where Pearl can get away from cooking and dishwashing. I think it will be good for all of us to get away from the city awhile.

JANUARY 1, 1914. I have been pretty lucky with both Christmas and New Year's Day coming on Thursday—my day off. Pearl and I had planned to celebrate the passing of the jinx year with a show and a little wine at a restaurant at midnight, but Mrs. Castro turned suddenly very ill and we had no other place where we felt like leaving Byron.

Mrs. Castro has been looking very bad lately and she has a ghastly cough. I have felt that she looked as if she had consumption and sometimes have been reluctant to leave Byron with her. She, however, has told Pearl several times that her trouble was only bronchitis, which is serious enough but not contagious.

So Pearl and I saw the old year out in the apartment. I went out and got a bottle of claret and a dozen hot tamales and we had a midnight lunch that reminded us of the old days before we were married and Pearl used to wait up for me with a lunch at her mother's rooming house.

JANUARY 14, 1914. Mrs. Blanche Castro died Tuesday morning after a terrible hemorrhage and we went to her funeral today. She was a fine young woman and one of our very best friends in San Francisco. For two years and more she has been taking care of Byron when Pearl and I went out. Byron loved her like a second mother. We shall miss her very much.

She never should have stayed in this climate, but Frank Castro loved San Francisco and she never would think she would be better off elsewhere. She must have had tuberculosis, but she tried to bring herself to health by sheer will power.

It is too bad the scientists have been unable to find a real cure for this awful disease. It is too bad that the German Dr. Friedmann and his turtle serum turned out to be a fake.

This is a very bad climate for lung trouble. Since I have been on the *Tribune* one reporter and one copyreader have died of consumption.

APRIL 23, 1914. American marines occupied the city of Vera Cruz, Mexico, last Tuesday after warships shelled the forts. There was a regular battle through the streets with the marines using machine guns against Mexican snipers and killing many.

It all happened for the afternoon papers and most of the

excitement was over by the time we came out at night. The battle followed repeated insults to Americans and the American flag by cohorts of President Huerta.

Perhaps a display of force is a good thing at times. I am satisfied that President Wilson and Secretary of State Bryan never would have allowed such an episode if it were not necessary. But I will admit if Taft or Roosevelt were President now I should believe the attack on Vera Cruz were inspired by the vested interests who hold large investments in Mexico.

I have just read Sigmund Freud's "Interpretation of Dreams." I imagine there is a good deal of truth in his observations on sex, but he certainly is an extremist.

There definitely is no carnality connected with my dreams of Frances. Our associations were always on a plane above that and I never think of her in that connection.

Then Freud lists dreams as "wish dreams" and "fear dreams." And I cannot place my strange visions of Frances in either category. For instance, there was the dream of her marriage. Certainly I did not wish her to be marrying Paul Clark. And I did not fear it either. As I am unable ever to associate with her again, I could have no objections to her marrying anybody she wished. I do want her to be happy.

Freud has nothing to say about vision dreams like mine, of a person dreaming events as they actually occur. If there are no records of such phenomena, my experiences may be unique. Or, of course, there may be nothing to them at all. I am convinced in my own mind that Frances married Clark just as I visioned it, but as a matter of fact, I have no proof. She may be married to somebody else. She may still be single and working as a stenographer for the insurance company. But I do not believe it.

For two months I have been having vivid dreams of her at least twice a week.

She has not seemed in good health ever since her baby Carol was born a year ago. In February she was sick in bed for several weeks and when she got back to her housework she had much the same appearance as Mrs. Castro.

I will give her husband credit where credit is due, for he at least must have recognized the symptoms or have taken a doctor's advice. They moved early this month out west, probably to Colorado, although I cannot be sure of the location.

They have a cottage on the outskirts of a small town which I have seen quite plainly several times. It is painted gray and has green shutters. There is a wooden picket fence around the yard and several large cottonwoods in front. I do not know what Paul Clark is doing there for I never see him in my dreams. But I do see Fran and see her baby sitting in its high chair in the kitchen while she is about her housework.

Frequently Fran will pause in her work and step to the kitchen window and push back the curtain to look out. There is a wonderful view of a mountain range from that window.

Now it might well be that they have not moved west at all, but are living in the Alleghenies or the Adirondacks. But the mountains do not look like Eastern mountains. And there is the matter of time.

While Frances was in Buffalo I often would waken after dreams about her at 4:30 to 6 o'clock. Now I never dream of her before 8:30 or 9 o'clock.

I am positive in my own mind that Frances is thinking of me when I am dreaming of her. In Buffalo she probably would think of me after Clark had gone to work and while she was starting her housework. She would be too occupied and too much in a hurry while getting breakfast.

Thus the change in time of my dreams indicates to me that she now is living in the Mountain Time section rather than in Eastern Time. That would place her either in Montana, Wyoming, Colorado, New Mexico, Arizona, eastern Utah, or Idaho.

Inasmuch as the climate of Arizona, Montana, Idaho and Wyoming is rather harsh for invalids, they probably are living in Colorado or New Mexico and possibly Utah. Colorado is the most likely, I should say, because the health-giving properties of Colorado are better known. But of course the economic question enters. I suppose Clark has continued with his father in the real estate business in Buffalo. I don't suppose he knows anything else. Necessarily, then, they would have to go someplace where he could go into business or where he could find a job. And, after all, the main thing for lung trouble is a dry climate and a reasonably high altitude.

Wherever they are it is agreeing with Frances, I can see, for she looks much better than when they left Buffalo.

I won $5.50 in a curious "win-place-show" office pool a week ago Monday. It was Jack Cullen's idea. He got it up Sunday night on the electrocution of the four New York thugs who killed the gambler Herman Rosenthal a couple of years ago.

Cullen made up twenty-four slips of paper each bearing the names of three of the four murderers in one, two, three order. He called it the "Hot Squat Parlay" and sold chances at 25 cents each. The slips were folded and shaken up in my derby.

My first chance listed Dago Frank, 1; Whitey Lewis, 2; and Gyp the Blood, 3. I didn't like that ticket because there had been some intimation on the wire Sunday night that Governor Glynn of New York might give Dago Frank Cirofici a reprieve. It was rumored Cirofici was willing to give more information that might help convict Lieutenant Becker in his second trial. So I bought another ticket quickly and quietly.

The second ticket read Gyp the Blood, 1; Lefty Louie, 2; Dago Frank, 3. I had hoped to get a ticket that didn't list Dago Frank at all. This second ticket was no better than the first if the governor granted a reprieve, but I decided I couldn't afford to invest any more and let it go.

But as it turned out, Glynn didn't grant any reprieve and my second ticket won. That is the order in which they went to the chair—Gyp the Blood, Lefty Louie, Dago Frank and last, Whitey Lewis. So I collected $6 which left me a profit of $5.50.

JULY 9, 1914. A crisis broke in Europe early last week that looked very serious for a few days. But it has been happily cleared up.

The Archduke Francis Ferdinand of Austria and his wife were touring in Bosnia when, at the town of Sarajevo, a young anarchist named Gavrio Princip shot and killed them both. Of course Princip was arrested for the murder. But for the fact that a bomb had been thrown at the Archduke and his consort earlier in the day the incident probably would have been considered the act of a madman and would have been closed with his execution.

However, there is a great deal back of this assassination. First, Austria-Hungary occupied Bosnia under the Berlin treaty of 1878 for the express purpose of "pacifying" the Bosnians. The country formally was annexed by Austria-Hungary in 1908.

The people of Bosnia are said to be largely Slavic and unfriendly to the Germanic rule. There are many Servians living there and the Vienna government charges Servia has been attempting to stir the Bosnians to revolt against Austria-Hungary.

Archduke Francis Ferdinand, who would have succeeded to the throne of Austria-Hungary on the passing of Emperor Francis Joseph, was too ambitious for his own good. He had imperialistic dreams of a German-Magyar-Slavic kingdom that could control Europe. And his dangerous ambitions raised a hatred among the Bosnians that resulted in the Archduke's death.

The murdered Archduke's successor, on the other hand, is 27-year-old Charles Francis who is said to be very able and not too ambitious. He is better liked in his own kingdom than was Francis Ferdinand. So, inasmuch as Servia has promised a thorough investigation into the possibility that the plot originated in Servia, the assassination may actually insure the peace of Europe rather than jeopardize it.

For a few days it looked as if the Bosnian affair might embroil all Europe in warfare, for Russia with her army of millions has sworn to protect Slavic Servia from invasion by Austro-Hungarians. And Russia is bound by the Triple Entente treaty with France and Great Britain, who, if they lived up to the treaty, would help out Russia. On the other hand, Austria-Hungary is bound to Germany and Italy by the Triple Alliance treaty.

European leaders realize, however, that a general war would do no one good, but would cost millions of lives and billions of dollars. It is apparent now to thinking people that science has advanced so far that another great war is practically impossible.

Growing out of the war talk last week came a statement from Admiral Sir Percy Scott of the Britsh navy, which shows the turn a war at sea would take.

According to Sir Percy, the battleship is a thing of the past. British submarines could control the seas.

At present Britain has 69 submarines and is building 35 more. Her ally, France, has 50 submarines and is building 31 more.

Germany has only 24 submarines and is building 31.

"Realizing the power of British undersea boats," Sir Percy said, "at the first signs of a foreign war the enemy would lock up its battleships and cruisers in some safe, protected harbor and never venture out into the high seas. Britain would put down a submarine blockade then that would effectively prevent any merchant ships moving in or out of the enemy ports. The submarines thus could protect British commerce while starving out the enemy."

Now that the war scare has been put down the papers are full of a proposed aeroplane flight across the Atlantic.

Glenn H. Curtiss, an early aeronaut, has just built a large hydroaeroplane for Rodman Wanamaker. It has the hull of a boat so it could land in the ocean and is driven by two gasoline engines.

It would be navigated by Lieutenant John Cyril Porte of the British navy and piloted by an American, George Hallett. They propose to take off from Newfoundland, fly to the Azores Islands and thence to England.

There is a good deal of enthusiasm over the project, but experts are doubtful. Even Lincoln Beachey, who is probably the foremost aviator in America, says a flight across the Atlantic cannot be done—at least not with Wanamaker's aeroplane, *America*.

Beachey does not believe the plane can get aloft with sufficient fuel to take it to the Azores. Also he feels that it is beyond the endurance of one pilot to fly an aeroplane from Newfoundland to the Azores.

"Perhaps," says Beachey, "one man could pilot a plane for fifteen hours or so over the ground. But he has the comforting sight of good Mother Earth beneath him. When there is nothing in sight except the dismal watery waste of the Atlantic it would have a shocking effect on the pilot; it would increase his nervous strain many times.

"I don't believe it possible for one pilot to fly across the ocean. Porte may be a competent navigator, but he should have another pilot so they could spell one another every four or five hours. If they ever fly across the ocean they will have to build a plane that will fly like a streak. Wanamaker's ship is too slow."

My dreams of Frances have been continuing on the average of once or twice a week. Usually nothing is taking place. I just have a sudden picture of her at her work or playing with baby Carol. Frequently she is just leaving the little gray cottage and pushing the baby buggy down and out the wooden gate and then down the street toward the businesss section where she does her shopping.

The sidewalks are made of flagstones. They are rough and red and coarse grass and weeds grow up between the flags. Along the picket fence in the shadow of the big cottonwoods hollyhocks grow. And beyond the hollyhocks there is a tall sheaf of black-eyed susans and even half a dozen huge sunflowers. The street in front of the house is unpaved and rutty, but the soil is light and gravelly. It is quite dry there now and sun-baked and sometimes the wind swoops down from the mountains sending the dust in swirls toward Frances' house.

I witnessed a minor tragedy there the other morning. Frances must have risen early to wash, for she had the clothes hung out by 8 o'clock our time, which was probably 9 o'clock where she is. I could see the clothing fluttering in the breeze—the baby's little dresses and underthings, Paul Clark's shirts and socks and underwear and Frances' own house dresses and teddies and stockings and towels and sheets and pillow cases. Then a sudden gust came howling down the canyon, rustling the silver-gray leaves of the cotton-woods and making the sunflowers and hollyhocks bow down before its onslaught. It caught the clothes and whipped them violently for a moment. Then the rope clothesline snapped and the whole wash went slithering down into the dirty gravel of the back yard.

Poor Fran, already tired from the washing, was sobbing to herself as she gathered up the dirt-streaked clothing in the washbasket and carried it in to do over. I should think Clark could at least put up a wire clothesline for her.

JULY 16, 1914. There is a great deal of unemployment in San Francisco. As a matter of fact, we have had dispatches from all over the country about the jobless.

Now it is impossible to walk along lower Market Street without having at least one or two down-and-outers sidle up to you and ask for "a dime to get a cup of coffee." It is significant that while coffee costs only a nickel a drink of whisky costs a dime.

The other evening when we were walking around a little after lunch a panhandler came up to Tom Rogers and me and whined out his plaint.

Rogers glared at the fellow. "Don't you know," he boomed, "that coffee is bad for your stomach? It'll give you nervous dyspepsia quicker than most anything. Now I'll give you a dime if you promise me you'll spend it for whisky instead of coffee."

The bum grinned sheepishly and promised.

I believe most of these bums could get work if they really wanted it. For instance, they need men down in the apricot and prune districts of Santa Clara County and a self-respecting man would go down there even if he had to walk.

Also, the city offered jobs with pick and shovel to all who would apply the other day. And while there is estimated to be at least 15,000 jobless in San Francisco, only 800 applied. In this rich country there is little excuse for an able-bodied man being out of work.

Little Byron has a bad summer cold and has been quite ill. His throat has been swollen at the sides and he had such a high fever day before yesterday that we got a doctor in. The doctor prescribed cod-liver oil, but we can't make Byron take it.

The child is too thin and pale to suit me. I'm afraid Pearl is inclined to humor his whims too much. I'm afraid she lets him eat too much sweet stuff. He won't touch any vegetables except navy beans and canned corn. I have tried to force him to eat beets and turnips and things, but then he cries and Pearl takes his part.

And practically every day he begs a penny or a nickel from Pearl for candy and she thinks it's cute to see him toddle down to the corner grocery and come back with his face smeared with chocolate or licorice or red-hots.

Pearl blames his thinness and paleness on the San Francisco climate. "Children need good hot sunshine in the summer," she says. Well, I see a good many sturdy-looking children here.

AUGUST 6, 1914. The unthinkable, the unbelievable has happened. Virtually all of Europe is plunged into the greatest war in history. And it all was precipitated by an incident which we in America had well-nigh forgotten—the assassination of Archduke Ferdinand of Austria.

Austria had demanded that Servia conduct a thorough investigation of alleged plotting against Austria by Servians in Bosnia. This was agreed to by Servia. We thought that all was settled. But Austria also demanded that Austrian officers be permitted to take part in the investigation and Servia denied them that right.

A week ago last Tuesday Austrian troops marched on Servia to force their point. They were fired on by Servian soldiers.

The next day Russia began mobilizing more than a million men, declaring Austria was waging a war of conquest on her treaty ally.

Kaiser Wilhelm of Germany ordered Russia to cease mobilization, threatening to declare war. Czar Nicholas ignored the command and Germany started general mobilization. France followed by calling all her reservists to the colors.

Still it all seemed impossible to me, to almost all Americans. It seemed like a colossal game of bluff.

It was announced in Berlin that Germany longs for peace, but the Russian mobilization is a threat that cannot be ignored.

In St. Petersburg it was announced that Russia longs for peace, but the German threats were too serious to be ignored.

In Paris it was announced that France longs for peace, but the German mobilization endangers the Republic.

Last Saturday Germany declared war on Russia. French and German border patrols exchanged rifle shots. And Sunday Russian troops invaded Germany while Germans marched into France and Belgium. When Belgium appealed to her treaty ally, England declared war on Germany Tuesday. There was a naval battle in the Baltic Monday in which a German fleet drove Russian warships to cover.

Last night the German army had penetrated Belgium as far as Liége where they apparently will be stopped, for the forts at Liége are said to be absolutely shellproof and impregnable. Military experts declare no army can get by Liége.

The war promises to be the most terrible in history, but also the shortest. The resources of the world are not large enough to carry on this conflict more than a few weeks as it will cost hundreds of millions of dollars each day. Estimates of experts generally run from one month to three months. One man figures it could last a year before the world was bankrupt, but it is generally agreed that long before a year passes the soldiers would have to be fighting with stones and clubs because there would be no more ammunition and that the European governments would be overthrown by revolutions.

As it is Germany is doomed to defeat, despite her present marvelous military machine. She is hemmed in and the British and French submarines will lay down a blockade, sinking any merchant vessels which attempt to bring food and supplies to the Central Powers.

Italy has refused to join the war, declaring her treaty with Germany is simply for a defensive war. Tom Rogers and I are agreed that Italy is holding off for a while to see which way the wind is blowing. When it appears certain that Germany and Austria are being defeated, Italy probably will join the side of the Triple Entente.

At present, while the combined armies of Germany and Austria number approximately 6,400,000 men, France, England and Russia have 10,600,000.

For the duration of this war I as telegraph editor shall have my hands full. I am going to work at noon and don't get away until the Dawn Extra is put to bed at 3 o'clock in the morning. I have a huge map of Central Europe and colored tacks representing the various armies which I must keep in place. It is very exciting, but lots of work. I really need an assistant because there is so much happening and the wire services disagree so much that I have to get out a long summary of reports which we run in 12-point on Page One, set two or three columns.

I asked the Old Man to give me Tom Rogers as assistant, but he said it'll probably be all over in a week or so.

MARCH 15, 1915. I have been too busy, working too long hours and too tired after work to keep up this record. The war has been going for seven months and a half and it is more terrible now than ever.

I notice in my last entry that nobody thought the Germans could pass Liége. Well, they brought up new heavy artillery which blasted the Liége forts flat. They captured Brussels. They nearly captured Paris, but were stopped by the French in a terrific battle on the Marne in which French reinforcements were rushed to the front in taxicabs.

There is a great deal of confusion about what is actually happening because both sides are lying at a mile-a-minute clip. But this much is certain: Germany and Austria are doing their fighting on Allied territory and thus far the immense resources of Britain, Russia and France have made no headway toward whipping the Kaiser.

Britain's vaunted submarine power has not been produced.

Instead, while the British navy certainly controls the sea and has driven German shipping off the ocean, German submarines have sunk numerous British and French boats and they have established a blockade of the British Isles.

Last winter we had a dramatic running story concerning the exploits of a German cruiser, *Emden,* which harried British shipping for weeks, sinking many merchantmen until she finally was destroyed by the Australian cruiser *Sydney* at Cocos Island in the South Pacific.

The Germans have been pursuing a most ruthless warfare in France and Belgium with a cruelty almost impossible to believe under this modern so-called civilization. Apparently authentic reports sworn to by priests and other responsible people tell of Frenchwomen crucified on barn doors and we have had many eyewitness stories of German officers slashing off the hands of Belgian children with their sabers.

These stories seem too authentic to doubt, but they are difficult for me to understand. Both my grandfathers were born in Germany as was my mother, although she was brought to America when a small child. Frances Harbach's father was born in Germany and came to America when he was 16 to avoid military service. I knew literally dozens of German-born men and women in Buffalo and I have always felt that Germans were about the kindest race in the world. It is very hard to think of child-loving Germans deliberately crippling children, even if the children are of another race. The only explanation is the brutalizing effect of military life, the fact that these German soldiers have been driven insane with killing.

I have developed a new respect for my grandparents' good judgment in emigrating to the United States.

Yesterday Lincoln Beachey, the foremost aviator in the United States, was killed when he fell into the Bay. He was putting on an exhibition for the Exposition and while straightening out after a spectacular dive the wings broke from his machine. Thousands saw him fall to his death.

We took Byron to the Exposition late this afternoon and stayed until the lights were turned on the Tower of Jewels. It is a beautiful sight.

Although the war halted foreign participation in the Exposition, it is more beautiful even than the Pan-American in Buffalo because of the wonderful setting. Byron was entranced with the Tower of Jewels—as were Pearl and myself. I took him on the merry-go-round and while he was frightened at first and clung to me desperately, he wanted to ride again and I had to ride the thing three times. I finally got him off by bribing him with a promise of popcorn. That boy has a determination that will make him succeed in anything he undertakes.

MAY 13, 1915. Last Friday came the most terrible occurrence of the war. A German submarine torpedoed and sank the British liner *Lusitania* near Ireland, killing 1,195 men, women and children, of whom 124 were Americans.

The German embassy had warned Americans to keep off the ship with advertisements and placards before the *Lusitania* sailed from New York. But that cannot excuse the ruthless warfare the U-boats are conducting. There is a great deal of agitation now for the United States to enter the war on the side of the Allies, but it certainly will not be necessary to go that far.

England has been sinning against America also in stopping American ships, forcing them to steam into British ports to be searched for alleged contraband bound for Germany. We went to war against England in 1812 for that very offense.

I am glad that wise, levelheaded Woodrow Wilson is President and that William Jennings Bryan is Secretary of State. Theodore Roosevelt is shouting from the housetops for America to teach Kaiser Wilhelm a lesson and wants to

recruit a brigade of cavalry which he would lead against the
Germans. If he were President we should have declared war
within twenty-four hours after the *Lusitania* sank.

While Wilson is telling Germany where to get off, I feel
he will lead America safely through this crisis. Terrible as
the *Lusitania* sinking is, there is another side to the case. After
all, the Germans claim the *Lusitania* was loaded with shells
and cartridges which would have killed thousands of German
boys had not the submarine fired the torpedo. There is talk
also that the ship carried cannons capable of sinking a submarine. In that case, had the submarine come to the surface
and hailed the *Lusitania,* shellfire would have sunk the U-boat
and the British liner would have gone blithely on her way
with her cargo of shells. And after all, again, why didn't
these Americans sail on an American ship if they had to go
to Europe? And if they were traveling for pleasure, they
had no business imperiling their nation's peace by going to
Europe at all at this time. Why don't they come out here
and see the Exposition?

Tonight we all went to the best motion picture ever. It is
"The Clansman," which is being shown back east under the
title of "The Birth of a Nation." It is based on the recon-
struction period in the South following the Civil War. It
reveals the terrible experiences of the Southerners after the
slaves were freed and, encouraged by the carpetbaggers, began
to take control of the country.

Henry Walthall as Ben Cameron, the "little Colonel," did
a wonderful piece of acting as did two new actresses named
Lillian Gish and Mae Marsh.

The scene where the Ku-Klux Klan assembles and rides
with flaming torches to battle is one of the most thrilling
I have ever seen. We were in the balcony (which is a good
place to see a movie for the flickering is not so pronounced
at that distance) and when this scene came on an old man

downstairs leaped up in his seat, waved his hat and let out a blood-curdling yell.

No doubt he was a Southerner himself and probably had taken part in just such an event in his youth.

There was another scene which reminded me forcibly of my own brief experience with the movies. Several negroes attacked a very muscular blacksmith, played by an actor named Wallace Reid, and the blacksmith picked up one of his assailants, swung him high over his head and hurled him through a glass window. At least I was spared the experience of crashing through glass. They had a large orchestra that played throughout the picture and the music was arranged to match the action.

JUNE 10, 1915. Honest, fearless William Jennings Bryan has resigned as Secretary of State and has been succeeded by Robert Lansing.

Bryan believes first in keeping this nation out of the war. He believed the notes the United States has been sending Germany regarding the *Lusitania* are far too severe and threatening. And rather than affix his signature to them he has resigned his post.

Sentiment is growing for the entry of the United States into the conflict. I suspect much of this sentiment has been manufactured by the Wall Street bankers who have been lending hundreds of millions to the Allies and want to protect their investments. At the war's outset Bryan vigorously opposed allowing these loans to be made. Permission for them was made over his protests.

Many of the papers are lampooning the Commoner viciously for "deserting the ship" and because he refused to serve intoxicants at state dinners. I admire him even more because of his fearless adherence to his principles.

I have been altogether too busy for the last year to think of putting down thoughts here for future use in my writings.

I am even too tired at the end of my 12- to 15-hour grind
to think of reading. I don't believe I have read anything
except the newspapers since the war started last August.

But I still dream of Frances.

I have just finished a series of dreams that left me heart-
broken.

It started on a warm afternoon when Frances came out
on her front porch with little Carol. Fran was wearing a
house dress of blue print and Carol, with her hair the color
of a sunflower's petals, wore a little frock of the same material
as her mother's.

Fran sat down in a weather-beaten rocker on the porch with
a basket of stockings to darn and Carol, who was only two
last April, was romping in the yard with her little fox terrier.

The cottonwoods were rustling softly in the spring breeze
and there were bright-colored tulips blooming along the side
of the house. Fran, now looking the picture of health, darned
her stockings and smiled at the little girl and the little dog
chasing each other around the gravel and sparse grass of the
lawn.

There is a wooden picket fence in front of the yard, but
the gate is broken and will not shut. Through this gate a
huge mongrel suddenly dashed and set upon the little fox
terrier. The terrier yelped and tried to escape, but the snarling
mongrel bore him down.

Little Carol screamed, "Go away, bad dog!" Frances dropped
her workbasket and called to the baby, "Carol, come here
quick!" But the child apparently did not hear her mother
in the chorus of growls and yelps and she ran toward the
dogs to rescue her pet. She kicked the mongrel in the head
with her tiny foot and the big dog turned on her. In a flash
his teeth were sunk into her baby throat and he was shaking
her like a limp rag.

Frances was running down the walk to fight the brute
with her bare hands when a heavy rifle cracked from a

window across the street and the mongrel dropped the baby and bit at his own hindquarters. The rifle cracked again and he fell twitching in the gravel beside the inert little girl.

Fran picked up the child and the blood was streaming from her mangled throat. The neighbor came running from his house carrying his Winchester.

"Is she—is she—" he called.

Frances half turned and the sun glinted in Carol's yellow hair, now smeared with red.

"Oh, *please* get a doctor!" Frances sobbed.

The man turned and sprinted down the street still carrying his gun while Frances hurried into the house and neighbor women came running to help and children gathered to gaze at and to toe the brindle body of the dead mongrel in the yard.

That was one dream. And the next night or morning I saw little Carol die. It is all too real. I had a terrible battle to keep my own grief from growing hysterical. Pearl noticed my pallor and jumpiness and made me take some epsom salts. Albertson at the office noticed it and thought perhaps I was on the point of a nervous breakdown from working too hard on the war. So he got Mr. Rothstein to approve making Marvin Blue, a young copyreader, my assistant. Marvin is a nice boy and willing and he'll be a lot of help as soon as I get him broken in properly. I am having him come to work early and get the day copy sorted. There has been far to much work for one man for the last year and a half. Not many men could have stood the strain of 12 to 15 hours work a day the way I have been doing. My health is a great asset to me.

But I can't get over these dreams of little Carol. I scarcely could have been more upset were it my own child.

I wonder how Freud would interpret these dreams of mine Certainly there could be no sex connection to this last series. I suppose if I told anybody of these dreams I have of Frances they would think me nuts—especially the fact that I can't

but take them seriously. As far as actual evidence is concerned
I don't know that Frances ever had a child, let alone a two-
year-old named Carol. Yet Carol has been as real to me as
any baby I ever saw—even Byron. As far as actual evidence
is concerned, I don't know that Frances isn't still living in
Buffalo. I don't know that she ever married anyone, let alone
Paul Clark.

Usually I dream of her in the morning while she might
be doing her routine housework and might be thinking of
me. Thus it could well be telepathy which causes the dreams
or visions. But the dream of the dog attacking Carol came
soon after I had gone to sleep. Its vividness woke me and I
could sleep no more.

I have thought over this a good deal and my only explanation is this: The thing occurred, apparently, in the early afternoon. At that time I was very busy on the telegraph desk
and my brain necessarily was not receptive to telepathic im-
pulses. But could not my subconscious have received the
message and filed it away to be brought forth as a dream
when I fell asleep and my subconscious finally gained
ascendency?

OCTOBER 14, 1915. Still the war continues, growing more terrible week by week. A fleet of Zeppelins flew over London
last night, dropping bombs that killed 41 men, women and
children and causing millions in damage. Millions of young
men have been killed on both sides and the Germans now are
using poison gas for attack.

We are lucky in having a calm and wise President who
cannot be swept off his feet by the interests who would
have us enter the war to save the Allies from the "Hun."

The J.P. Morgan interests have just signed a half billion
dollar loan to Great Britain and France.

Little Byron is sick again with a cold on his chest and
has been in bed for a week. I wish Pearl could make him
take cod-liver oil.

JANUARY 13, 1916. Byron has been sick a great deal this winter and now is in bed with another heavy cold on his chest. There has been so much fog this winter and Pearl feels the San Francisco climate is entirely to blame for the child's condition. She also has a notion that the boy may have contracted consumption from Mrs. Castro when we used to leave him with her on my night off.

We have had several doctors and while none has said definitely that Byron has tuberculosis, they do say he is delicate and that his lungs are not strong. Pearl feels that doctors are reluctant to come right out and tell parents their child has consumption and when a Dr. Banks said it would be a good thing if we could move him to a sunnier, drier climate for the winter, she became almost frantic.

I am reluctant to leave San Francisco, for I feel I have a real opportunity here on the *Tribune*. Sam Rothstein, the managing editor, has let it be known that he expects to move to New York City in the spring. That, undoubtedly, would place Jimmy Albertson as managing editor and leave the news editor post open. And I feel Albertson almost certainly would make me news editor.

Albertson always has been most kind to me and has a high regard for my work. And the record I have made in handling the war news should offset any advantage in seniority that Pete Van Camp, the city editor, and Hugh Murphy, head of the copy desk, might hold.

I am now drawing $42.50 a week, which is very good salary for a newspaperman, and I understand the news editor job pays at least $60. If I had that salary, I really could save some money. My bank account now amounts to $280.

But the health of a man's family comes before his business opportunities. If Byron would be better in a drier climate I naturally am willing to make any sacrifice—if I can get a job.

Consequently I have written letters to four newspapers in Denver, to three in Salt Lake City, two in El Paso, Texas, and two in Oklahoma City, outlining my qualifications and the reasons for wanting to leave San Francisco. These all being smaller papers in smaller cities, I cannot hope to get a salary anywhere near as good as the *Tribune* pays me, but I do believe I should find a job. Telegraph editors, competent telegraph editors, are most important in these days of the European War.

JANUARY 27, 1916. I gave Sam Rothstein two weeks' notice last Saturday, terminating more than five years on the *San Francisco Tribune*. I have got a job on the *Denver Call,* a morning newspaper. The managing editor, Fred Gotchell, wrote me I could have a job on the copy desk rim at $30 a week and, while he gave no definite promise, indicated I should be put on the telegraph desk soon if my work was satisfactory.

Rothstein and Albertson both were very kind and told me if it were a matter of salary they could give me a raise to stay. And when I told them the reason for making the change they both assured me I could have a job on the *Tribune* any time I felt I could come back. That made me feel much more secure.

One never knows what situation he will run into when he changes jobs. It may be that the Danver job will be impossible. I could be fired before I got my feet on the ground should I make some minor error. That possibility is always confronting any new man on any newspaper.

For that reason I shall leave Pearl and Byron here for a week or so until I see what conditions are and can get a furnished apartment.

Pearl wasn't enthusiastic about being left here even a fortnight, but she finally has seen the wisdom of it.

5. Denver

FEBRUARY 11, 1916. I arrived in Denver Wednesday afternoon and went to work that night on the *Denver Call* copy desk. The editorial room is not nearly as good as the *San Francisco Tribune,* but the men on the copy desk at least are friendly and helpful. It is not a difficult desk on the rim, but the slot man, George Empey, a fat, nervous fellow about 30, is also telegraph editor and has his hands more than full.

I worked Wednesday and Thursday nights and Empey gave me tonight off. I don't believe I shall have any trouble making good as a copyreader. But advancement is another thing. The combined telegraph and slot of copy desk job doesn't look very good to me.

On the way from San Francisco I had the strangest experience of my life. And I still can't decide whether I did right or committed a terrible wrong.

Because I knew I should go to work as soon as I reached Denver and didn't want to be tired out from the trip, I took a Pullman for the first time. Pearl and Byron, who is feeling much better, took the ferry with me across the Bay for the ride and saw me on the train in Oakland.

On top of the Sierras at Truckee there was a great deal of snow—more snow, in fact, than I ever saw before. Because of the snowsheds along the way I didn't realize how much there was until we stopped at the town and could see drifts piled up almost to the eaves of some cottages. And from there clear across Nevada we crawled through a blizzard.

The train was an hour late the next morning. At about 10 o'clock we came to a stop at a small town in Utah. I was in the smoking compartment reading a magazine and smoking my pipe when the porter stuck his head in and said the snow had blocked the track ahead and it would take about four hours to get it cleared.

I looked out the window at the station and the sign under its eaves which read, "Raleigh, Altitude 6,120 feet." The storm was over and several men stood on the platform kicking their feet together. You could see from their actions and their steamy breaths that it was very cold.

From the window I had a view of the town water tower and a church steeple and part of the business district and it all looked strangely familiar to me.

"Raleigh," I said to myself. "When have I ever been in Raleigh, Utah, before?" And I knew I never had been. Then I thought that perhaps the train had stopped there quite a while five years before when I was on my way to San Francisco from Kansas City. Then I thought that perhaps the town only reminded me of some other place. So many little Western villages look alike.

But I really knew I was kidding myself all the time. I had a thought which was too crazy to consider. I tried to forget it. But in the end I put on my overcoat and hat and went out on the station platform.

I had forgotten it could get that cold. My blood was thin from five years in California and my overcoat was scarcely heavier than a mackintosh. But I walked briskly through the snow up and down the platform a couple of times and then stepped up to a fellow who had a red muffler tied around his neck. I asked him if he knew how long the train was going to be held there.

He shook his head. "No telling," he said. "There's a cut

over east of here what's clear full of snow. Plow's on the way but it may take 'em hours to clean out the cut. Doubt if you get out of here before four o'clock this afternoon."

So I talked to this man for a while about the weather and railroading and the war and about Henry Ford's peace ship and him failing to "get the boys out of the trenches by Christmas" and he said, "Henry makes a rattling good car," and laughed at his pun. Then he took a chew of tobacco and observed that whenever a man makes a pot of money in the real estate business or pawnbroking or manufacturing corsets he immediately puts himself up as an expert on everything in the world.

Then I asked him as casually as I could, "Do you know a man named Paul Clark here in Raleigh?"

He squinted his blue eyes and spat a brown stain in the snow. "Paul Clark?" he said. "Oh, sure. Sure I do. He's a foreman over at the smelter."

I felt oddly hot and suffocating despite the weather.

"Do you know his wife?" I asked.

He shook his head. "No," he said. "I know he's got a wife, but that's all. They live down at the end of Pine Street—last house on the right-hand side going out. Ain't far from here. Pine Street's the second street over from Hemlock and Hemlock's that street right over there that ends at the railroad track."

My head was buzzing and I felt faint and dizzy. But I tried to appear casual as I asked, "Is it a little gray frame house with some cottonwood trees in the front yard?"

"Yes," he said, "yes, that's the place."

And I said, "Wooden picket fence in front?"

He nodded his head. "You know the place. Clark won't be home this time of day, though. You know his missus?"

"Yes," I said, "I know them both."

"Well," he remarked, "you got plenty of time to go down

and call on her before this train'll be ready to go." Then he left me and went into the freight house of the station.

I don't think this fellow noticed it, but cold as it was, the sweat was running down my face. Here I was, in all likelihood, less than a quarter of a mile from Frances. Everything checked. This must be the western town I had seen so often in my dreams. The description of the house fitted. Paul Clark —of course that was a fairly common name—but my intuition told me that Mrs. Paul Clark of Raleigh, Utah, was, beyond the faintest shadow of a doubt, my Frances.

I walked down to the east end of the station platform— toward Pine Street. I was going down to see Fran after all these years, after all these sad years.

But when I got to the east end of the platform I turned and walked back.

I found that I was afraid to see Fran. I was afraid of what might happen. If it were truly Fran, it could not be doubted that her thoughts of me had inspired my dreams. In that case she surely still loved me. And if she still loved me, could we continue living apart after we met again?

Then what of my responsibilities? Pearl might get along, but what of little Byron, my poor semi-invalid baby son? Could I desert him even for love? True, I knew I wanted Frances more than anything this side of hell. I knew I actually needed her and I felt she needed me. But I was responsible for Byron. He also needed a father. And it was my job to be a good father to him.

But when I reached the west end of the station platform I said to myself, "God meant that Fran and I should be man and wife. That was plain from the first day we looked into each other's eyes in high school. If Pearl is unable to take care of Byron properly she can give him up to me." And I thought of the many differences Pearl and I have had. I thought of how little we have in common. I thought that I never really have loved her, that I was her husband only because it was convenient to her that I be her husband. I thought of all the dreams of Frances and I said to myself, "God sent me those dreams or visions. Now God has shown me the way. I will go."

I turned and walked fast eastward along the length of the station platform with the steam from my hot breath billowing up before me. But when I got to the east end of the platform my steps began to drag and I turned and walked west again.

A hundred times I walked back and forth along that platform. A hundred times I decided I would go down to Pine Street and a hundred times I changed my mind. My ears were stinging from the subzero temperature, but my light overcoat seemed oppressively warm.

About noon I went back into the train feeling I had won a victory. I ate a small lunch in the dining car and smoked a cigar. I went back to my seat and settled myself with the magazine story to pass away the hours. I congratulated myself on my will power. But the first thing I knew I had my overcoat on again and was pacing back and forth on the station platform, changing my mind at each end. Passengers on the train, watching me through the frosty windows must have thought me crazy. And in fact I *was* crazy.

Shortly after 2 o'clock the battle had worn me to a point of reckless exhaustion. My sense of responsibility was drugged. Everything in me was worn out and dying except my love for Fran, my desire for Fran.

At the east end of the platform I kept on walking. I went plowing desperately through the hard fine snow toward Pine Street, toward the girl whom I had not seen in ten years, but whom I never would cease loving in a century. I was going to see Fran and to hell with consequences. The very least I could do was to see her when I was in the same town.

I had gone nearly to Hemlock Street when the locomotive blew its whistle. And before I knew what I was doing I was running back through the snow and climbing aboard the train. And then I was sitting in my seat, scratching the frost off the window and peering out the peephole at the Raleigh town water tank and the church steeple and the bare cotton-wood trees around a small house up a street I judged to be Pine and at a trickle of blue smoke rising from this small house's chimney which might be coming from a fire that was warming my golden-haired Frances.

And as the train whirled on through the snow toward Wyoming I asked myself why I came back. And I didn't know the answer.

To satisfy my own mind, I should have gone and seen if the Mrs. Paul Clark of Raleigh really is my Frances. I know she is. But again, I don't know. The whole thing is so fantastic. It has been so for years. I could have settled the matter of my strange dreams if I had only acted. But I didn't act. Could I have but seen Frances and talked with her awhile things would be so much better now. We wouldn't have run away together. Frances, knowing my responsibility, wouldn't have permitted it even though I had been willing, even though she wished to.

Perhaps, if I stay on the *Denver Call,* I shall get a vacation next summer or in 1917. I never have had a vacation by myself. Perhaps if things go right I can convince Pearl I need to go fishing or something into the hills. And Raleigh, Utah, is not impossibly far from Denver.

I could drop in there casually and discover by accident she is living there. That coincidence would not be greater than many of the actual coincidences of life.

FEBRUARY 18, 1916. My job on the *Call* is apparently secure, so I have rented a furnished flat on East Nineteenth Avenue of the type they call a "terrace" in Denver and have sent word to Pearl to come on with Byron.

There are numerous terraces here—low, flat-topped apartments that in reality are a series of square, brick cottages all joined. While they are practically flush with the street there still is a community back yard where the children may play. In that they are much better than the huge, rambling apartments of gray-painted redwood such as we occupied in San Francisco.

Denver is not a large city—only slightly above 200,000, or approximately the same size as Oakland—but there is a quality to it I like already. There are no very large buildings, except that the Daniels and Fisher department store has a slim tower which is 20 stories or so high, and the gold-domed capitol building sitting on the only eminence in the city—a slight rise called Capitol Hill—appears huge from a distance.

The Rocky Mountains, which rise sharply to the west, dominate Denver. In the clear air, this snowy range seems to be only a couple of miles away, but today, being my day off, I took a trolley car to the village of Golden and was surprised to discover that the nearest foothills are 13 miles from the city.

Golden nestles between huge, flat-topped hills called buttes. One of these, Castle Rock (which really resembles a castle) has a funicular railway running up its 45° slope to the summit, which I should judge is 1,500 or 2,000 feet above the surrounding country. There are two tracks and a car on each track connected by a steel cable. I understand there are water tanks in the cars which are filled at the top and emptied at the bottom of the butte. Thus the weight of the water takes one car down the incline and pulls the drained one back up by the cable. The railway operates only in the summer when there is tourist business.

There must be a magnificent view from the top of Castle Rock and I must take Pearl and Byron up next summer.

From an awesome, steep-walled canyon Clear Creek boils down from the mountains and through Golden. The water is no longer clear, but milky from the mine dumps far up the gorge.

A queer little narrow-gauge railroad runs up the canyon clear up into the high mountains to a mining camp called Silver Plume and stopping at the other mining camps of Idaho Springs and Georgetown. I walked a short way up the canyon and presently a whistle shrilled, echoing weirdly among the sheer rock cliffs. I got off the track and here came a train from out of the past. The tiny locomotive had a tall, swelling smokestack such as those in pictures of Civil War times.

I understand there are a number of such railroads running into the mountains and that in the summer they have one-day excursions at ridiculously low fares. We'll have to take some of those on my days off.

The newspaper gang in Denver is the most friendly I have seen anywhere. There is bitter rivalry between the papers, but away from work the reporters and copyreaders are good friends. There is a press club where the fellows meet after work to play pool or poker and drink and gossip and banter about who got scooped and why.

Last Saturday night after work I went to the press club with John Soibelman, who sits next to me on the copy desk. We found a dozen or so there from the *Call* and the *Rocky Mountain News* and the *Denver Post*. The steward, a dour Chinaman named Jim Wong, was grumbling about the work and serving sandwiches and scrambled eggs and beer and whisky highballs to those who put in orders.

In the main room of the club are a billiard table, a pool table and player piano and rack of rolls and some bookcases of oddly assorted books. In the room adjoining to the back there is just one large green-topped round table with a green-shaded light and chairs. The other room is the bar with Jim Wong's gas range and refrigerator back of it, a couple of pine

tables and chairs and one of the Dewey gambling machines
such as they had on the gambling boat in Kansas City.

When John Soibelman admitted us with his passkey a poker
game already was in progress. Soibelman introduced me to
the players and they invited us to buy a stack of chips. It
seems the club sells $4.50 worth of chips for $5 which is one
of its means of raising revenue.

At the table already were Harvey Thorpe, slim and satur-
nine reporter for the *Call;* Roscoe McNamara, florid and a
little pompous, who is state editor for the *Rocky Mountain
News;* Bill Cunningham, city editor for the *Call;* who is
about my size and who wears a worried expression and an
odd, round black felt hat on the back of his head; and Charley
Murray, a bright-looking young Irishman with a caustic
tongue who is a reporter for the *Times.*

Thorpe, I discovered, had put in several years as a clown
with John Robinson's circus and McNamara had been a circus
advance man. So between deals Thorpe and McNamara were
putting on, with all seriousness, an act which they loved.
McNamara, unsmilingly, was a small-town mayor. Thorpe
was a circus claim agent, or whatever they call it. And
McNamara was trying to collect damages.

"Now, your Honor," protested Thorpe, "surely you know
that the great Adam Forepaugh circus wishes to be fair with
everyone."

"I know, *I* know," McNamara drawled with heavy sarcasm.
"Nothin' but fairness about a *circus.* Come into a town, stay
a day and take out thousands of dollars what ought to go to
the merchants."

"You look," said Thorpe, "into the merchants' tills on circus
day and you'll find they do bigger business than any other day
in the year. But I needn't tell *you* this, your Honor. You know
as well as I. And it's all beside the question. Where now was
this damage done?"

"Right at the corner of Main and Clay streets," attested McNamara with some heat.

"But you can't be certain it was done by the circus, can you, Mr. Mayor?"

"Can't be *certain?* Why, gol darn it, Fred Hackett was right there and he seen it and Miss Mamie Pinkham, she plays the organ in the South Methodist Church, why, she was right there and she seen it and—"

"Oh, can the comedy, Sureshot," Murray interrupted. "Are you playing or not?"

Thorpe looked at his hole card. "*I* stay," he said, throwing in a red chip.

"Well, I raise you a blue one," announced Murray, who had a deuce and a five of diamonds showing.

"On what?" asked Cunningham, irritably.

"Possible straight flush," said Murray.

"Raise you another blue one," said McNamara. "They all seen it. I got half a dozen witnesses, I have, that your dad-gummed old parade wagon with the hippypotamus painted on the side turned the corner too brash and run right over the curbing at Main and Clay and smashed off a great chunk of the stone."

"I stay," said Cunningham.

"I stay," said Thorpe.

"I'll see your blue one and raise you another," announced Murray.

"I stay," said McNamara, "— a great unsightly scar on the face of our beautiful town and all because of criminal reck-lessness on the part of a money-grabbing circus that comes in and—"

Cunningham scowled. "Not afraid of you, Murray. But I fold my tent like the well-known Arab."

Thorpe threw in another blue chip and began to deal the cards around. "If," he said, "any damage whatsoever has been done by the Adam Forepaugh circus, the Adam Forepaugh circus, greatest show on earth, is ready and willing to make any reasonable restitution. Well," as he dealt an ace to himself, "up jumped the devil. No pairs in sight and the ace bets a blue one. What do you consider, Mr. Mayor, to be a fair price for repairing the allegedly damaged curbing?"

"You bet," said Murray, testily, "right in the face of my possible straight flush? Well, I raise you a blue one." Murray now had the three, five and six of diamonds in sight.

"I'll see the raise," said McNamara, sadly. "We estimate the damage at three hundred dollars."

"But, Mr. Mayor, Mr. Mayor, that's *ridiculous,* unheard of, positively preposterous." Thorpe threw in another blue chip. "I'll just call the blue chip. Three hundred dollars for a little piece of concrete chipped off a curbing by a parade wagon that was giving thrills and pleasure to your own townspeople and your own kiddies? You *can't* be serious."

"Oh, deal the cards," snapped Murray.

Thorpe dealt Murray a very black jack of clubs, a four of diamonds to McNamara that would have made Murray's hand look very dangerous and then the three of diamonds to himself, which showed Murray hadn't even a chance for a straight from the beginning.

"Ace bets a blue," observed Thorpe.

"It ain't just the actual *value* of the curbing," said McNamara, "though it'll cost plenty to put in that whole corner. It's that unsightly scar on the face of the town, hurting our reputation when visitors come in and—"

"I call," said Murray.

"You can't be serious, your Honor," said Thorpe. "How could a small piece of chipped curbing damage a town's reputation?"

"I also call," said McNamara, "and Main and Clay is right on the direct road from the Katy station to the Austin House. When visitors are coming in on the station bus, how can they *help* seeing that unsightly scar? How can they help, gol darn it, saying 'My, what a slovenly town Wilsonville must be.'"

"You're called, Thorpe," said Murray. "What's your hole card?"

"Another ace." Thorpe flipped over the ace of spades.

"Just tops my ladies." McNamara turned over a queen which matched his third card.

"Come to your drunken father," drawled Thorpe, raking in the chips.

Jim Wong brought Soibelman and me stacks of chips and we sat in the game. On and on the dialogue between the mayor and the circus agent continued. The town must protect itself. Suppose some citizen tripped on the broken curbing and was injured. Suppose he or she won $10,000 judgment against the town before the curb should be repaired. What then? The mayor thought he was betraying his constituency even in accepting $300.

Murray continued raising the bet at every turn. Sometimes he won. More often he only built up a substantial pot for someone else. Both Soibelman and I were lucky. Cunningham seemed to be playing a conservative and sensible game. But luck was against him. Thorpe and McNamara were more interested in their debate than in the cards.

About 2 o'clock a lanky and rather drunken fellow of around 35 let himself in with a passkey. He was introduced to me as Judd Watson, political reporter for the *News*. For a minute or so he stood grinning at the Thorpe-McNamara act. "At it again," he said, mildly. Then he went to the bar and drank a couple of straight whiskies. Then he went to the player piano and began to pump out "A Perfect Day" very fast and as loud as he could make it. When that roll was ended he played the "Sextette from Lucia" equally fast and equally loud. Then he played "A Perfect Day" over. Then he played the "Sextette from Lucia."

"For G—'s sake," called Murray, "don't pump that thing so hard, Judd."

"I like it loud," said Judd, smiling happily. "Sounds prettier when it's loud." Then he played "A Perfect Day." Then he played the "Sextette from Lucia."

Then there was a vigorous rapping on the door and Jim Wong opened it before two very large policeman. They pushed into the room.

"Hello, fellows," hailed Judd, waving his hand. "Come in and sit down. I'll play you some music and buy you a drink." He began to pump once more on "A Perfect Day."

The policeman walked over by the piano. "Listen, Watson," said the bigger one, "you're making too much noise for three o'clock Sunday morning. We got a complaint. You got to stop that."

Judd stopped pumping and "A Perfect Day" died gasping for breath. He turned and squinted owlishly at the officers. "Now," he said, "who would complain about a little music? I love music. Don't you cops love music?"

"Sure," said the smaller policeman, "I like music, but that ain't the question. The girls next door is complaining. They say they can't sleep for the noise over here."

Judd got up from the bench and put his arms around the policemen's shoulders. "Now, fellows, listen," he said. "No girls ought to be sleeping this time of Sunday morning, anyhow. You're not sleeping. I'm not sleeping. Jim Wong's not sleeping. Nobody ought to be sleeping."

He led them to the bar. "Now you fellows have a nice drink with me and then I'll tell you what to do. You go over and have the girls come up here and I'll play them some music. I'll play 'em some swell music about a Perfect Day."

"We'll have a drink," said the bigger policeman. "But we can't do *that*. The girls complained to the captain. You got to quit pumping that piano, Judd."

Jim Wong put a bottle and glasses on the bar and they all

drank. The smaller policeman put a nickel in the Dewey slot machine and pulled the handle. He didn't get anything.

"Fellows," said Judd, "you make me sad. I *love* music. I don't get much chance for music and now you say I can't play. I can't understand folks that don't love music, and I think if those girls next door don't love music they aren't nice girls and to h— with them."

"Well, they complained," said the bigger policeman.

"Have a drink," said Judd. And they all took drinks.

The smaller policeman put another nickel in the slot machine and didn't get anything.

"Listen, Judd," said the bigger policeman, "haven't you got a soft pedal on that thing?"

"Yes. Got a soft pedal."

"Well, you promise to keep the soft pedal on so's it won't disturb the girls and we'll go."

"Fine, fine." Judd was glowing and slapped the policeman on the back. "You're gentlemen and you love music."

So the policemen departed and Judd went back to "A Perfect Day" and the "Sextette from Lucia." But he didn't use the soft pedal.

When he was rerolling a record Cunningham called to Judd. "Listen here, Watson, you promised those cops to soft-pedal that thing. You'll have 'em back here presently and they'll take you down to the jug."

"Pardon *me,* Mr. Cunningham," said Judd, "but I didn't promise the cops a thing. Legal technicality. They asked me to promise but I gave 'em legal technicality. Don't you know cops have to operate on legal technicalities? And besides the music isn't so pretty when it's soft."

So the piano continued its deafening bam-bamming. And at 4:30, after Jim Wong had sold a bottle of whisky to the poker table, there was vigorous rapping on the door again. Judd himself left the piano and opened the door and there were the policemen again.

The larger policeman was stern. "We got another complaint, Watson, and you got to stop that noise," he said.

"We could hear you a block away," said the smaller policeman.

"Aw, please," begged Judd. "I didn't really promise last time. I just gave you a legal technicality. But I'll promise and cross my heart this time I'll use the soft pedal."

"Let's see that piano," said the larger policeman. He looked over the battered instrument and scratched his chin. Then, "If we had a piece of string maybe we could tie that soft pedal lever over so it would be all right."

"Give you my shoestring," volunteered Judd, eagerly.

"Let's have it."

So Judd fumbled and finally got the string out of his shoe and the policemen lashed the soft pedal lever over and had Judd try the piano. He played very softly.

The policemen warned Judd that if they got one more complaint they'd take him to the cooler and departed. He left the soft pedal on then, and pumped away at "A Perfect Day" and the "Sextette from Lucia" until about 5 o'clock. Then he found the "Second Hungarian Rhapsody" and added that to his repertoire and played until 7 o'clock.

When we adjourned and went to a restaurant for waffles and sausage, Judd's legs were so lame he scarcely could walk. Also he had to limp to keep one shoe on because he'd left his shoestring on the piano.

Because I had won the most in the game—$14—I had to pay for the breakfasts, which came to nearly $3.

Soibelman is a very interesting fellow. He was born in Russia and couldn't speak a word of English when he came to America at 12. Now he hasn't a trace of accent. He went to Columbia University in New York City for three years and has worked on newspapers all over the United States and in Europe.

He lives out on East Twentieth Avenue and we walk out

together in the morning after work. The other morning we got to talking literature and he confessed he has written four long novels and several hundred short stories without ever selling a line. I think that proves that one shouldn't start writing seriously until he is fully prepared for the work.

I told him about the novel I shall write someday and he asked me how I liked Tolstoy and Dostoevski. When I admitted I had read neither he told me no one should even think of writing until he had read "Anna Karenina" and "War and Peace."

MARCH 21, 1916. There has been a heavy snowstorm, which kept Byron in the house for several days. But generally the child is feeling much better and he looks better than he has in a year. Pearl is feeding him lots of milk and eggs and getting him out in the sunshine whenever possible.

Pearl, however, does not like the terrace we are occupying and believes we owe it to Byron to have our own furniture and our own house (rented at least) while we are in a city like Denver where almost everyone lives in separate houses.

She has found a store that will sell complete house furnishings on credit with a small down payment and when spring comes we shall look for a cottage with a nice yard.

The United States is practically at war with Mexico and while I have felt that war can be avoided always if the statesmen don't act like small boys, I admit there is a great deal of justification for America's action in invading Mexico.

About ten days ago the Mexican rebel leader, Pancho Villa, led a party of 2,500 Mexican brigands across the American border and attacked Columbus, N. M. They raided the town, looting stores and setting fire to residences and attacked the near-by United States cavalry camp. Sixteen Americans were killed and many wounded while the handful of American troopers managed to exterminate about forty of the bandits.

When President Carranza showed little enthusiasm for running down the murderer, Villa, General Funston sent Brigadier General John J. Pershing at the head of an army to cross the border and chase down the sometimes rebel and sometimes bandit Villa in the hills of Chihuahua.

Villa has been a thorn in the side of Mexico for many years. There is no estimating the number of his robberies or the number of his murders. That he has a great following in Mexico cannot be doubted, nor that many Mexicans believe him capable of anything—even to capturing the United States. Two or three days ago a newspaper in Durango, Mexico, printed the startling information that Villa had captured Texas and New Mexico and that President Wilson and his family were fleeing to Canada to escape the conqueror.

Pancho Villa, however, made his fatal mistake in crossing the American border. He has learned now that making attacks on Mexican communities and raiding American towns are horses of a different color. We received information tonight that Pershing's cavalry has trapped and captured Villa in the mountains 110 miles south of the New Mexico border without loss of a single American trooper. There may be international complications over Villa's trial as Carranza has expressed resentment at the American invasion. Perhaps, however, things may be simplified. Perhaps Villa may "attempt to escape" on the way back to the border and one of his guards regrettably may be forced to shoot him.

Last Friday afternoon we took Byron to the Isis Theater and saw French government films of actual fighting on the western front. The pictures were very interesting although not very plain. The other picture was Theda Bara in "Gold and the Woman." Pearl liked it, but I don't care so much for the vampire. And of course Byron didn't know what it was all about.

I am trying to talk Pearl into having the child's hair cut. He is nearly 5 years old now and should be quite a boy. But his yellow curls make him look more like a little girl. Pearl feels he will be a baby no longer once his hair is cut.

That is one of the troubles with the boy, as I see it. Pearl doesn't give him a chance to be a boy. I never see him except when he is with his mother and he is with her alone in the evenings when I have gone to work. Thus he always turns to her instead of to me and he actually seems jealous of me when Pearl and I are talking.

I don't like that, but I don't seem able to do much about it. I have suggested several times that I take Byron out alone on nice afternoons but Pearl naturally doesn't want to be left behind. So when we are all together it is, "Mama, what's that? Oh, Mama, looky. Oh, Mama, can I have an ice-cream cone?"

Pearl thinks the situation is a joke and I believe she may even encourage it. But I don't think it is very funny. I certainly don't want Byron to develop into a sissy, and I can only hope the situation will change as he grows older.

Taking John Soibelman's advice, I have "Anna Karenina" from the library, but am having a little difficulty in keeping the characters straight because of the names. Arkadyevitch and Golitsin and Vronsky and Dmitrievitch and Shtcherbatsky probably seem as plausible and common to Soibelman as Jones or O'Brien or Schwartz to me.

If the European War should last until the first of August it will have run two years. In the beginning nobody believed it would continue for a year. At last, however, everything points to a termination of hostilities before summer.

Germany is at the end of her resources—money, materials and man power. The stupid Crown Prince has killed off tens of thousands of German young men in a foolish assault on the forts at Verdun. Army after army was hurled into these attacks, always with the same result. The Germans were mowed down by French machine guns and light artillery. It is reported that at least 50,000 German dead are lying before the French trenches. Among these are the corpses of Germany's proudest cavalry brigade—the "Death Head Hussars," which were called the "Crown Prince's Own." He ordered these horsemen to charge the array of machine gun nests and to take them at any cost. The Brigade was wiped out. It is noteworthy that the Crown Prince did not charge with them.

JUNE 11, 1916. I am now telegraph editor of the *Call* and incidentally head of the copy desk. It is a terrific job, but probably will be easier when I get more used to the routine. On any other paper I have seen it was considered a man-sized job to be head of a universal desk. And it certainly was a man's job being telegraph editor of the *Tribune* in San Francisco. Here, however, they aren't as particular about the copyreading and the headlines as in San Francisco and also there is not quite as heavy a burden of telegraph copy. We have the Associated Press night wire and the Universal Service.

George Empey, who formerly was in the slot and telegraph editor, took a job on the Associated Press, which made the opening for me. But I had been led to understand I should replace him in any event. My pay has been raised to $40 a week, which, I am told, is $2.50 more than Empey was getting.

There is at least one unhappy circumstance connected with my promotion. A copyreader, an old-timer named Morris Johnson, whom everyone calls "Peg" because he has an artificial leg, resents my advancement over him and has been acting very surly. He doesn't actually stall on the job, but he does a lot of grumbling about the stories I give him and asks me many questions where the answers are most obvious. Especially does he ask me questions about office policy which he really should know better than I. Of course what he is trying to do is to show me up before the others.

We have rented a red brick cottage on Tejon Street (pronounced Tee-hone) in North Denver and have furnished it from an installment house. I paid $100 down and owe more than $300, which I am supposed to pay off at the rate of $25 a month. Normally one would think that this would pay off the debt in a year. But the interest and brokerage charges and whatnot bring it up to 15 months.

We have a golden oak library table in the living room and four chairs and a couch which can be opened out into a bed. Two of the chairs are rockers. And, of course, we moved our phonograph from San Francisco. Two fairly large framed pictures, one of a brightly colored mountain scene, which Pearl selected, and one called "The Lone Wolf," which I picked out. It shows a snowy hill and a wolf in the foreground. It is night, which makes the sky a dark blue and the snow a light blue. The wolf is looking down into the valley at a small cluster of buildings and the whole effect is good, although Pearl says it makes her cold to look at it. There is a mantel and fireplace and I have stacked my books on the mantel on each side of the clock. I do not care much for the clock. It is gilt and quite fancy and it strikes too loud and fast. In the living room we have a rather pretty flowered rug. But the dining room rug is a mixture of yellows and purples which seems loud to me. Then we have a round dining table of golden oak and six chairs.

Our bedroom has an iron bed painted bronze and a mahogany veneer dresser and chiffonier with fancy brass handles on the drawers. Byron has a small iron bed and a dresser and a little chair. We already had a high chair for him, which he has outgrown, but Pearl keeps it in the kitchen now. She has taken the arms off and sits on it to work.

There was a gas range in the house, so we didn't have to buy that. But we got an icebox and kitchen table and chairs and a kitchen cabinet because there wasn't enough cupboard room. And we got an ironing board and flatirons and kitchen pots and pans and spiders, which they call skillets out here, and dishes and some silverware.

After we were moving in Pearl discovered there weren't

any lace curtains and, being used to living in furnished places, hadn't thought about needing them. So she had to rush over to the Golden Eagle and buy some lace curtains and rods to hold them up. After that we discovered there weren't any electric bulbs left in the sockets and we had to go buy them.

Our house is across the Twentieth Street viaduct from the downtown section, so it is too far to walk. This is bad in one way because if I miss an owl car in the morning (which I often do) I have to wait an hour for another. Perhaps, however, I shall get my schedule routinized later so I can catch the regular 2-o'clock car.

I have made one discovery already in the matter of systematizing work. Empey always went out to lunch right after the North Mail edition and stayed out half an hour or so. I tried that at first, putting Soibelman in the slot while I was gone. But of course Soibelman couldn't send any copy to the composing room while I was out, not knowing what I had handled before or not knowing the status of any running stories except those he had handled himself. So necessarily the copy stacked up, both telegraph and local, and it would take me the best part of an hour to get things straightened out after I returned. The solution of this was quite simple. I don't go out to lunch now. I send a copy boy to the near-by "Greasy Spoon" and have him bring me a tray with a big bowl of chili con carne and crackers and a ham sandwich and a cup of coffee. Chili is very nutritious and I am fond of it. I can eat the chili with a spoon in one hand and sort and deal copy with the other. Thus I am in pretty fair shape for the inside of the home edition even before Bill Cunningham, the city editor, and I go into conference with Harvey O'Brien, the news editor, on Page One.

The Republican convention nominated Charles Evans Hughes for President and Charles W. Fairbanks for Vice-President. Hughes is a former governor of New York and probably too good a man to be used as a burnt offering against Woodrow Wilson. Naturally, the Democrats will renominate Wilson and he should win a larger vote even than in 1912. The nation owes Wilson a debt of gratitude for the fact that he has kept us out of the European war despite the clamorings of such jingoes as Theodore Roosevelt.

Still the war goes on, although it appears that Germany is near exhaustion. But the fact remains that the Germans still are doing their fighting in France, Belgium and Russia. And their submarine warfare is becoming more terrible week by week. Last week the British cruiser *Hampshire* hit a mine and sank, taking to death with its crew, Lord Kitchener, British minister of war.

JUNE 23, 1916. Sunday, being the lightest night, is my night off now and Pearl and Byron and I took the "far-famed Georgetown loop" trip today. The narrow-gauge train goes up Clear Creek canyon to Georgetown and Silver Plume, making a loop across an awesome gulch over a spindly bridge. Never have I seen such wonderful scenery. We took a picnic lunch and ate it above Silver Plume between trains. Byron was greatly excited over the brawling stream and all. It was the first time I had ever ridden on a train with him. He is looking much better and apparently is feeling fine. Certainly it was a wise move, bringing him to Colorado when we did.

Friday Carranza troops attacked the column of cavalry led by General Pershing in search of the bandit, Pancho Villa. Twenty-three Americans were captured. It would seem that Pershing is on a hopeless quest. It would seem that he better be withdrawn before the United States is embroiled in a war with Mexico. Because our manufacturers are persistently shipping ammunition and guns to the Allies, Germany might welcome an opportunity to aid Mexico in warring on America and thus stop the flow of supplies to their enemies.

Last week I had another vivid dream of Frances. She was standing before the ironing board in her kitchen ironing clothes and from the clothesbasket she brought out the blue print she was wearing when little Carol was killed. The baby was wearing a frock of the same material at the time. When Frances brought out this dress it suddenly reminded her of Carol. She held it in both hands and burst into tears.

My eyes have been bothering me a great deal lately. Sometimes they ache so much after I have got home and to bed that I can't sleep. I'm afraid I shall have to go to an oculist and get glasses. But I hate to give in to that. My eyes have always been so strong, but I must admit I have abused them a lot.

Peg Johnson is making a great play for favor in the eyes of Harvey O'Brien, the dyspeptic news editor, laughing loudly at anything even faintly resembling a joke that O'Brien tells.

Saturday night O'Brien came over to the copy desk during a lull and he said, "You know last winter on the western front the Germans put up a sign calculated to disconcert the British in the opposite trenches. The sign read 'Gott Mit Uns,' which meant of course, 'God is with us.' But that didn't feaze the Tommies. They put up a sign reading, 'We got mittens too.'"

At that Johnson burst into such a gale of laughter he could have been heard a block away. "We got mittens too," he chortled and slapped his thigh. "Say, that's good. We got mittens too."

And O'Brien minced back to his desk as pleased as a dog that's just chased an automobile out of the block. I don't think O'Brien cares much for me and I can see Johnson is working on that. Perhaps I should feel worried about the situation if it weren't for Fred Gotchell, the managing editor. Gotchell, a burly fellow with great nervous energy, is the man who matters around the *Call*. And I know he likes my work and is very friendly with me. He'll come in along about 10 o'clock and stop at the copy desk to slap me on the shoulder.

"How's everything, Homer, old boy?" he'll ask. Then I'll tell him what is going on and he'll go on into his office often without even going over to talk with O'Brien.

I always try to handle the lead story of the night myself. Gotchell often comes out after an edition and asks who wrote this head or that 8-column line. Sometimes he has most emphatic objections and tells me not to let them get away with things of that sort. At other times he has high praise for the line or head, and most often on those occasions it has been my own work that met his approval. So I feel I have nothing to worry about despite the O'Brien-Johnson combination.

Of course O'Brien is in a position to make me look very bad if he chooses. I don't believe he could actually fire me, but if he set out to do it, he probably could make me appear sufficiently bad that Gotchell would want to fire me. But nevertheless, I am in a position to make O'Brien look very bad also.

Usually he is late in getting his Page One dummy scheduled, so we have to work like fiends to get the copy to the composing room in time. It would be a simple matter for me to hold back some key story for three or four pages, making them go into the stereotypers in a bunch. I could make every edition late except the first street edition, which O'Brien doesn't dummy. He couldn't prove a thing and it would give him a bad record. Of course I wouldn't do a thing like that unless he forced me to it, but at least he should know that I have several potent weapons at my command.

I have found out how Johnson lost his leg. He was working on the *Times* during the bloody mine strike in southern Colorado two years ago. His sympathies were with the strikers so strongly that he quit his job and went down to help the miners fight the National Guard. Because he had served an enlistment in the regular army during his youth, he knew something of military affairs and he tried to organize the strikers on semiarmy lines for the battle.

Then he saw that the militia had some machine guns trained on the camp and conceived what seemed to him to be a bright idea. One night late he got a good-looking sister of a miner to play a vampire role on one of the sentries and while the sentry was thus engaged, Johnson and several of his followers slipped down and stole a machine gun and a box of ammunition.

They took the gun to a promontory which overlooked the militia camp, set it up and at dawn opened fire. But the machine gun jammed after a few shots and Johnson, old soldier though he was, didn't know enough about a machine gun to get it going again. Consequently the National Guardsmen opened a heavy fire which killed one of the strikers and wounded Johnson in the leg. His pals carried him off, but it was long before he got medical attention and the wound became infected. A doctor in Trinidad amputated his leg to save his life. From my present perspective that seems to have been a somewhat unnecessary procedure.

SEPTEMBER 17, 1916. We have had a very pleasant summer and now Byron is a schoolboy. He started to Bryant School kindergarten last week and is most proud of himself with his new boy haircut and suit of clothes. It is about three blocks to the school on West Thirty-sixth Avenue and he trudges off in the morning, very much the big boy. It about broke Pearl's heart to have his hair cut and to see him going to school, but she has some other interests now and is quite content.

Boyd Ferguson, who is assistant city editor on the *Call*, lives only a few blocks away on Umatilla Street and Pearl and Violet Ferguson have become good friends. Mrs. Ferguson has made Pearl acquainted with several other young women who live near by and they meet frequently to play bridge.

We made several trips into the mountains on Sundays. Once we took the narrow-gauge railroad over to Mount

Morrison, hired a burro to carry Byron and the lunch basket and walked up into the Park of the Red Rocks where the great slabs of upended sandstone have been eroded into wonderful and fantastic shapes. While there I killed a rattlesnake with a stone and Pearl ripped a heel off her slipper. With a spike heel on one foot and no heel on the other she was unable to walk back to the railroad, so she had to ride the burro and I had to carry Byron most of the way. I was exhausted by the time we got back and felt pretty sorry for the little donkey. They are amazingly sturdy, however, and he didn't seem any worse for carrying Pearl's 150 pounds two or three miles.

A more wonderful trip was on the Moffat Road to the crest of the Continental Divide at Corona. It was a hot day in July that we took this trip but there were snowbanks at the top and hot coffee and hot hamburgers in the restaurant were most welcome.

I finally had to give in and go to an occulist. Now I am wearing horn-rimmed glasses which don't look as bad as I had feared. And certainly I feel a lot better and am not troubled so much with headaches.

We now are in the midst of one of the most bitter political campaigns on record. Governor Hughes has been touring the country, but he is a man of frigid personality and an indifferent orator. He was given a fine reception in Denver, but it was the reception which would be accorded any person who has been distinguished by the presidential nomination of a major party.

Theodore Roosevelt is doing the major campaigning for Hughes, attacking Wilson with such unrestrained bitterness that I imagine he is making votes for the Democratic Party rather than for Hughes.

Roosevelt charges Wilson with being a weakling who has compromised the honor of America. Particularly does he rant at the government's failure to send a huge military force into

Mexico and capture Pancho Villa. He shouts that Wilson is guilty of the murder of the women and children in Columbus, N.M., because he had not displayed firm enough a hand to frighten the Mexican bandits. He also makes the ridiculous charge that had Wilson been firm enough with Germany in the beginning Germany would not have dared to engage in her submarine warfare, that Germany would not have dared sink even the *Lusitania*.

The Democrats are not even bothering to stress the great works of the present administration, to emphasize the Federal Reserve act which will prevent panics such as that which gripped the nation in 1907 during Roosevelt's administration, nor of the Adamson bill signed this month by Wilson which provides an 8-hour day for railroad men, thus preventing the wave of railroad wrecks which killed thousands during Roosevelt's term. There is a good deal of argument that a man is never injured by the hours he works, but by what he does when he is off work. No doubt there is a great deal of truth to that attitude, ordinarily. An 8-hour day never would be practicable at many occupations—notably the newspaper business—but it has been proved that many wrecks have been caused by fatigue relaxing the vigilance of a railroad engineer. Despite Republican opposition, most people agree now that 8 hours is enough for an engineer to stay at the throttle when the lives of hundreds depend on his wakefulness.

The Democrats are waging this campaign on one premise. That is, "He Kept Us Out of War." And what a potent sentence that is with wise Americans.

But there are others, not so wise, who assail Wilson for a "wishy-washy" foreign policy and not only are going to vote for Hughes, but firmly believe he will be elected.

It is difficult for me to understand how anyone can attack Wilson's foreign policy unless he actually wants the United States to enter the European War. Wilson's consistent policy

is to preserve peace. The only other possible policy would
be war.

I am going to save every penny I can above what we need
for living expenses and to pay the furniture installments and
bet all I can on this election. In that I have a dark plot forming. I shall say nothing to Pearl about my bet and I shall
salt away my winnings carefully for a purpose.

Next summer I shall have a vacation coming. And I shall
start promoting the idea in the spring that I need to get
away from everything for a while, that I need to go back in
the hills and rough it. Then I shall take a train to Raleigh,
Utah.

NOVEMBER 12, 1916. Last Tuesday undoubtedly was the most
terrific national election in history. President Wilson was re-
elected for which the whole nation has reason to thank Providence. But it was by a narrow margin and the result was in
doubt until well along the next day. Even now the betting
commissioners will not pay off until after the official count.
I had bet $35 at even money and eventually will get my $70,
minus the commissioner's 5% but I have been somewhat
embarrassed financially, as they say, while the money is held
up. As a matter of fact, I took it for granted the commissioner
would pay off as soon as the result became evident. And, as
Pearl has been clamoring for a new coat, I gave her $25
Thursday which was to go to the furniture house, because
I supposed I could collect my $66.50 on the way to work.
When that was impossible I tried to stave off the furniture
house for a week and they grew practically insulting. Then,
much as I hated to, I borrowed $25 from John Soibelman.
It is very bad policy to borrow from a man who is working
under one, but I know Soibelman is not a man to presume
on that sort of thing. Also, I knew he had the money.

The election itself was a great strain on me. I felt the issues
so keenly that I couldn't believe the people at large could

help seeing the situation as it is. But about 10 o'clock Tuesday night I realized I had been too confident. There are so many obscure items to be considered in a national election, so many hidden elements of which even a telegraph editor cannot be cognizant.

Of course I expected New England to go for Hughes. One couldn't expect anything else except when the Republican Party was split as in 1912. But I had taken it for granted that Wilson would carry New York State and when the returns showed that Hughes was sweeping both New York and Pennsylvania I felt actually ill. Then New Jersey and Illinois gave substantial leads to the Republicans and Michigan joined the parade. All of the big states seemed to be falling into line with each succeeding bulletin.

Then about 10 o'clock the Associated Press boy spiked a piece of paper on the spindle, calling out, "Flash!"

I pulled off the sheet and it read:

NEW YORK WORLD CONCEDES
HUGHES ELECTION

And the *World* had been Wilson's staunchest supporter in New York.

I called out the flash to Gotchell and O'Brien. Gotchell grinned. "Well," he said, "it's all over. Shoot an extra."

So I wrote the saddest 8-column line I ever turned out, in 120-point. It read,

HUGHES WINS IN LANDSLIDE

and we put out the extra.

The office was jam-packed with politicians and others who had enough influence with the management to gain entreé. They crowded around the copy desk, leaning over my neck to read the bulletins as I got them, breathing stale, secondhand

Cheyenne whisky in my face. The whole staff was at work on the local and state angles and returns, including those off all the runs except the police beat. And in addition virtually the whole business office crew was working at benches, running adding machines and computing the returns as they came in by telephone. Also at a long table were six or eight girls from the business office and Miss Murray, the society editress, with telephone headsets on answering the hundreds of queries that came in. Their soprano voices rose above the general din and clatter of typewriters, telegraph instruments and excited male voices. Now excitement entered the girls' voices too. They were higher pitched and louder.

"Yes, Hughes is elected. Hughes is elected. Yes, Hughes has won New York. Hughes . . . Hughes is ahead in Illinois. It looks like a landslide. No reports from New Mexico yet. Pennsylvania? Hughes wins Pennsylvania."

And the visiting politicians, almost all of whom were Republicans, were jubilant. They cheered when they caught sight of additional Hughes victories over my shoulder.

One sleek young fellow with a big cigar held importantly in his mouth slapped me on the back. "Ain't that great, old man?" he chortled.

"Yes," I said, "if you're ready to shoulder a gun and go to France."

At midnight the office had sandwiches, pie and coffee brought in for the workers who hadn't had time to go to lunch. The visiting politicians made great headway. They dropped sandwich crumbs down my neck as they read bulletins over my shoulder. We on the copy desk were too busy getting out the North Mail to eat for half an hour. By that time the food was pretty well pawed over. But we did get some lukewarm coffee and Soibelman rescued an apple pie from the debris which hadn't much coffee spilled on it, and Frank Chapin was lucky enough to find a big dill pickle which he divided, cutting it up with his copy shears.

Along then the tide began to turn. Wilson was leading in Ohio. Of course the solid South was going Democratic and most of the returns from the West were going right. Colorado unmistakably was for Wilson.

"It doesn't make any difference," O'Brien said. "Hughes has got New York and Pennsylvania and Michigan. He's way ahead in Illinois. Wilson can't win without those."

But by dawn it appeared that Wilson might win without the big states. At any rate the election was very close.

The phone girls were sent home about 3 a.m., but more were brought on at 6:30. And by 7 o'clock their voices were chanting a new song as people got up and phoned for more information. They had gone to bed with Hughes apparently elected by a landslide. Now they were incredulous as the girls reported, "It's very close, but Wilson is leading. That's right. New York is for Hughes. Wilson wins Ohio. Colorado's gone Democratic. California still is in doubt. Yes, but Wilson's ahead. No, Hughes is not elected yet. It's very close."

All day Wednesday we worked, putting out extras, for the election service continued EOS, or Extraordinary Service, which means papers can extra on A.P. news at any time. And we worked all Wednesday night, too, although young Frank Chapin went to sleep in his chair at 10 o'clock and I made him go home.

In all, I worked steadily from noon Tuesday until 3 o'clock Thursday morning, a total of 39 hours.

When he went out to lunch Wednesday evening Peg Johnson brought a quart of whisky from the Press Club. He was pretty drunk on the job by midnight, which, with Chapin gone, made the burden very heavy for Soibelman and me. But I couldn't censure him very well, because both Soibelman and I had taken several drinks from his bottle.

On the way home I went to sleep on the streetcar and slept to the end of the line. The conductor woke me at my stop on the return trip.

"Must have been quite an election for you," he said. From my unshaven, bleary-eyed appearance, he judged I had been on a two-day drunk.

As it turned out, California went for Wilson—466,200 to 462,394 and was the deciding factor in the election. Wilson's electoral vote will be 277 to Hughes' 254. Thus, had less than 2,000 California voters cast their ballots for Hughes instead of Wilson, California's 13 electoral votes would have gone into the Republican column and Hughes would have been elected with 267 electoral votes to Wilson's 264.

We can all be thankful for a very stupid political blunder made by Hughes on his West Coast campaigning tour. There can be little doubt that this blunder cost him many times 2,000 votes.

Had Hughes been acquainted with the 1912 election he would have known Hiram Johnson's immense popularity in California. The mere fact that Johnson was running for Vice-President on the Bull Moose ticket carried California for Roosevelt in 1912. Yet when Hughes was on the Coast he seemingly snubbed Johnson deliberately. He not only failed to go to see the senator but didn't invite Johnson to visit him. As a consequence, everyone in the state knew Johnson was deeply hurt and that he had refused to take the stump in his own state in behalf of the icy New Yorker.

FEBRUARY 4, 1917. Right after Christmas, when he had eaten too much candy and stuff, Byron came down with a protracted cold which necessitated keeping him from school. Finally Dr. Valentine decided his frequent colds were a result of adenoids and infected tonsils. He urged us to have them out as soon as his current cold was better.

So last Tuesday we took him to the Children's Hospital and had the operation.

It took a great deal of argument on the part of the doctor and on my part too to get Pearl to agree to the operation.

"I can't bear," she would say, "to think of the little precious being taken into the operating room and smothered unconscious with chloroform or ether. I can't bear to think of him lying there unconscious while all those white-coated men and nurses slash away at his poor little throat with shiny, sharp knives."

"But it won't last but a little while," I told her. "And in a few days the soreness will be gone and he'll grow into a sturdy, healthy boy."

"I don't like this business of operating on babies," she said. "Like as not he'll outgrow these colds anyhow. He's been a lot better since we moved to Denver."

"Now, Pearl," I argued, "you know he has one cold after another in the winter. Something's got to be done or he'll be an invalid all his life. Don't you trust Dr. Valentine when he says Byron's tonsils are infected? Don't you know he's said the boy's system can't absorb the poison from the tonsils indefinitely? And his adenoids make him go around with his mouth open and cut down his resistance so he can be a victim to most any disease that comes along."

"Of course he has his mouth open when he has a cold," Pearl objected. "Who don't? And children do die from having their tonsils taken out. I've heard of ever so many cases. Suppose we take him to the hospital and he dies there. Whose fault will that be?"

"Suppose," I said, "we don't take the doctor's advice and the poison from those diseased tonsils affects Byron's heart and he dies because we neglected to give him the treatment the doctor knows he needs. Whose fault will that be?"

So finally Pearl gave in and we took him to the hospital. Byron wasn't nervous, not knowing what was going to happen to him. He really was interested in the whole proceeding and was laughing when they wheeled him away on the rolling stretcher. He called out in his high-pitched voice, "G'bye, Mama; g'bye, Dad!" as they rolled him through the door.

Then Pearl broke down completely. She cried until they came to us and told us the operation was over and that Byron was coming out from under the anesthetic in his room. Pearl stayed with him all that night and we brought him home Wednesday evening. He was a pretty sick boy for 24 hours, but he's recovering in fine shape now. I feel certain we have got to the root of his trouble and he will be a different boy from now on. And now that it's over Pearl is glad we had the operation.

I had to dig into my secret vacation fund which I won on the election to pay for the hospital and operation. But I certainly don't begrudge it. Probably it would be a bad thing for me to go to Raleigh, Utah, anyhow. Much as I should enjoy seeing Frances, it would be an upsetting experience.

My dreams of her continue on an average of once a week. I awoke this morning at 10 o'clock from a dream in which I saw her working in her kitchen, which I know now better than our own. Frances has no gas to cook with as has Pearl. She burns wood in a range and was having trouble finding sticks in the woodbox which would fit. Most of them Clark had brought in were too big and knotty to go in. So Frances had to put on an old sweater and go out in the snow and chop some more wood. One would think a husband would be more considerate of his wife.

Frances still is looking too thin. And she still is sorrowing over the death of little Carol.

It now seems that war with Germany is practically inevitable.

Thursday the Kaiser broke his agreement with President Wilson and opened unrestricted submarine warfare on merchant ships. As a consequence, Wilson broke off diplomatic relations with Germany yesterday. Germany apparently is bound to force America into the war and the Kaiser will live to regret it.

Tonight Pearl and Violet Ferguson went down to see a

movie, Annette Kellermann in "The Daughter of the Gods."
I am reading Harold Bell Wright's latest novel, "When A
Man's a Man." It is a story of Arizona and a stranger from
the city who proves himself a man on the unfenced range.
Somehow I find the writing rather florid. It annoys me.

JUNE 3, 1917. Tuesday every man in the United States between
the ages of 21 and 31, inclusive, must register for military
service.

While I certainly would find no joy in the army, especially
living in the mud of French trenches, I cannot help a strange
sense of regret that I am 34. There is a sense of being left
out of something very important and very exciting. Of course
I wouldn't think of volunteering. I have Pearl and Byron to
think of. But if I were summoned and couldn't help it, that
would be another matter.

I am much opposed to war. It seems to me to be the height
of international insanity. But I must admit the United States
did everything possible to keep out of the conflict and that
Germany, or rather the Kaiser and his Kultur, forced us in.

As a matter of fact, President Wilson has made it plain
we are not waging war against the German people—it is
only the imperial German government that has provoked
America into using force. Germany was given warning after
warning. Then in February the Kaiser opened unrestricted
submarine warfare and Wilson gave his final warning in
breaking off diplomatic relations. Germany's answer was sinking three American vessels.

So Wilson called a special session of Congress and on
April 6 war was declared. In order to make it fair to all,
it was decided in May to use selective conscription in raising
the army. That is the draft registration which is called for
Tuesday.

Frank Chapin didn't wait for the registration. Early in
May he gave me a week's notice and enlisted in the regular

army. He is in camp down in Texas now. His place has been taken by Warren Reeves, a middle-aged ex-copyreader who has been working as a bond salesman. Business has been bad of late and he was glad to take a copyreader's job.

Dana Garfield, who had been covering the courthouse for us, is at Fort Riley, Kansas, learning to be an officer as is young Barney Pratt, who was going to the University of Denver and working as a cub reporter nights.

Boyd Ferguson, who is 32 and exempt from the draft, is trying to convince his wife that she could make her own living if he went to training camp. He put in some time in the Indiana National Guard and likes military life.

Fred Gotchell has an automobile and he took Bill Cunningham and me out to Fort Logan one morning while Frank Chapin was there. We watched the recruits drilling across a field. They hadn't got uniforms yet and didn't look particularly soldierly, but when we picked out Chapin in his familiar, battered felt hat we all had a strange thrill.

Gotchell's face was beaming. "There's the boy," he cried. "On the end of the second row. See him? Good kid. Good kid."

And Chapin whom I knew so well slouched over the copy desk, using that same old hat as an eyeshade, now was standing straight with his chest out and obeying like a machine the barking commands of a blue-jawed drill sergeant.

When they finally called a recess, we shouted to Chapin and he came over to our car. His face was red with sunburn and he looked weary. But he was very pleased to see us.

Gotchell shook hands with him and held to his hand. His voice was husky. "Frank," he said, "I'm proud of you, boy. I'm proud of you. Give the Kaiser a kick in the pants for me. personally, and when you come back you've got a job as long as I'm in a position to give jobs—even if I've got to fire such stick-in-the-muds as Zigler and Cunningham here."

Frank said he expected to be sent to join some regular army

regiment in a day or so and believed he would be in France by mid-July. Sure enough, I got a short letter from him in about ten days. He said he had a uniform and rifle now and was learning how to take care of both.

He is such a boy, not quite 21, and he seems much younger as he isn't very robust. He came to the *Call* when he was 17 and just out of high school. For three years he was a reporter and has been reading copy for a year. For his experience, he is a very good copyreader too. I have had to watch his editing a little, but he has a knack of expression and writes a better feature head than most of the older fellows.

I have just read a little book called "Speaking of Operations—" by Irvin S. Cobb. It is mildly funny. I wish Mr. Cobb wouldn't try to be a comic writer. He can write serious fiction so well and it's a shame for him to waste his time and talents on humor.

October 28, 1917. This war is to be no picnic even for us stay-at-homes. One day a week we are supposed to eat no meat. One day a week we are supposed to eat no wheat. We must conserve on every foodstuff that can be shipped to the Allies, for it has become apparent that food will win the war.

In September Congress prohibited the manufacture of intoxicants for the duration of the war. The grain must be used to feed our soldiers and the soldiers of England and France. And pending in Congress (already passed by the Senate) is an amendment to the Constitution which would prohibit the manufacture and sale of intoxicating liquor forever.

There is a good deal of opposition to that amendment, but I am inclined to believe it a good thing. I have enjoyed drinking. But I must admit it has caused me a good deal of trouble also. I seriously believe the world would be better off without liquor and saloons. I know that saloons are a breeding place of political corruption and crime. I know that many lives have been ruined by liquor. And I know I shall be happy in the knowledge that there will be no liquor and no saloons when Byron grows up, that there will be no danger of drink ruining his bright future.

Whisky is of doubtful value even as a medicine, doctors are now beginning to recognize. It really is a relic of the Dark Ages and it is inevitable that the prohibition amendment will be enacted.

Another progressive measure, inevitable of adoption, is woman suffrage. Of course some of the suffragettes have made nuisances of themselves, such as picketing the White House last summer and being thrown in jail. But William J. Bryan has spoken in defense of the movement several times and last week President Wilson urged the states to adopt woman suffrage.

Political corruption has been the bane of American democracy. And the one sure way to clear out the crooked politicians is to give women the vote.

The war has hit our staff pretty hard. Ferguson is a lieutenant at Camp Dodge, Iowa. Garfield and Pratt are officers at Camp Kearney, California. Harvey Thorpe, although he was over draft age, joined the marines as a private and nobody has heard from him. Chester Loomis, Karl Schlossen and Jimmy Manguso, the office boy, who no one dreamed was 21, were drafted and are in General Wood's division and John Soibelman enlisted in the navy because, he said, he admires Joseph Conrad's sea stories so much.

Frank Chapin is in France. I got one letter from there headed "Somewhere in France," but it was heavily censored with indelible ink and we couldn't make out much except that he is well.

One thing that delighted me about Wilson's conduct of the war was his refusal to allow Theodore Roosevelt to raise a division and take it to France.

Secretary of War Baker told him that all generals for volunteer troops were to be taken from the regular army.

Roosevelt's reply to that was that he is a retired commander in chief of the army, meaning President, and that he was eligible to take any position of command over United States troops. When they still refused, Roosevelt said Wilson was afraid he would do his service too well.

It is more likely that Wilson feared Roosevelt, by excess of zeal, love of grandstanding and lack of judgment, would get 25,000 men or so killed off needlessly.

As a matter of fact, Roosevelt's military experience consists of being appointed lieutenant colonel over a group of volunteers in the Spanish-American War. Even in his famous charge up San Juan Hill, the story is he blundered into a trap and would have got his command annihilated if a negro regiment hadn't come to his rescue.

JANUARY 21, 1918. The war is having a profound effect on us all. For one thing, we are so shorthanded at the office I am forced to work seven days a week virtually every week. Today was the first day off I have had since early in November. We celebrated by going downtown to a movie and seeing Charles Ray in "His Own Home Town." Ray is a good actor. He portrays the role of the guileless small-town boy to perfection. He must have made a long study of the type.

I am glad that my name doesn't sound as German as Schultz or Hegendorfer. People with German names are automatically suspected of giving aid to the enemy or planning to wreck something American. Consequently their windows are broken and they have to endure insults from the ultrapatriotic unless they can display service flags in their windows.

Business of the Kaiserhof Hotel at Seventeenth and Welton streets was falling off badly. So they changed the name of the place to the Kenmark.

I believe the most spectacular headline of the war so far was printed in the *Denver Express,* a little labor newspaper published by the Scripps-McRae syndicate. It was an 8-column line on the occasion of General Allenby's entering Jerusalem after 600 years of Turkish rule. The line read:

British Capture Christ's Home Town

FEBRUARY 9, 1919. This is the first day off I have had in more than a year. The war is over. The flu is virtually over. And I feel truly as if I had been in a war. Seriously I wonder if we who stayed at home in the newspaper business didn't have a harder time than Dana Garfield and Barney Pratt who fought the war in a California training camp and came home in splendid uniforms and boots and spurs to be regarded as heroes.

We at home worked night and day without rest, went without sugar and meat and wheat so the soldier boys like Garfield and Pratt could have plenty.

Of course it was different with those who did the fighting. I understand Frank Chapin was badly wounded, but we have heard nothing from him in months.

Last fall, before the Armistice, I got a postcard from John Soibelman from Brest, France, saying he was in the transport service. "Having wonderful time," he wrote, "wish you were here." So did I.

Now President Wilson is in Paris working to make the peace permanent. He is forming a League of Nations which will outlaw war, using the combined power of the United States, Britain, France and the other Allies to force peace upon the rest of the world. There can be no doubt that Wilson will go down in history as the greatest man ever.

Last month Nebraska ratified the Eighteenth Amendment to the federal Constitution. Being the thirty-sixth state to take such action, the prohibition of the manufacture and sale of intoxicating liquors in the United States will become a fact next January.

I was amused at the attitude of Jim Wong, Press Club

steward, on prohibition. I rarely drink any more, but this morning after work both Bill Cunningham and I were very tired and we decided to step over and get a "shot in the arm" before taking our owl cars home.

So while Jim Wong was fixing our hot rum slings I asked him what he thought of prohibition coming.

The old Chinese twisted his mouth. "Damn good," he said. "Whisky no damn good. Whisky cy'nide. Drinkum cy'nide, fall down dead."

Two or three years ago there was a reporter here named Paul Underwood who wanted to become an author. He took his writing very seriously and put in all his spare time, including many, many hours when he should have been sleeping, in writing short stories. But he hadn't prepared himself fully for that career and consequently couldn't sell a single story. In that Underwood was similar to Soibelman. But he apparently didn't have the moral stamini to accept rejections as philosophically as did Soibelman. Or perhaps there was a girl.

At any rate Underwood brooded over his failures and became convinced he never could make a success at anything. So he stole a little cyanide of potassium from the engraving room and went to the Press Club. He slumped into a chair in the lounge and called to Jim for a double whisky. And when Jim served him Underwood dropped the cyanide into the glass and stood up.

"Well, Jim," he said, "here goes nothing."

He tossed off the drink and fell dead at Jim's feet. Jim heard there was cyanide in Underwood's whisky and no matter of argument could convince him there wasn't a certain amount, sometimes more and sometimes less, of cyanide in all whisky.

I don't believe he has served a drink of whisky since that he hasn't expected the drinker to fall dead as did Underwood. Thus his warning, "Drinkum cy'nide, fall down dead."

Of course Colorado has had state prohibition ever since I

have been here. But it has not been very effective. Cheyenne, Wyoming, is only a little more than a hundred miles away and there has been a big business trucking whisky down from there. It will be different when there is a federal law.

The war brought me raises in salary which have increased my pay to $50 a week. From that I have managed to accumulate $200 in Liberty Bonds and would have more except that Pearl got the flu and we had to have a nurse. I was lucky to find one at that.

It has been more than a year since I have read a book. And I believe it has been that long since I have read a magazine or gone to a picture show.

There has been nothing but work and I find I am too tired to get rested in less than two or three weeks of doing nothing and sleeping all I want to sleep. It is showing on me too. My face is becoming lined and gray hair is beginning to be noticeable at the sides of my head.

Well, we should have a good staff by summer when the soldiers are all demobilized and we should have vacations again. Then I shall get a rest. And then I mean to do the thing I have been planning to do ever since I have been in Denver. That is, go over to Raleigh, Utah, and see Frances.

My dreams of her have been less frequent of late, but that has been mainly because I have been too tired to dream.

Last November, I believe it was, I had a series of vivid dreams, however, wherein she was very sick with the flu. For a while there was an old neighbor woman who dropped in to care for Fran, but finally this Samaritan came down with the plague herself and died. Several times Fran herself was near death.

Fran would be 36 now, but in my dreams she is just as beautiful as when I first saw her 20 years ago. I wonder if my dreams are fooling me in that. She has had so much trouble and so much sickness. It doesn't seem possible that her charms haven't faded. I may be shocked when I see her next summer. But I don't think so. Fran's beauty came from within. I don't believe it will ever fade.

OCTOBER 19, 1919. I seem to have got out of the habit of keeping this record. President Wilson's peace treaty which contains the League of Nations plan has been ratified by Great Britain and Italy and last Monday by France. The new German Republic headed by President Ebert has signed it. But in the United States Senate there is opposition. The Republican enemies of Wilson and the traitors in his own party such as Jim Reed of Missouri are trying to keep us from entangling alliances with foreign powers.

They should know that the only possible way to prevent future wars is by such a covenant. They should know from experience that our national affairs are so entwined with those of Europe as to imperil our own peace when war flares forth across the Atlantic. And I don't believe there is record of the gentlemen who are fighting the League of Nations voting against entry to the World War.

In any event it seems that Wilson is strong enough to force Congress to ratify the peace treaty.

I took my vacation at home and thoroughly enjoyed it with two new books which I bought, although I could ill afford them. They are "Winesburg, Ohio" by Sherwood Anderson and "Twelve Men" by Theodore Dreiser, a former newspaperman.

"Winesburg, Ohio" opened a new door of fiction to me. It gives the impression of being not fiction, but reality. After reading it I suddenly realized that practically every book I have ever read was following a set formula just as newspaper stories follow set formulas. And the formula has not been based on actuality, but a romantic pattern developed ages ago which has been followed by novelists as if it were law.

Anderson follows no law except the law of life, the law of reality. His book is most refreshing and thought-provoking.

Dreiser does not write as well as Anderson. I have the impression that he was like many reporters—too careless to read over his news stories in the paper to see what the copyreaders did to them. Had he done that he would have learned a few fundamentals of English construction which would help his serious writing. Nevertheless, Dreiser has wonderful powers of observation and the faculty of remembering what he observes. His book is a series of twelve essays about men he has known—some of them newspapermen. And despite his clumsy writing, he manages to paint very vivid pictures. I should say Dreiser is a magnificent reporter, but he should be required to phone all his books to a good rewrite man.

I spent my vacation reading these books on the front porch of our house on Umatilla Street. We moved a block west and a block north from our old Tejon Street house this May. Our new place is much better and newer and costs only $2.50 a month more than the other.

We also bought a piano this spring (on time) for $350 and started Byron taking music lessons. I don't know enough about music to tell, myself, but they say the boy is doing wonderfully well, although he requires a great deal of coaxing to keep up his practice.

In June Pearl came down with acute appendicitis and had to be rushed to St. Luke's Hospital for an operation. She came through very well, but was unable to do her housework for five weeks.

That took my Liberty Bonds and the rest of my savings. Now, counting the piano, we are so badly in debt that it frightens me to think about it.

Last Sunday night we went to a bridge party at the Fergusons. I had a miserable time. I can't play bridge well and I detest the game. But Violet Ferguson was my partner and she grew quite nasty in criticizing my play. Boyd had to work, but got home around midnight. He refused point-blank to play and he and I adjourned to the basement where he is accumulating a stock of liquor against prohibition. We had several drinks and he told me about the war—or at least his part in it. He was stationed at Bordeaux in the Service of Supply and had some wild times.

Poor Frank Chapin didn't get back until last month. He had been in a hospital in France for several months. Frank's right arm is gone above the elbow, shattered by shrapnel. Three days passed after his wound before he could reach a base hospital and by that time gangrene had set in, necessitating amputation.

The boy (he looks 40 now) is trying bravely to learn to write with his left hand and is reading copy on the desk. He says when the stump gets healed enough the government will give him an artificial arm which he can use to hold the copy down. Now he has a block of lead from the composing room which he rests on the copy while he is editing it with his left hand.

No one has heard a word from John Soibelman. I suspect he has gone back to Russia. He held the czarist government in hatred and his political views were definitely socialistic.

JANUARY 10, 1920. The League of Nations now is a fact, despite the mad action of the United States Senate in refusing to ratify it.

Today representatives of thirteen nations will meet in Geneva, Switzerland, to complete organization of the League, which will act as a central government over nations of the world—excluding the United States. That is, excluding the United States until after election this fall. Those senators who repudiated President Wilson's magnificent plan will get their own repudiation at the hands of the voters.

I have just read "Moon and Sixpence" by Somerset Maugham. And I am finding my whole attitude toward literature undergoing a renascence. My whole attitude toward life, as a matter of fact.

I believe I have been overinfluenced by an artificial standard of life and literature. And I am more than glad that I did not start writing while under that influence.

Byron now is wearing glasses. The boy had been troubled with headaches and finally his teacher suggested he might need glasses and we took him to an oculist. We found he was suffering from astigmatism and that he is slightly near-sighted. The oculist believed the glasses might correct the faults and that he may be able to discard glasses when he is 10 or 11.

The glasses give his thin little face an odd, owlish appearance, but it can't be helped. I could wish that he were inclined to play more with the other boys. That would be good for his health. But he is a very studious child and he prefers to read or to play with his blocks or train than to get out and snowball and coast with the other boys. He is doing very well in school, getting grades in the 90's in every subject.

Harvey Thorpe is back on the paper from the marines and is working on the copy desk. In slack periods he and Frank Chapin have some great discussions of the war. It would appear that the war was one long wild party with French-women and cognac.

Thorpe is an awful liar. One day he pulled a handful of medals from his pocket—the French Croix de Guerre, the French Médaille Militaire and the American Distinguished Service Cross.

I asked him what heroic action gained him those decorations and he grinned.

"I got 'em because I thought I might have some grand-children someday," he said. "They'll want to know what I did in the great war for civilization and I'll show these medals. I'll have a swell story worked out by that time. I'll have it worked out that I won the war singlehanded."

"How'd you really get them?" I asked.

"Different ways," Thorpe said. "This craw-digger [holding

up the Croix de Guerre] I got from a Frenchman after the
Armistice. I traded him a pack of Camel cigarettes for it.
This yellow one I got from a redheaded mademoiselle named
Veronica. A Frog had given it to her for some favor or
another. And she gave it to me for some favor or another.
But I like the American one best. Anybody could get the
French ones for five francs, but the stores didn't have the
D.S.C. I had to fight for that."

"How do you mean?"

"Well, I was going down a street in Orleans one night and
there was a M.P. [military policeman] who got God-damn
cocky. He yells, 'Leatherneck, get your hands out of those
pockets.' And I tells him where to get off at and one thing
led to another and he makes a pass at me and I connect and
I land on top of him in the gutter. Well, this M.P. was
wearing this Elks Lodge badge, so I took it for a souvenir."

When Thorpe was out at lunch Chapin came around to
me and said, "Zig, don't believe a word that fellow tells you
about the war. He was lying about the way he got those
medals. The other night I was up in his room having a
drink and Harve was feeling pretty high. We were talking
about the war and he dug out an official citation and showed
me. The citation said Corporal Harvey Thorpe captured a
machine gun nest singlehanded and I finally pried out of
him how it happened. I forget just where they were, but
there was a German machine gun nest about fifty yards away
raking their shallow trench. They were having to keep on
their hands and knees and even then the machine gun was
knocking off somebody every few minutes.

"Finally Harve noticed how they were working. The gun
would lay bursts into them steady for a while then there
would be a lull of about forty-five seconds. Harvey timed the
lulls with his watch and figured that was when they were
changing belts. He figured, too, that the crew would be

occupied in making the change and wouldn't be paying particular attention to what was going on outside.

"He waited for a lull and then jumped out of the trench with his rifle. He ran across the fifty yards and jumped down among the Germans with his bayonet. There were six of them there and they all surrendered without an argument. So he took their Luger pistols and turned the machine gun around on the Germans until his leathernecks came on over.

"Harve says there wasn't any particular danger, because he knew how it would work out. But suppose one of the Germans saw him coming. They all had pistols. And suppose they hadn't been sick of the war and ready to surrender. It they'd put up a fight, what chance would one man with a rifle stand against six with automatics?"

I think Thorpe is almost as old as I am. Anyhow he is grayer.

A few nights later I jumped Thorpe privately about his lying and told him he should be proud of his exploit. He was embarrassed but admitted he really was proud in a way. "But, hell," he said, "there are enough phonies running around now telling how they won the war."

AUGUST 8, 1920. Denver is under martial law. Armored war tanks are rolling and rumbling through the downtown streets. Bronzed soldiers in steel helmets, veterans of the war, are patrolling everywhere with bayoneted rifles. Mayor Dewey C. Bailey is virtually deposed and ensconced in the mayor's office is Colonel C. C. Ballou of the regular army, commander of the city.

This came about yesterday following three days of virtual civil war.

Employees of the Denver Tramway Company called a strike a week ago today. They had asked wage increases from 58 cents an hour to 75 cents an hour, a two weeks' vacation annually under pay and several other concessions which the company refused to grant. Instead, when it became apparent that a strike was coming, the streetcar officials engaged John ("Black Jack") Jerome, San Francisco strikebreaker, to come in with a tough crew and keep the cars running. There were no cars running Monday, however, and all Denver either walked to work, caught rides with obliging motorists or rode in jitneys—private automobiles with signs on the windshields indicating they would carry passengers for a nickel or a dime.

I walked to the Twentieth Street viaduct and caught a ride on a truck. Going to work at noon, there naturally was not much of a crowd. But at 2 o'clock in the morning there were neither obliging motorists nor jitneys and I had to walk clear home.

The *Call* handled the story as it should be handled—strictly as news without bias. The *News* and *Times* expressed some indignation at the inconvenience. The little *Express,* however, bitterly assailed the company and came out flatfootedly for the employees. And the *Post* was even more bitter against the men, decrying the fact that a thousand utility workers led by an "outside agitator" could inconvenience a whole city of 300,000 people.

The company promised that cars would be running Tuesday and they did run one car through the downtown district. Its windows were covered with steel grating and it was filled with strikebreakers armed with rifles and shotguns. Black Jack Jerome, with a three-day growth of beard on his hard face, was at the controller and the car was escorted on a circle trip through the downtown district by four police automobiles.

There was no real disturbance for the reason that the police were quick to leap from their cars and arrest anyone who even jeered at the strikebreakers.

Trouble really started on Thursday. And before midnight Denver had seen its wildest day in history.

The company was making an attempt to resume actual service. Cars with windows so heavily grated that you could see only shadowy outlines of the passengers were hooked together tandem. And each of the tandem cars carried crews of four armed strikebreakers.

When I climbed from a jitney at Sixteenth and California streets early Thursday afternoon I saw a commotion down on Fifteenth. People were running down California and I joined in the rush.

There stalled and surrounded by a crowd of hundreds was one of these two-car trains. There was a great deal of yelling and movement down front and I climbed on top of a refuse can to see over the heads of the crowd. First I saw the grating ripped from the side of the leading car. Then there was a rippling crash and clinkle as stones and paving bricks smashed through the windows. There were cries, "Kill the scabs, kill the scabs!" Then both streetcars toppled over with a terrible roar and a cloud of dust.

Near me two men plowed out of the crowd carrying the inert and bleeding body of another. Then two policemen pushed into California Street supporting slim, old Chief of Police Hamilton Armstrong. Armstrong was capless and was bleeding badly from a wound in his head. He appeared badly dazed. One of the policemen also was bleeding from his nose.

Then I went to the office, figuring we should get out an extra on the riot. One of these strikebreakers, it developed, was beaten to death and all of them were badly mauled.

The company and Black Jack Jerome, undaunted, made an effort to open service on the East Colfax Avenue line and shortly before 6 o'clock started two trains up Capitol Hill. But by the time they reached the crest there were 5,000 people congregated. The track was blocked and the cars came to a stop at Pennsylvania Street in front of the Cathedral of the Immaculate Conception. All four cars were tipped over. Several of the strikebreakers were caught and beaten to unconsciousness. The others fled up the steps of the cathedral, followed by the mob. The strikebreakers dashed through the doors as Father William Higgins stepped out.

His black robe whipped in the wind. He held up his hand.

"You can't enter the House of God with violence in your hearts," he cried. And the mob stopped. They went back down the steps. Then they set fire to the cars. The upset streetcars blazed and smoked and smoldered for hours, melting the asphalt paving, because the fire department couldn't break through the mob, couldn't even get to fire plugs to attach a hose.

Finally the mob left the burning cars. They left in a body, marching down Colfax past the Pioneer Monument and into Fifteenth Street. From somewhere two or three drums had appeared and they marched to their rhythmic rattle. Leading the mob were numerous young men in soldiers' uniforms. They were either ex-service men or regular army soldiers from Fort Logan and Fitzsimons Hospital. In front was a soldier carrying a large American flag. And he was leading the battle chant that swelled and swelled in volume as they marched.

"Let's get the *Post!* Let's get the *Post!* Let's get the *Post!*" That is what they were chanting.

In that chant was distilled hate for a commercial institution which harps daily on its own self-styled altruism.

"The *Denver Post,* the paper with a heart and soul. The *Denver Post* is your big brother." These are phrases that appear in every issue of the *Post.* And over the country are billboards painted a gleaming chrome yellow with this inscription in black: "Yes, the *Denver Post* is yellow, but it's shore some pumpkins." But most of all, the *Denver Post* had been attacking this strike with extraordinary bitterness. Probably there were but few actual Tramway employees in this marching, chanting mob. There were huskies from the Denver Rock Drill. There were rough customers from the Burnham shops and the smelters.

And they marched down Fifteenth Street, turned into Champa and crowded from curb to curb in front of the *Post* building where no doubt most of them had crowded before to see Houdini wriggle out of a strait-jacket while suspended by the heels; or an Empress Theater juggler catch a turnip on a fork held in his teeth when Mr. Bonfils threw the turnip from the *Post* roof; or to hear prize-fight blow-by-blow announcements bellowed from a megaphone; or to receive stiff and bloody jackrabbits killed in drives sponsored by the *Post* and doled out by the altruistic Mr. Bonfils and Mr. Tammen.

The street lights gleamed dully on the broad golden inscription across the front of the building:—"O, Justice, When Expelled From Other Habitations, Make This Thy Dwelling Place!"

And a half-pound locomotive nut hurled by a Burnham shopman crashed terrifically through one of the huge plateglass windows. In an instant stones and bricks and scrap iron carried by the mob were showering through all the windows— even those on the third floor. From some source the soldier with the flag had obtained a long, heavy plank. He wrapped old Glory around his shoulders like a toga, shouted for a following and charged his plank into the front door like a battering ram. The door gave way and the cheering, howling mob followed him into the business office. They tore down iron grillings. They ripped up a drinking fountain so water geysered up, flooding the floor. They smashed desks, wrecked typewriters, pounded cash registers to pieces.

On the second floor the emergency night crew of the editorial staff fled across the areaway into the Symes Building and thence down into Sixteenth Street. On the third floor the night crew of linotype operators turned off their machines and fled also down into the Symes Building.

The mob spread out. Some of them found their way to the basement and the big presses which most of them probably had watched with awe from the Champa Street windows.

They hacked at the rollers with axes. They poured printer's
ink over everything. One of them found he could start a
smaller press by pushing a button, so they fed a roller length-
wise into the press. The roller smashed one cylinder and then
blew a fuse, stopping the machine. They started a fire, but
water gushing down from the broken pipe extinguished it.

In the editorial rooms they upset desks and threw typewriters. They wrecked the furniture in Bonfils' "Red Room."
They broke the glass case which held Tammen's stuffed baby
elephant, the former prize exhibit of Sells-Floto circus, which
the *Post* owns, and made away with the elephant. They went
through the morgue like a whirlwind, dumping out the con-
tents of all the files and ruining whatever they could, destroy-
ing the librarian's work of years.

Up in the composing room they did little damage outside
of upsetting a few linotypes. With a hammer they could have
disabled every machine for days merely by battering the
matrix-distributing bar, but they apparently did not know
this.

But in spite of all this, the *Post* came out as usual the next
day. City Editor A. K. Stone moved down to the police
reporters' room at police headquarters where it would be
safer. The paper was set largely in 10- and 12-point type
because the upset linotypes were mostly body type machines.
But in this case the *Post* no doubt would have set the major
part of the paper in big type anyhow.

The lead story was written by Bruce Gustin, a mild-man-
nered blond fellow of about my size. And his lead, set in
fullface 14 point, read:

Hell broke loose in Denver Thursday.

When they left the *Post* the mob somehow pushed two
gigantic rolls of paper out in the street and unrolled them

all over town. The streets were cluttered with miles of news-print.

Another mob later engaged in a battle at the South Denver carbarns where strikebreakers were billeted. When they began throwing stones as well as taunts at Jerome's men, the strike-breakers opened fire and wounded two of the crowd seriously.

Friday morning Mayor Bailey announced that police were unable to cope with the situation and asked for 2,000 volun-teers from ex-service men to help preserve order. He did not wish to ask for the National Guard because intense bitterness against the state militia still exists on account of the Ludlow mine massacre. It was feared that if the militia were called out it might cause bloodshed rather than prevent it. The ex-soldiers responded. They were armed with pick handles and arm brassards and were put to directing traffic.

That evening came the worst riot of all. Bill Cunningham had reporters stationed at all the danger points and at the hospitals. Our composing room deadline for the first street edition is 8:40 p.m. And about 8:20 Cunningham began to get calls from people on the East Side. "What's the shooting about?" they asked. And, "We just heard police sirens going by here. Is there any trouble?"

Cunningham didn't know and was pretty unhappy about it. From the location of the calls he assumed something might have happened at the East Side carbarns at East Thirty-fifth Avenue and Gilpin Street. But he had a young reporter named Simpson stationed there and he had heard nothing from him.

O'Brien, tired out from the strain of the last 24 hours, had gone out to lunch. So had Gotchell. Cunningham called over to me that some kind of hell was popping out east, but he didn't know what.

"Well," I said, "you better get it unpopped pretty soon because we've got to go to press."

Cunningham got hold of another reporter and sent him to Thirty-fifth and Gilpin in a taxi. Minutes went by and

people kept calling in wanting to know what the shooting
was about and still no report from Simpson.

Then at 8:35 Simpson called. "I've got the names of some
of the dead and wounded," he said.

"For God's sake, man, what's happened?" demanded Bill.

"Well," said the cub, "you know I phoned you at eight
o'clock that there was an orderly crowd of two or three
hundred out here. Well, they weren't doing a thing. Just
standing. There were men and women and children. Just
standing."

"But what happened?" Cunningham's voice was a scream.

"Well, an automobile load of American Legion men drove
up," said Simpson. "They drove up to the crowd. And they
had rifles and shotguns. First they fired a volley in the air.
I was right there close and saw it all. The crowd backed up
a little. Then the American Legion fired right into the crowd.
I don't know how many they killed yet. The ground was
covered with bodies of dead and wounded. Men, women
and children."

"Great God, Simpson," said Cunningham, "be sure what
you're saying. Are you certain they were American Legion
men? And how are you sure?"

"I was as close as from here to that counter," declared
Simpson. "Well, of course you can't see the counter. I'm in
a drugstore. But I was close and I saw their arm bands and
everything."

So Cunningham could do nothing but take Simpson's word
and started hammering out the story himself, sending it
paragraph by paragraph over to me by the copy boy. And
old man Hewitt, the composing room foreman, came fuming
up the stairs yelling, "Where in hell's your eight-column line?
Where in hell's your lead story? What in hell's wrong up
here? Haven't I got enough trouble downstairs without having to wet-nurse the God-damn editorial department, too?
We ought to be going off the floor now, God damn it."

I was trying to rush out two 8-column, 120-point lines that would tell the story and still protect us. Then the lights went out.

Hewitt let out a scream that could be heard two blocks. "Now look at that. The God-damn power's off. The God-damn machines are off."

And Harvey Thorpe lit a match and held it so I could see what I was writing.

And Hewitt said, "Let me have your God-damn lines. Those are set by hand, anyhow."

I said, "Just a second." And the copy desk phone rang and Frank Chapin answered it and said, "It's for you, Zig." I took the phone, thinking perhaps it was Gotchell just as Cunningham shouted over, "Wait a minute, Zig, Joe West is calling. Maybe something important." And Hewitt howled, "Ain't got any God-damn minute to wait, important or not important. *What* the hell." And I said "Hello" into the transmitter. It was Pearl. She said, "Homer, our lights are off and we're playing bridge. You know what's wrong?" I said, "Will you go to hell with your God-damned bridge?" and slammed up the receiver. And Cunningham yelled, "For Christ's sake don't let that story get away. Kill it, *kill* it!"

Hewitt yelled back, "What the hell's wrong now?"

"That story's wrong."

Then the lights came on, but Hewitt didn't notice. "Everything," he said, "that the editorial department does is wrong. We're late right this minute and it's on you. Don't care a damn if we never get the God-damn paper out." Then he stalked back downstairs.

Well, we finally got the paper out about fifteen minutes late. And what really had happened as Joe West reported accurately was this: an automobile taking Black Jack Jerome and his guard out to the East Side carbarns for an inspection was halted by the crowd. Someone recognized Jerome and threw a brick through the windshield. The men in the car, trying to frighten the crowd back, fired into the air. But the strikebreakers in the carbarn thought Jerome was being fired on by the crowd and poured a volley from rifles and revolvers into the strike sympathizers. Four were killed and thirteen wounded.

Young Simpson was simply so frightened he didn't know what he had seen. It was a miracle that we didn't put the paper out blaming the American Legion for the massacre. It would have meant the jobs of Simpson, Cunningham and myself and very likely a boycott of the *Call*. It is very dangerous to say anything bad about the American Legion even when it's true.

The East Side carbarn massacre brought the call for federal troops. Colonel Ballou came up from Fort Logan with his men and the veteran Second Division troops were rushed up from Camp Funston, Kansas. Things quieted immediately after their arrival. Streetcars are running with soldier guards. I understand, however, that the troops, who are quartered in the Municipal Auditorium, grumble a lot over strike duty.

Pearl is still mad at me for swearing at her over the telephone. She scarcely will speak to me. This afternoon she took Byron and left the house without saying where she was going. Byron told me this evening that they went to the Tabor and saw Mary Pickford in "Pollyanna." He didn't care so much for the picture but liked the animated cartoon of Andy Gump. I apologized to Pearl and tried to explain how it was. I don't believe she's really so mad. I believe she is merely trying to teach me a lesson. Well, I can stand Pearl's silent treatment. Usually she talks a little overmuch. In a way her "punishment" is sort of a relief.

November 7, 1920. After the quietest presidential campaign I have ever seen, Warren G. Harding, United States senator from Ohio, was elected Tuesday over his Democratic opponent, Governor James M. Cox, also of Ohio. I believe every copyreader in the country was hoping for Cox's election. His name fits into a head so well. And above that I hoped for his election because he was the champion of Wilson's principles. Poor Wilson, broken from his own desperate battle to save the League of Nations, has been an invalid or semi-invalid since he collapsed following a speech at Pueblo a year ago.

I am convinced that Cox is a much abler man than Harding, but public reaction to the present state of affairs was too much for him. Prices have been skyrocketing. There is much unemployment. And there is an overwhelming desire to break away from all things connected with the war. I did have hopes for Cox's election. But I can see now that, despite (or perhaps because of) the campaign for the League of Nations, his defeat was inevitable. The voters, and especially the women who cast their first ballots Tuesday, want to pull away from all things European.

Harding called for a "return to normalcy," probably meaning normality, and the people wanted "normalcy" bad enough to give him a landslide victory. His vice-president is a sour-faced, taciturn, former governor of Massachusetts named Calvin Coolidge, who attained some prominence last year by calling out the National Guard when police struck in Boston. If he had called for federal troops as did Mayor Bailey here, I suppose he would be President now instead of Harding.

Cox's running mate was Franklin D. Roosevelt, a vigorous young man, Assistant Secretary of the Navy in this administration. He made some very good campaign speeches as, in fact, did Cox. Harding limited himself to "front porch talks" from his home in Marion, Ohio, where he runs a newspaper.

Harding looks like a President. He is big and dignified and has distinctive, bushy black eyebrows. No doubt he is a good man. He does, however, seem somewhat confused and not quite confident. Tuesday night when it became apparent he was elected his statement to the press was not one of thanks to the voters nor of elation that now he should be able to undertake his program. He said, "I pray God to make me capable of playing my part." No doubt that also should be the nation's prayer.

Pearl has allowed Byron to stop taking his piano lessons. I thought he was progressing satisfactorily, but she says she had a battle with him every day to force him to practice and that if he doesn't care enough for music to want to practice there is no use spending money for his lessons. I suppose there is something to that, but I did want him to learn the piano. Perhaps he will take it up again when he is a little older. I wish, however, I had got my way about the piano. I wanted to buy a Pianola such as they have at the Press Club. I enjoy pumping the rolls through and we could have some music. Pearl says she detests player pianos. But our piano now is just a piece of furniture—and it isn't paid for yet, either.

A 30-hour search for an air-mail pilot lost between Salt Lake City and Cheyenne ended last night when they found the wrecked De Haviland near Tie Siding, just across the Wyoming line on the Laramie road. The pilot, John P. Woodward, who apparently had become lost in a storm, was crushed to death in the wreckage.

June 19, 1921. Pearl and Byron are in Kansas City visiting her mother. Byron is 10 years old now and, although he is not large for his age, I had to buy a half-fare ticket for him.

Byron is developing into a very bright boy with an inquiring mind. He does well in school, especially in arithmetic. He is eternally asking questions which leave Pearl and me at a loss for an answer.

This spring Pearl bought a set of the Book of Knowledge from a house-to-house salesman, which we are paying for on the installment plan. They are quite expensive, but Byron is showing such an interest in looking up things that I am sure they are worth many times the cost. I believe the boy probably will develop into a scientist.

I am getting my vacation in the middle of July. Pearl and Byron will be home by that time.

We have had a very wet spring with disastrous floods. Pueblo was virtually destroyed by a flood on June 4 when cloudbursts ripped out reservoirs in the upper reaches of the Arkansas River. A wall of water swept down on the city taking everything before it. Loss of life is estimated at 500 although no one will ever know the exact toll. Peppersauce Bottoms, a congested Mexican district, was swept clean. Houses, bodies and everything were taken down the river.

We had night and day work for three days during this period, for more floods were in prospect and Pueblo, with all utilities paralyzed, was in grave danger of fire. Every available man was sent down from the *Call*—even Thorpe off the copy desk, leaving us shorthanded.

As no trains were running they had to go by taxicab, and as all highway bridges were out, they had to drive over the railroad tracks, bumping thirty miles or so over the ties. Because all the hotels were underwater except the Congress and the Congress was filled up, even to all the chairs in the lobby, the boys had no place to sleep except where they could find a dry space and very little to eat. I am glad my reporting days are over.

JANUARY 29, 1922. An unusually heavy snow in Washington caved in the roof of the Knickerbocker Theater there last night. At least 100 persons were crushed to death.

The wires handled this story very poorly. Not only were they inexcusably slow, but their facts were contradictory and the stories were as poorly written as you would expect from the rawest cub police reporter.

This impressed me as strange, inasmuch as it is assumed the best reporters in the country are in Washington. To be

sent to Washington is counted a great honor and the greatest
promotion possible for a newspaper writing man. I suppose,
however, that reporters go to seed in the capital. They are
so accustomed to receive their news on a platter in the form
of "handouts" from the various governmental departments
that they have forgotten how to dig out facts on their own
initiative. And confronted with a major disaster, they all
blew up.

Bootlegging now is very pronounced in Denver. There are
several bootleggers who "deal off the hip" in the vicinity of
the *Call* building. Some of them make regular trips to the
editorial room. Others "hang out" in the poolroom down the
block. They sell whisky made from beet sugar at $3 a pint.
The price is scandalous, but the whisky is worse. It is impossible for me to drink it without a quick chaser of water.

I have read two impressive new books this winter—"Three
Soldiers" by John Dos Passos, a stark and realistic picture of
the war, and "If Winter Comes" by A. S. M. Hutchinson,
an Englishman.

I read "Three Soldiers" first. And I believe that was a
mistake. I'm afraid it hurt my perspective for "If Winter
Comes," which probably is a much better book than Passos'.
As it was, the raw, blasphemous vigor of "Three Soldiers"
made the character of Mark Sabre in Hutchinson's book seem
a little too lovable. It was like eating a sugary French pastry
on top of a healthy slug of moonshine whisky.

It would seem that somewhere between these two distinctive books would be the proper level for a truly great novel.

Bill Cunningham, for years city editor of the *Call,* has taken
a job with an advertising firm in St. Louis. Boyd Ferguson
is the new city editor. Boyd gave a party at his house in
celebration two or three weeks ago and both he and I and
several others got fairly well lit on moonshine mixed with
ginger ale. The ginger ale can't rob the moon entirely of its
vile taste.

AUGUST 6, 1922. For once I managed to save out enough money for a vacation by myself. I announced firmly that I needed to get away, that I was going into the mountains by myself so I could think and regain my perspective. Pearl was somewhat sarcastic, but offered no violent objections.

I planned out the whole project in detail. I bought some army breeches at the Army and Navy store and a pair of laced boots. In that costume I would leave home, but instead of taking a train for the hills, I would take the Union Pacific through Wyoming into Utah.

My vacation starts today. For a month I have been counting the days until tomorrow, when I could take the morning train. All week I have been excited over the prospect, as excited as a child during the week before Christmas.

But Friday night I had a dream. Frances was on a train. I saw her sitting in a Pullman looking dreamily out the window while a landscape of trees and fields and farms, distinctively Eastern, floated by.

That was most disturbing. If Frances were on a long trip, naturally there was no sense of me going to Raleigh, Utah. From the landscape I judged she probably was on her way back to Buffalo. But still, many parts of California have trees and fields and rolling hills. And even the landscape in the valley close to Salt Lake City might be mistaken for the Middle West.

But it was all settled last night. I saw Frances in her old home on Lemon Street, Buffalo. She was with her mother in the kitchen, wiping dishes while her mother washed them. Mrs. Harbach seemed much older. But Frances looks little different than when I last saw her sixteen long years ago.

They were talking, but their conversation meant little to me. It was almost as if they were speaking in German and I could understand a word here and there but not quite enough to catch the sense.

Finally Mrs. Harbach said, "Wait a minute, honey, I'll rinse those."

Then she got the teakettle and poured hot water over the dishes on the draining board.

Mrs. Harbach put the teakettle back on the stove and said, "Did you know Mrs. Zigler was back visiting Ethel this spring?"

Frances started. "Oh," she said, "how is she?"

"I didn't see her," Mrs. Harbach explained. "Ethel lives in Kenmore, but Mrs. Zigler was over here to church. I didn't go that day, but Mrs. Seifert was telling me about meeting her. She looked fine, Mrs. Seifert said, and Mr. Zigler is doing so well down in Pittsburgh."

"Did she say anything about Homer?" Fran's voice sounded queer.

"Mrs. Seifert said he's way out west in Denver or some place working on a newspaper and doing fine."

"He was in Kansas City," said Frances. She was wiping a long time on a dinner plate.

"No, it wasn't Kansas City," insisted Mrs. Harbach. "I'm pretty sure Mrs. Seifert said Denver."

Then the dream changed to something irrelevant.

I wish I had enough money to go back to Pittsburgh on my vacation and see Mother. Last winter she wrote she was suffering from sciatica in her hip, but she got over that with the coming of summer. If I could go back to Pittsburgh I could run up to Buffalo and probably see Frances before she left. But I haven't enough money and I don't know where I could get it without going to a loan shark and I'm afraid of starting that.

So I shall take the sort of vacation Pearl thought I was going to take in the first place, although it doesn't appeal to me much. I have Sherwood Anderson's "Poor White" to read while vacationing. I have only started it, but find it gripping.

NOVEMBER 12, 1922. Pearl has become a disciple of Emile Coué, the French country town druggist who has developed a health system called "Self-Mastery by Autosuggestion." Thousands of people who have ills or fancy they have ills are going around saying, "Every day in *every* way I grow better and better." It is something like faith healing and something like Christian Science only there is no religion connected with it.

There is nothing particularly wrong with Pearl except that she has been putting on weight. She has tried dieting, but didn't like that. So now she has a string with ten knots tied in it and she says this "rosary" every morning and every night, repeating ten times, "Every day in *every* way I grow thinner and thinner."

For the last year there has been virtually a civil war in some sections of Italy. Italian Socialists, who were opposed to the World War, refused to fight. They stayed at home and dug themselves in. As a result the red labor unions gained control of factories and many farms.

We have had stories about the red flag and the scythe and hammer of Bolshevist Russia being in evidence everywhere and a Socialist bloc in Parliament virtually paralyzed the government. It had begun to look as if a Communist minority would subdue the nation as it did in Russia.

Then Benito Mussolini came to the front. Mussolini is a highly educated and widely traveled member of the Italian aristocracy who once was a Socialist, but who sympathized so strongly with the Allied cause that he enlisted as a private soldier and was wounded a hundred times at the front.

After the war Mussolini formed an organization of war veterans something like the American Legion called the "Fasci di Combattimento," or the "Fasces of Combat."

And as the red terrorists grew more bold the war veterans began to meet the peril with armed resistance. With pistols and clubs and grenades the patriots drove the reds from the factories and restored the mills to their rightful owners. They burned red newspapers and broke the power of trade unions on the farms.

The principle which the "Fascisti" are fighting for and the battle cry of Mussolini is, "The state is made for man, not man for the state."

Two weeks ago, when it became more apparent that the Italian government was powerless in the clutches of red destructionists, Mussolini at the head of his veterans marched into Rome. It was practically a revolution, a bloodless revolution. King Victor welcomed "Il Duce," as Mussolini is called, to Rome and invited him to form a cabinet.

Mussolini formed the cabinet and showed his fairness by including representatives of other parties.

Some commentators believe Mussolini can form a dictatorship in Italy under the sanction of the King, but most observers in Italy who know Mussolini doubt if he will do so. The correspondent for the *Christian Science Monitor,* for instance, declares he knows Mussolini will not take undue power for himself, attesting that "the striking characteristic of Premier Mussolini is lack of personal ambition."

The Premier's first step in straightening out the sorry postwar mess into which Italy has fallen was to begin disbanding the costly Italian army.

It is the consensus of experts and observers that Mussolini is too much of an idealist to last long as Premier of troubled Italy. But he may sow enough seeds of peace and good will before he is overthrown to work good for his nation and for the world. More often than not idealists fail to see their epoch-making ideas succeed. Honor comes to the martyrs of great causes usually after their deaths.

SEPTEMBER 9, 1923. I have been news editor of the *Call* for nearly a month. My promotion came after a row with Harvey O'Brien in which Fred Gotchell took my part and O'Brien quit his job. He has gone to Los Angeles.

On August 2 President Harding died in San Francisco. For days there was nothing else in the papers while they were taking his body across the continent to Washington and while he lay in state at the Capitol. The whole nation was in a state bordering on hysteria of grief. The newspapers and wire services worked themselves into such a frenzy that one might have judged America was doomed to disintegration now that its great leader was gone. Harding no doubt was a good man and a reasonably competent President—for a Republican. But, if one could judge from the millions of words of tripe published, he would conclude that Harding was a far greater man than Lincoln or Washington, to say nothing of Wilson. Kirke Simpson, the A.P.'s star Washington man, who gained fame and the Pulitzer award for his "Unknown Soldier" piece, wrote the Unknown Soldier all over again for Harding. And every other writer on the job tried to show that he knew at least as many solemn adjectives as Simpson.

So when it came time for them to move Harding's body from Washington to the Marion, Ohio, burial ground, there wasn't much left to say—especially in 8-column lines.

I worried out a line myself for the home edition which read, "WARREN HARDING GOES HOME FOREVER."

O'Brien was in the composing room when he saw the line in proof. He came upstairs. "Who wrote that line?" he demanded.

I admitted authorship.

"For Christ's sake," O'Brien said. "A man to sit in the slot of a copy desk should know enough to stop any copyreader from writing such generalized applesauce. But when he writes it himself, there's no hope for him. Here, Thorpe, write an eight-column eighty-four saying something to the effect that Harding's body is taken to Marion."

That made me mad. "Listen here, O'Brien," I said, "while I'm head of this desk I'm giving the orders to copyreaders. If you don't like this line we'll change it. But I'll have it changed and I'll have it changed by whomever I want to change it."

O'Brien started to say something, then quieted down. "All right," he said, "have it changed then."

"First tell me what you don't like about it." I was standing up and talking right into his face.

"I don't like any part of it," he said. "It's a lousy head. It doesn't say anything. Warren Harding Goes Home Forever. In the first place, a corpse can't go anywhere; it has to be taken. In the second place, where is home? In the third place, everybody knows who Harding is by this time and Warren is superfluous padding as well as being practically disrespectful. And in the fourth place, the forever is unconfirmed and superfluous."

"All right," I said. "You're news editor and I'll change the line myself." So I wrote, "HARDING'S BODY TAKEN TO MARION" and sent it down.

In twenty minutes or so Gotchell came in and went into his office. In a little while he came out with his face beaming. He was carrying a proof of the first line I wrote. He held up "WARREN HARDING GOES HOME FOREVER."

"That's a swell line, Zig," he said. "Who wrote it?"

"I wrote it," I said, "but it's not going in the paper."

"Why not?" Gotchell chewed his cigar and squinted his eyes.

"O'Brien killed it. Had me write another."

"What's the new line say?"

"Harding's Body Taken to Marion."

"Oh, hell! Hey, Harve."

O'Brien was up from his desk and his face was white.

"Why change that line, Harve?" asked Gotchell. "It's got everything. It's practically poetry."

"Poetry's got no place in an eight-column line," said O'Brien.

"Why," declared Gotchell, "that line tells the whole story. It tells everything. Every paper in the country will have Harding's body taken to Marion. Just trite tripe. Here, Harvey, put this line back."

"Mr. Gotchell," said O'Brien. His voice was quivering. "You put that line back on the paper and you'll have to get a new news editor."

"That's entirely up to you, Harvey," said Gotchell.

"I'm giving you notice then," said O'Brien. "I'm through."

So I was put on the news desk and Harvey Thorpe went in the slot. I like this job better than the other. There is more responsibility, but not the rush. And besides, my pay was raised to $60 a week with promise of more. It is pretty lucky for me all the way round. If Bill Cunningham hadn't left when he did he would have become news editor instead of me without a question.

I feel now I am getting somewhere. News editor is only one step from managing editor. And $60 a week is not a bad salary anywhere. Now I shall be able to save some money.

My vacation was scheduled for the middle of August, but I waived it because of the promotion.

Pearl, Byron and I went to "The Covered Wagon" tonight. It was a great picture with marvelous photography and stirring scenes of the westward march of the empire. It made me think of my own novel and it made me wonder when I shall ever have time to write it. I have even less time to myself as news editor than I had as telegraph editor and head of the desk. I really feel that I should drop in the office and look over proofs on my night off.

Byron is starting in the seventh grade at Skinner Junior High School this fall and is doing fine. This afternoon I was sitting in the living room reading the *Literary Digest* when he spoke up in his oddly drawling voice.

"Dad," he said, "what's the capital of Australia?"

"Canberra," I said, without looking up.

"That's right, Dad," he said, "I thought you'd probably say Melbourne."

He wasn't looking for information at all. Just trying to trap his old papa.

JULY 26, 1925. I dropped into the office this warm Sunday afternoon to see how Harvey Thorpe was coming with preparations for a baseball extra. I had eaten a big Sunday dinner at home of roast pork and had a touch of indigestion. In my desk I keep a can of bicarbonate of soda, a glass and a spoon. So I put a spoonful of soda in the glass and was going to the water cooler for some water when the Associated Press boy brought in a flash. *William J. Bryan dead.* I had to go back to my desk and sit down. Until that moment I had not really appreciated how much the Great Commoner meant to me.

For three weeks, however, I had been conscious that Bryan was getting old. All during the "monkey trial" in Dayton, Tenn., the proceedings had been very painful to me for Bryan, in his sublime and literal faith in the Bible, had permitted the cunning Clarence Darrow to trap him time after time in ridiculous statements.

Bryan was never one to compromise. He would not compromise even with President Wilson. He resigned as Secretary of State rather than give in one inch on the stand he believed was right concerning notes to Germany. And history perhaps will show that he was right in this instance.

At Dayton it was different. Bryan was no scientist. He was a humanitarian and a Christian. He believed firmly in the Bible and his unswerving mind was incapable of rationalizing Biblical tales with science. It was a very sad spectacle. Bryan of the "Cross of Gold" speech; Bryan the former idol of millions; Bryan, who, virtually singlehanded defeated Champ Clark at Baltimore and elected Woodrow Wilson President —being made a monkey of by a criminal lawyer.

And then he died. Three times defeated for President and

then last year patronized at the New York convention which battled back and forth for more than a hundred ballots between Alfred E. Smith and William Gibbs McAdoo before compromising on the J. P. Morgan man, John W. Davis. Probably the Great Commoner died in the belief that he was a failure. But he was not a failure. He failed many times, but there was a sublimity in his failing. He had a profound influence on America and on the world.

I have been neglecting this record for more than a year. But as a matter of fact there has been little for me to record. I have read virtually no fiction. I have had practically no time to think of anything but my job. Certainly I have thought none at all about writing a novel.

This spring after my pay was raised to $70 a week we moved to a larger house on Federal Boulevard. Pearl was set for a while on moving away from North Denver. She felt that the prestige of a news editor would not be helped by the fact that his residence was listed on the North Side. She felt it would be more fitting for us to live in Park Hill.

Byron, however, wanted to stay in North Denver. He will be in the ninth grade this fall and go to North Denver High next year. His friends are here and he didn't want to leave them. Especially, there is a gangling, sleepy-eyed youth named Wallace French with whom he chases butterflies and studies birds and concocts vile-smelling chemical compounds in a laboratory the boys have set up in Byron's room.

Byron is the most interesting 14-year-old boy I ever saw. He has a strangely blasé and adult manner and, despite the fact he was always a very timid child, he has developed great self-assurance. He is a lad who is marked for success in whatever lines he enters. Really he studies his school lessons very little, being more interested in affairs far beyond his years, but nevertheless he manages to keep well up in his class with a minimum of effort.

Sometimes of an evening when Wallace French and Byron

come downtown to attend a lecture or go to a movie they will drop into the office and pay me a dignified visit and borrow a dollar on Byron's next week's allowance.

Last Wednesday was typical. Byron sat down at the edge of my desk and picked up a copy of the first street edition. He read the "scream line"—"SIX DIE AS TRAIN HITS AUTO."

He pursed his lips. "Hmmm, down in Tennessee," he said. "Dad, any of these people known in Denver?"

"Not that I know of, Son," I said.

"Why, then, is this accident in Tennessee worth such a big display in Denver?"

I couldn't help laughing. The boy had hit one of our sins squarely on the head.

Byron leaned back in his chair and put one of his shoes on my desk. He looked over the page and frowned. "I should think," he said in a manner strikingly like some dignified managing editor, "that this story on the Washington Arms Conference should be regarded the most important news."

I explained to the best of my ability that we doubtless would use that arms conference story for the lead in the home edition. I explained that he was reading the first street edition and that the circulation department demands lots of gore in street editions so they can sell papers.

Byron still frowned. "But, Dad," he said, "that sort of thing is essentially dishonest. With a big line like that, 'Six Die as Train Hits Auto,' you're implying the accident was in Denver. People will buy the paper and then feel cheated when they see where it is."

I could only laugh and tell him we never had any complaints on that score and that, after all, putting out a newspaper is a commercial enterprise. You've got to have exciting lines in a street edition to sell papers. You've got to sell papers to get circulation. You've got to have circulation to sell advertising. But of course Byron was right, dead right. And such insight and reasoning on the part of a 14-year-old boy impresses me as remarkable. I doubt whether more than a few of our reporters could analyze this fault of newspaper publishing as surely and succinctly as did Byron.

At last we are going to have an automobile. Pearl and Byron have been arguing for a year and finally I have become convinced a family misses a lot of life without a car in this modern age. They have been building many improved roads through the mountains and it would be possible for us to take some wonderful drives on my day off.

So we started saving for the down payment early last spring and last Monday I paid $350 down on an Essex coach. I expect to get delivery this week.

I had favored a Ford as being more simple to operate and cheaper both to buy and to operate, but Pearl and Byron are prejudiced against flivvers.

The Essex seems to be a very fine car. They claim you can drive it 50 miles an hour all day long. Of course we never will drive that fast at any time. Speed is what causes accidents. I shall lay down a set rule that the car never must be driven more than 35 miles an hour.

Both Pearl and Byron are wild to learn to drive. But I do not anticipate any great degree of pleasure until I have mastered the machine. I shall, however, go at the matter in a scientific manner. I shall paint a white mark in the exact center of each front mudguard. Likewise, I shall paint a white stripe down the center of each front tire. Then in driving I can keep the tire stripes on the mudguard or fender marks and be certain I am holding the automobile exactly true. That device should help all of us.

FEBRUARY 14, 1926. It has been a bright Colorado winter Sunday. But my spirit is sodden with grief. Since Thursday night I have been wandering about in a daze, doing my work automatically.

Tonight I sat here and thought over my life and I remembered that this was Valentine's Day. I remembered back twenty years—my first year on the old *Buffalo Morning Journal*—when I took Frances a huge box of candy in the shape of a red heart and that the next night was my night off and how we popped corn and ate it with the candy.

A week ago this morning I had a particularly vivid dream of Frances. She was out with Clark in an old Ford touring car on an isolated road. The road was covered with snow and there was snow in the air.

Presently the car stalled. Clark got out and cranked and cranked but couldn't get the engine started. And finally he walked off down the road for help, leaving Frances.

She sat in the open car for a while and then got out and paced back and forth in the snow. She slapped her hands to warm them. She stamped her feet. Then she got back in the car and wrapped herself up in a robe.

When Clark finally got back with a rancher in another car Frances was so chilled she scarcely could talk. Had she been in a coach like ours, she could have kept comparatively warm with all the windows closed, but in this touring car she would have needed arctic furs to keep comfortable. As a result she was ill before they reached home.

I worried about her until Thursday. Then came one of the most vivid dreams I ever had.

Frances was very ill in bed. She was gasping desperately for breath and the bearded doctor by the bedside said to a middle-aged woman, apparently a practical nurse, "God, if I only had some oxygen. And there's none closer than Ogden."

Frances coughed, pitifully weak, and the woman wiped her mouth with a towel.

Then Clark came in with a priest and the priest knelt by the bedside praying. Then he administered extreme unction. And when he anointed her eyes, saying, "By this holy unction and through His most tender mercy, may the Lord forgive thee whatsoever sin thou hast committed by sight," Frances opened her beautiful blue eyes that once I was privileged to kiss and she spoke softly, "Homer!"

"The poor dear's delirious," said the nurse. "She's calling her mother."

Then Frances closed her eyes again and the dream snapped off as a motion picture stops when the film breaks. Then I awoke realizing I never would see her again.

How many times I have planned and hoped for the day when I might go to her, when I might talk to her again, even for a few minutes. But Fate had decreed that should never be so. Always there was something which interfered. Once I was starting for Raleigh, but that was the time I saw her going back to Buffalo.

It is all so strange. Actually I know nothing of Frances since I left Kansas City and stopped writing to her. That was before Byron was born. That was before she was married.

I suppose most people would believe me mad to put such faith in my dreams. Perhaps I am mad. But they have seemed as real as my real life—in some instances more real.

A practical person could say, "Why, man, for all you know Frances is still living in Buffalo. The business of her marrying Paul Clark, the birth and death of little Carol, the life in Raleigh, Utah, the visit back in Buffalo and now this last sad chapter are all inventions of your perfervid dream mind."

But that person would discount altogether the matter of telepathy, which was well proved by the fact that we answered each other's questions in letters before we received the questions.

I have wondered so often whether she had equally vivid dreams of me. That was one of the things I planned to ask her. But now I shall never know.

True, I have never seen Frances in nearly twenty years. No doubt I am a sentimental middle-aged fool, but now that she is gone life seems an empty thing and not worth while, except that I have my duty to Byron—and of course to Pearl.

I censure myself for my silly blunders in the past, especially for my insane flight from Buffalo in 1906. But no one ever wrote a truer sentence than Omar when he said:

> The Moving Finger writes; and, having writ,
> Moves on: nor all your Piety nor Wit
> Shall lure it back to cancel half a line,
> Nor all your Tears wash out a Word of it.

I say if I had but controlled my outrageous jealousies then, Frances might be well and happy now. But then I was so unstable emotionally that I could not control myself. Can I censure myself for my own chemical make-up? The fact that the elements which make up Homer Zigler respond a certain way to a certain stimulus and the elements which make up Harvey Thorpe, for instance, respond in another way to the same stimulus is beyond the control of Harvey Thorpe and Homer Zigler. I tell myself I might as well curse a bottle of milk for souring when I add a tablespoon of vinegar.

Then, what can I know of Fate? Apparently Fate decreed that I should love Frances Harbach all my life, but that we never should marry. It was ordained that I should love her for twenty years in silence. Now it is ordained that I shall mourn her in silence for the rest of my life.

MAY 22, 1927. I am very much annoyed at Pearl. Last night she attended a party at the Franks' a couple of blocks up Federal and when the party was becoming dry about 11:30 she volunteered to drive a young dentist named Blumberg downtown after some liquor. Coming back (and probably driving too fast) she crashed into another car at Osage Street after turning off the Twentieth Street viaduct. Of course there happened to be a police car handy and the first thing the coppers saw was the gallon jug of moonshine in the back of the car.

Fortunately no one was injured, but both cars were badly damaged. When they smelled liquor on Pearl's breath they literally "threw the book" at her. They took her and Blumberg down to headquarters and charged her with reckless driving, operating a motor vehicle while under the influence of liquor and possessing and transporting intoxicating liquor in violation of the state prohibition law.

Joe Moley, our police reporter, phoned me about midnight and told me I had better come down and see if I could help straighten things out. So I got Fred Gotchell and went down in a taxi.

They had Pearl locked up in the matron's quarters, Blumberg in the bull pen and they had dragged our car down and impounded it. Under the law they can confiscate any car that is used to transport liquor.

Fred Gotchell and I fixed things up with the chief and got Pearl's and Blumberg's names scratched off the blotter. They released our car but refused to give Blumberg back the gallon of whisky. And I had to promise to pay all damages to the other car to prevent any flareback, so I went to see the other driver, a man named Schmidt who has a fish stall in the City Market, and told him to have his old Maxwell repaired and send me the bill. Our car wouldn't run so I had it towed from the city pound by Tom Botterill's garage. I don't know yet what the two repair bills will be, but it certainly was an expensive party.

Perhaps Pearl was under the influence of liquor when she had the accident, but she was certainly sober when the matron unlocked the door for her to come out—sober and tearful.

Her main worry was fear that Byron would learn of his mother's being locked up. There is little danger of that, however. I gave Chuck Kelley, the *Rocky Mountain News* police reporter, a pint of moonshine not to report it to his paper. I also told him we'd been watching his work over on the *Call*. The *Post* and the *Times* won't find out about it because the names were scratched from the blotter.

Pearl was inclined, as usual, to place some of the blame on me. She said if I had got the brakes adjusted last week she could have avoided the collision.

I told her if she hadn't gone to a stew party and been chasing around town after liquor with a hot-eyed young Jew there wouldn't have been any collision either.

The party was celebrating the safe arrival in France of a young aviator named Charles A. Lindbergh, who hopped off from New York Friday morning and landed in Paris yesterday afternoon after 33 hours of flight. Of course he is not the first flier to cross the Atlantic, but he is the first to do it alone and there was tremendous excitement over his feat. He is a gawky-looking country boy and he inspires the public's imagination. In a way he is the Great American Fairy Tale come true—the shy lad from the farm who took a big chance and won. Lindbergh won a $25,000 prize for making the first nonstop flight from New York to Paris and says he is going to buy a garage in St. Louis, his home town. Well, the publicity will help his garage business for six months or so until the people forget. But if he is a good mechanic his business should be well established by then. This single flight may well have made him a success for life.

I recently have formed a very inspiring friendship.

For the last year or so our Sunday book page has been edited by a young widow named Syra Morris. Perhaps I should not say young as Mrs. Morris is, I should say, 36 or 38, but at least she has the buoyancy and vivacity and charm of youth. She is slim and mahogany-haired and her eyes are a dark sparkling blue.

Review copies of books come to her from the publishers. She reads the important ones herself and reviews them, others she "farms out" to members of the staff.

On Thursday evenings she comes in for a conference with me on the position of various reviews and gives me the "art" she has selected for the page.

Several weeks ago she was late coming in and I met her on the stairs as I was going out for lunch. So I invited her to go to the restaurant with me and hold our weekly conference over a cup of coffee. Before this happy occasion I always had regarded Mrs. Morris as just another member of the staff like Mildred Sommers, the society editor, and crochety Wilma Spence, the club editor. But at the Edelweiss Restaurant I discovered what a remarkable person she really is.

While in her teens she became an actress and mounted virtually to the top of her profession. She played in Belasco productions on the road and appeared with Ethel Barrymore and Jane Cowl. During the war she married a young officer. He was gassed and they came to Denver for him to receive treatment at Fitzsimons General Army Hospital. He died three or four years ago.

Syra was too long away from the stage to return, so, as she had inherited some money from her husband, she remained in Denver.

Now she is trying to become a magazine writer. She hopes to write for *Atlantic Monthly* and *Scribner's* and *Harper's,* but thus far her success has been confined to several minor works sold to *Ranch Romances*. She gets $10 a week for editing our Sunday book page.

Mrs. Morris is the most widely-read person I ever knew. Not only does she know all the contemporary books worth while, but she is well versed in the classics, having attended Vassar before she went on the stage.

She has lent me Theodore Dreiser's "An American Tragedy" which I have wanted to read for a year but couldn't afford to spend the $5 the two-volume novel costs.

I now am just in the middle of the murder trial, but I should say it is not only Dreiser's greatest achievement, but without a doubt one of the outstanding achievements of the century.

Many gifted writers start to work on ideas that would make great books, but spoil the effect with a certain flippancy that makes them appear insincere. This was Mrs. Morris' criticism of "The Green Hat" by Michael Arlen and of F. Scott Fitzgerald. I agree with her fully.

NOVEMBER 11, 1928. Herbert Hoover, the great engineer who had us eating alfalfa bread during the war, was elected President Tuesday by the greatest majority ever. He received 444 electoral votes to Al Smith's 87.

Hoover is an astute fellow and probably will make a good President. But I was hoping for Smith's election on the prohibition question, if no other.

The Eighteenth Amendment and Volstead act have turned out to be ghastly farces. Everyone is drinking more now than he did before prohibition and there is absolutely no regulation. The whisky and gin are terrible. There are countless cases of blindness and invalidism caused by poison liquor. When I think of Byron going out with the boys and know that virtually every other boy carries a pocket flask to parties, I scarcely can sleep.

Nobody wants the return of the old-time saloon. Al Smith has said time and time again that he would be the very first to oppose the return of whisky and the saloon. What he wants and what every decent man wants is legal light wine and beer. With light wine and beer of a low alcoholic content legal no one would think of drinking whisky. Drinking would be done as it is in Europe—for sociability, not drunkenness.

JULY 14, 1929. Usually on Sunday I drop down to the office early in the afternoon to look over the mail and go over prospects for the night's news and art with Harvey Thorpe. Then, if I have time, I slip over to Syra Morris' apartment on Sherman Street for a cup of tea and a chat on literature.

I didn't go today. Pearl had her teeth pulled Friday and was still feeling miserable. Lately she has been suffering more or less from neuralgia and the doctor decided her teeth were the cause of it.

She is living on thin soups and milk until her mouth heals enough for her to have false teeth. She feels very bad about it—not only about losing the teeth, but about the diet. She doesn't want anyone she knows to see her now so she is hiding out pretty much.

We did, however, take a ride up to Boulder this afternoon, with Byron driving. Byron was graduated from North Denver High School last month and will enter the University of Colorado at Boulder this fall.

I had hoped to send him to Harvard or to the Massachusetts Institute of Technology, for the boy has real talents for engineering or science. But the fact of the matter is I simply won't have the money this year. And, after all, a year or so general arts course at Boulder will be a fine preliminary to studying science.

Byron really is pleased at the prospect of going to Boulder. His particular friend, Wallace French, is going there. And I understand there also is a little girl named Geneva Berryman whom Byron admires who will be a co-ed at Colorado U.

Byron's mind frequently amazes me. At times it is difficult to realize he is only 18 years old. Never is he satisfied with simple facts. He wants to know the underlying reasons for the causes of the facts. He has a professorial tone of voice which gives me a big kick.

The other evening Frank Chapin and his wife were over to the house listening to our new superheterodyne radio and we were talking about the activities of Henry Ford. Frank said something about Commander Richard E. Byrd using a Ford plane to fly across the North Pole.

Byron scratched a match to light his bulldog pipe. "No, Chapin," he said, "you're wrong there. Byrd used a Fokker trimotored plane. What confused you was the fact the ship was named the *Josephine Ford*. You see, Edsel Ford was one of Byrd's sponsors."

Frank was so confused and taken aback that he flushed. He really couldn't think of a thing to say. The next day I checked up on the matter at the office and found Byron was dead right. A memory like that will prove a great asset to the boy.

Byron wanted to go to Boulder today to look over the ground and particularly to pick out the fraternity house in which he'll live. Pearl thought he should join the Sigma Chi, mainly because there is a song, "The Sweetheart of Sigma Chi," which she thinks is cute. Byron, however, was right-fully scornful of argument that he should join a particular fraternity simply because they had a "cute song." We drove by all the fraternity houses we could find and Byron finally decided on the Beta Theta Pi as being the most desirable. The place looks pretty grand and I had a thought it might be wise to find out just how much it costs to live there before Byron sets his mind too fully on it. There might be a possi-bility that only moderately rich boys could live in such a place.

Pearl overruled that thought violently, though. And she was right.

"All we'll be able to give the boy is an education," she said, "and everybody who has been to college admits the happiest time of their life was their college years."

We should be pretty poor parents, after all, if we weren't willing to make personal sacrifices for Byron while he is in college. Moreover, if he lives in a first-class fraternity house he may make social and business connections which will prove most valuable in later life.

Syra has lent me a couple of books of poetry in the last

few months which have opened new portals to me. One was Edgar Lee Masters' thought-provoking "Spoon River Anthology"; and the other was Stephen Vincent Benét's magnificent "John Brown's Body." The latter is really a novel in blank verse. It tells the story of the Civil War more vividly, more logically than has ever been done before. It settled definitely in my mind that my own novel will not touch on that conflict. It would take a brave author (or a foolish one) to undertake a Civil War story to follow "John Brown's Body."

I also have read a very great novel this year. It is "Arrowsmith" by Sinclair Lewis. Syra was surprised at first that I didn't care for Lewis' books, "Main Street" and "Babbitt." Then she agreed with me that they were rather "smartaleckish" and insisted on my reading "Arrowsmith."

It is the story of a doctor with ideals and his struggles again commercialism. It is vivid. It is true to life. And it is sincere from cover to cover. It is so mature in comparison to "Main Street" and "Babbitt" that one might think they were by different authors.

OCTOBER 6, 1929. One of the most serious prison riots in history broke loose in the Colorado State Penitentiary in Canon City Thursday and lasted through Friday. Convicts barricaded themselves with several captive guards and threatened to kill the guards and throw their bodies from the windows unless they were released. The warden refused and they threw out the body of a guard. They repeated their demand and again were spurned. Another guard's body was thrown out. In all seven guards were killed and five convicts. The mess hall, the chapel and two cell houses were burned. And, despite the work of militia and police, the rioting continued until the four leaders, finally convinced that their fight was hopeless, killed themselves.

In the cell of one of the leaders they found two books

DENVER

Species." The other was "Alice in Wonderland."

Byron now is a college boy and very proud of himself.
He is living in a boardinghouse until he moves into the
Beta Theta Pi house. He has met one or two of the Beta
boys and told them he would consider joining their frat. But
it takes a little time. Joining a fraternity is like joining the
Elks or Masons in that one has to be recommended by a
member and then voted on at a meeting.

As we didn't need a car with him gone, I traded in the
old Essex coach on a new Chevrolet roadster. It is a bright
yellow and very sporty. The roadster will help Byron socially
and will enable him to come home week ends. I also just
bought him a raccoon coat, which cost $150, on the installment
plan.

The college business has put me horribly in debt, but it will
work out all right, although I haven't paid the dentist yet for
Pearl's new teeth.

I have just read Ernest Hemingway's "A Farewell to Arms."
At last, Syra and I agree, the World War has produced some
literature. The young man has a strange style, but one that
grows on you. At times he is powerful. At times he is poetic.
At times he is shockingly vulgar. But always he is entertaining. I can learn something from Hemingway. In a way
I am glad I never had time to write until after I read him.
American literary style is changing rapidly. In this transition
period it sometimes is incoherent. But I believe the change is
for the better.

AUGUST 10, 1930. Byron and Pearl are in Kansas City. They
drove down in Byron's car. They wanted to go during my
vacation and have me go along. But I was tired and preferred
to rest at home. It is so hot in Kansas City this time of year
and it's no great pleasure riding in a rumble seat.

Business is very bad following the collapse of the stock

market last fall. The *Call* decided last month that it would be forced to put through a blanket reduction in wages of 10 per cent. As I was getting $85 a week, I was cut to $77.50—which hurt.

Also I was buying $500 worth of Cities Service stock on the installment plan. I bought it at 54 and now it is down to 15 or 20. I haven't had the heart to look for some time. They assure me, however, that it will be up again higher than ever. When it ever gets to 50, though, I shall sell.

Last week a conversation with Syra veered around to telepathy and I told her about my series of dreams of Frances. She was the first person I have ever spoken to about these phenomena.

She said it was one of the most amazing things she ever heard of and that I should have written to Raleigh, Utah, to confirm Frances' death. Perhaps I should have done that. But I was not interested in establishing scientific data. I was satisfied in my own mind. I needed no confirmation. And besides, I did not care to write to Raleigh, Utah. It is such a small town that inquiries by me could easily find their way to Paul Clark.

Syra is not exactly a Spiritualist in that she is not a member of the organization. But she does believe that certain mediums can bring messages from the other world and she believes she has got authentic messages from her late husband.

Last night she persuaded me to go with her to a séance held by a Madam Pinckney out on South Logan Street. When we entered the hall a horse-faced man asked us to write our name and a question on a slip of paper and seal it in a small envelope. There were five or six others in the old dimly-lit living room. There was a choking tenseness and the odor of Woolworth incense as the overstuffed Madam Pinckney enthroned herself on an overstuffed chair next to a towering rubber plant in the far end of the room. The audience or congregation or clients—however they designate a medium's

customers—were grouped in the other end. Syra and I and
a thin, pale young woman were on a davenport. The rest
were sitting bolt upright and expectant in their chairs. On
a stand near by was a goldfish globe containing small en-
velopes which purported to be the ones we had sealed.

Madam Pinckney closed her eyes and rested a forefinger
against her temple. Immediately she twitched a few times and
then began to speak in a queer monotone.

"I see a shape . . . I see a shape . . . It is a handsome gray-
haired woman . . . She asks me to find Florence."

"Oh!" The pale young woman next to Syra gasped.

"Is Florence here?"

"Yes, Mother, I'm here. Oh, dear Mother!"

"The woman," droned Madam Pinckney, "says she is
Florence's mother. She says she has a message for Florence."

Tears were streaming down the girl's cheeks. "I'm listening,
Mother. Oh, my *dear* Mother," she cried.

"I want you to know," went on the voice, "that I'm always
by your side. Haven't you sometimes felt me touch your
cheek?"

"Yes, I have, Mother, but I didn't know it was you."

"I want you to know, Florence, that I'm very happy over
here. There is no pain. There is no sorrow. Just happiness.
And I am watching over you always.

"And it's so fine to be able to talk to you, dear Florence.
I'm so glad to see you here."

"Oh, Mother, darling—I'm *so* happy too. I'm so happy
I've found you. I'll come again, Mother, and you'll be here,
too, won't you? I'll come often, Mother."

Madam Pinckney twitched again. Her lips moved silently,
then she droned in her queer monotone, "I see the shape of
a young man in uniform. He is a policeman with leggings—
no, he isn't a motorcycle policeman. He's a soldier. Yes, he's
a handsome soldier."

I could feel Syra tensing beside me on the divan. It would

have been evident to a less astute observer than Madam Pinckney that this lead was receptive to Syra.

"The soldier," said Madam Pinckney, "has a message for—" she hesitated at the name —"for Sigh-ra. Is Sigh-ra here?"

"It's Syra," breathed Syra, her voice almost a whisper. "Is it Hugh that wants me?" Her hands were clasped so tightly in her lap that the knuckles were white.

"Yes—it—is—Hugh. Hugh—says—you—are—following—the —proper—course—now. Hugh says you are now on the point of greater success than you expected. He wants you to know he is very happy and that he is watching over you, that he will try to protect you from all danger. But he wants to talk to you more. Hugh says, 'Won't you come here oftener, dear Syra, so I can talk to you? Sometimes I see danger before you and I want to give you warning. Now there is no danger, Syra. The course is clear. And I see some money coming to you through the mail.' "

Syra was smiling happily as Madam Pinckney by twitching indicated this interview was closed and that she was seeking another spirit. But Syra took a handkerchief from her purse and wiped her eyes.

"Is—there—" droned Madam Pinckney, "—someone here named Homer?"

"Yes," I said.

"I—have—a—message—for—Homer. It—is—from—a— woman—a—beautiful—young—woman. I—don't—quite—get —the—name. Repeat it please. Mary? No, is isn't Mary. Gertrude? Would you know a Gertrude on the other side, Homer?"

"No," I said. I was determined to give her no assistance.

"Could it be Frances?" asked Syra in a hushed whisper.

"Is—the—name—Frances?" inquired Madam Pinckney's monotone. "Yes—it—is—Frances. Frances wishes to speak to Homer."

In spite of the transparent hokum, I felt a prickling along
my spine.

"Frances is speaking," intoned Madam Pinckney. "Frances
says, 'I'm very happy over here, happier than I ever was on
earth. I am so glad to see you, Homer. It has been so long.
So very long.'"

The medium's voice had taken on a new quality, a strange
liquid quality that I could have imagined resembled the
voice of Frances Harbach.

"'I want to warn you, Homer, you must take better care
of yourself. You're not as strong as you think. You must
watch your health and not work too hard. I hope you'll never
forget me, Homer. And I do want to see you again soon.'"

Syra and I did not wait for more messages. We took advantage of Madam Pinckney's twitching interlude to make our
exit. In her car Syra asked, "What did you think of her?"

I lit her cigarette and mine.

"Well," I said, "it's a pretty fair act."

"I don't know," Syra mused. "It may well be more than an
act. She seems to get things."

So I passed it off. If Syra gets comfort out of thinking she
can communicate with her Hugh through Madam Pinckney
it is all right with me. But it puzzles me to see such an
unusually bright and levelheaded woman swept away by
this medium's show. Madam Pinckney's customers are so
anxious to get "messages" that they help her over the rough
spots. Even in my own case Frances' name was supplied by
Syra. And the so-called messages are so general that I fail
to see how they can give the bereaved much comfort.

The "warning" about my health was so obvious. I did look
tired that night. I do give the appearance of a man who has
been working too hard. And, if it is possible to communicate
beyond the grave, why did my dreams of Frances cease so
abruptly after the dream of her death? When we were so
closely attuned that we could communicate (if we *did* com-

municate) by telepathy in dreams for twenty years, why should it be necessary to call in a third party, a stranger, for further communication after death?

Also, it seemed to me the spirits were doing a little too much plugging for Madam Pinckney. They were urging over-much that their friends on earth make return visits to Madam Pinckney—who charges a dollar a séance.

I have heard of mediums who make startling revelations, who bring convincing information from departed friends and relatives. Perhaps these mediums exist. I don't know. But I do know that Madam Pinckney is not one of those, whatever Syra may think to the contrary. Well, this is the first flaw I have detected in Syra's good judgment. If she is wrong in this instance, I certainly can forgive her that.

DECEMBER 28, 1930. I had something of a row with Fred Gotchell last night. Byron, who is home for the Christmas holidays, wrote an essay pointing out the evils engendered by fraternities at universities and colleges. He proved them to be un-American breeding places of snobbishness and to be infiltrated through and through with favoritism, intimidation, bribery and all the elements that make for corruption in American politics. He pointed out that to be a fraternity man it is necessary for a college student to be a sneak; that the fraternity libraries contain "ponies," giving translations of all Latin exercises and French and German lessons, and that it is common practice for upperclassmen to assist freshman and sophomore fraternity brothers with their lessons and exam-inations. He closed by urging strongly that legal means be taken to abolish these sinkholes of deceit and student demoral-ization.

Byron himself has taken action against the fraternities at Boulder by leading an organization of clear-minded young fellows called "The Barbs" who are fighting the frats at every turn.

I am very happy to see Byron public-spirited and taking up cudgels for his fellows. He will go very far.

It impressed me that his essay would make a splendid editorial for us and I showed it to Fred Gotchell. Gotchell read it and shook his head.

"That," he said, "could have no place on our editorial page."

"Why not?" I asked.

"It's not of general interest," he said, "and, well, it seems to me to be too opinionated, too partisan."

That burned me. "Listen here, Fred," I said, "this paper needs to take a definite stand once in a while. And it can afford to run a few things of interest to the younger people. We're getting too stodgy. What we need is something to attract young readers."

He tried to soothe me. "Now, Zig," he said, "that piece is intemperate. And I don't believe the facts bear out the boy's charges. We certainly couldn't take responsibility for those statements."

"You don't believe the facts bear out the charges!" I blurted. "My boy is attending Boulder and he certainly should know the conditions there better than you or I could here in Denver."

"But he may be a prejudiced observer. You know, Zig, hot-headed young fellows sometimes see things a little strong. Now I'm a Chi Psi myself. I'll admit there were certain irregularities when I was going to college but nothing vicious, as this piece indicates."

"That was a long time ago," I said. "Things could change quite a lot since you went to school."

"True. But still—why don't you do this, Zig: Sign your son's name to the piece and publish it in the Letters to the Editor column?"

I pointed out that if it were printed over Byron's name the fraternities would be certain to take physical reprisals on him.

Gotchell grinned in his fiendish way. "Why, then," he said, "should the *Call* accept the reprisals gratuitously?"

I saw there was no use in prolonging the argument. "I hope," I said, "to work again someday on a paper that has guts, that isn't afraid to stand on its hind legs and fight for a principle."

I actually was on the point of handing in my resignation, but decided that discretion is the better part of valor. I probably could get another job in Denver without much trouble, but it would be a smaller job and at considerable less pay.

The argument with Gotchell upset me badly. I went out to lunch immediately afterwards. In a booth at Schultz's I was eating a bowl of chili when Judd Watson came in with a bottle of moonshine. I took one drink with him and it turned my stomach. On the way back to the office I became violently ill and had to go up an alley.

After all Gotchell is a fraternity man himself. It would take more nerve than he has to make a stand against his own gang.

AUGUST 2, 1931. We had a picnic in Berkeley Park this evening. Pearl drove Byron's roadster over with her mother, who is visiting us from Kansas City, with Byron and me in the rumble seat. Then Byron took the car and went after his girl friend, Geneva Berryman.

Neva is a frail, dark girl with a faint, birdlike voice. She is rather pretty, but her sallow, blotchy complexion is a handicap. She wears octagonal, rimless eyeglasses. If Byron has serious intentions in that direction, I could wish the girl were healthier looking. But she seems a very nice girl. She doesn't have much to say, but pays close attention to the conversation and laughs at the right places.

Mrs. Hawkins has been having a pretty hard time. The bank where she had her money in Kansas City folded up and her business has been bad. As her mother is getting along in years, Pearl is trying to induce her to sell her rooming house and move to Denver with us.

While Mrs. Hawkins is visiting us she is sleeping in one

of our twin beds and I have moved to a sanitary cot in the basement. In many ways I like this arrangement. The little basement nook is next to the furnace room and is dry and quiet and cool in the summer. I find I can sleep there days with less interruption than I had upstairs. Also, I can read in bed there after I get home from work in the morning.

Byron has been working this summer. He has a clerical job with the Tri-State Oil Company and likes it very well.

Either the salami or the potato salad we had at the picnic didn't agree with me. Tonight I had violent indigestion that bicarbonate of soda didn't relieve.

SEPTEMBER 6, 1931. Early this afternoon I was lying on the cot in my basement study deep in Thomas Wolfe's "Look Homeward, Angel." I had just turned a chapter and looked at the alarm clock thinking that pretty soon I must get up and shave and go downtown to look at the mail and talk to Harvey Thorpe and then run down to Syra's apartment for a cup of tea and a discussion of young Wolfe.

Then I heard Byron calling from the top of the basement stairs, "Dad, oh, Dad, can you come up?" There was a strange excitement in his voice.

I laid the book down on the bed, pushed my feet into slippers and, thinking there were callers, put on my coat. Pearl and Mother Hawkins and Byron and Neva Berryman were in the living room all smiling at me as I shuffled in brushing down my hair.

"Dad," said Byron, solemnly, "I want you to meet your new daughter." And he put his long, lean arm around Neva's waist.

"W-h-a-t-!" I said.

"Well," spoke up Mrs. Hawkins, "no need for you to faint. It's perfectly all right. You were young once yourself, you know."

"But—"

"I know, Dad, it's a surprise," said Byron. "But Neva and I have loved each other for ages, haven't we, honey?"

Neva put up her face and kissed him.

"But how about your college?" I asked.

Byron laughed. "To hell with college," he said. "It's too stuffy up there. I like my job and they offered me a raise to twenty a week if I'd stay. So I'm staying. You get your real education in the world of business, Dad, not at a stuffy school."

"Aren't you going to congratulate them?" demanded Pearl.

"Why, of course," I said, although I was sick with disappointment. I stepped up and put my arms around both of them and kissed Neva.

"Now that's better, Dad," said Byron. "I knew you'd be a sport."

I grinned as best I could. "But you won't be twenty-one until next spring," I said. "How about the license, Byron?"

He chuckled. "No trouble there, Dad. I'm in my twenty-first year, aren't I? Well, then there was no lie in saying I am twenty-one."

"O.K.," I said, "but I still don't see how you are going to support a family these days on twenty a week."

"Why, Homer," put in Pearl, "they can live here with us and everything will work out splendid."

"And," observed Byron, "if I'm not making a hundred a week inside of two or three years I'll be a mighty disappointed young man."

So that is that.

I had planned on Byron getting a college degree since he was a baby. And when, as a little boy, he showed a keenness toward scientific subjects I resolved that he should become a scientist.

But, after all, what right has a parent to attempt to direct a child's life? If Byron wishes to become a businessman that should be his own affair. He has two years of university behind him. If he doesn't like university, why should I wish him to continue?

In the last analysis all I ever wished for Byron was happiness. I regarded a lot of education as the road to happiness. But, as Mother Hawkins said, I was young once myself. I should be able to remember something of young love. I should realize that there is where happiness lies.

Yes, when I consider it well, I must admit that where I was stupid and fearful Byron has been wise and courageous. And I honor the boy for not being overinfluenced by his parents' ideas.

MAY 8, 1932. We were given another 10 per cent reduction in pay last week, which cuts my pay check down to $69.75 a week.

This makes the situation extremely serious, for Neva is to have a baby next month. Byron lost his job in February because the Tri-State was making extensive retrenchments. While they assured him there would be a job there for him when business gets better, people have lost faith in President Hoover's reiterated declarations that "Prosperity is just around the corner."

Byron has tried desperately to find a job, but he isn't strong enough for manual labor and everywhere else he is met with the same statement—"We're laying off men, not hiring them." He did try selling vacuum cleaners from door to door, but in ten days was unable to dispose of one.

Meanwhile bills are running up. I haven't a cent in the bank. And when the doctor isn't calling to see Neva he is coming to see Mrs. Hawkins or Pearl, both of whom are afflicted with many unidentified aches and pains.

Worry over affairs has given me something like dyspepsia, but I haven't found it necessary to see the doctor about it. There is a saying that when a man reaches 40 he's either a fool or his own physician. I shall be 50 next winter and I have found that a man can correct most of the ills of the flesh with a little bicarbonate of soda, aspirin and epsom salts.

For two months we have been playing what no doubt is the most remarkable story in the history of journalism. On March 1 the 19-month-old son of Colonel Lindbergh was kidnaped from its crib in Lindbergh's remote New Jersey home. A crude note demanded payment of $50,000 ransom. This ransom finally was paid in a Bronx cemetery by an intermediary, Dr. John F. Condon, an old schoolteacher known as "Jafsie."

But the kidnapers double-crossed Lindbergh. They did not return the baby. They apparently are demanding more money. At present they are dealing with John Hughes Curtis, a wealthy boatbuilder of Norfolk, Va., an Episcopal rector named H. Dobson Peacock and Rear Admiral Guy W. Burrage. The kidnapers make strange communications with the intermediaries who go out to sea in a cabin cruiser to contact them. It is believed that Lindbergh himself is in Norfolk and working with Curtis, Admiral Burrage and the Rev. Mr. Peacock.

It has been so long, however, that I fear the child has either died from mistreatment or has been killed. If so it is the most ghastly crime in history and perpetrated against the nation's idol.

NOVEMBER 13, 1932. The Zigler-Hawkins family cast five solid votes for Franklin D. Roosevelt on election day. Even Mrs. Hawkins, who has been a Republican all her life, was so bitter over business conditions that she voted against Hoover. And it seems auspicious that Byron and Neva, both voting for the first time, should pick a winner.

I didn't dare risk any money to speak of on the election, but I did take a dollar from Fred Gotchell on Denver County. He bet me a dollar to 50 cents that Roosevelt would not

carry Denver County by 10,000. The vote was 72,868 for
Roosevelt and 59,240 for Hoover.

My little granddaughter came on schedule and was named
June Berryman Zigler, the June in honor of her natal month.
She is a fine baby, although becoming rather spoiled with a
grandmother and great-grandmother in the same house. She
cries an uncommon lot, but I suppose I am fortunate in
having a bedroom in the basement where at least I can sleep
undisturbed.

Poor Byron still is unable to find work. I have tried to get
him to enroll at the University of Denver where he could
continue his studies cheaply, living at home. But he feels that
it is beneath the dignity of a husband and father to go to
school. He has oiled up my old typewriter and has been trying
to write some essays for the quality magazines, but thus far has
been unable to sell any.

I could get him a job as a cub reporter on the *Call,* but
the pay wouldn't be much and I should hate to have him start
on a newspaper. Byron has seen enough of newspaper work
to have no desire in that line, either—especially if he had to
work on my paper.

After Roosevelt is inaugurated I can't help but believe
conditions will get better and Byron can then find work for
which he is fitted. Then he and Neva will be able to set up
housekeeping for themselves. The present arrangement is
very unsatisfactory for the young people.

With three women in one not too large house there is
bound to be a certain amount of dissension and bickering.
The baby's crying annoys Mrs. Hawkins and Pearl thinks
Neva doesn't do enough work around the house.

Pearl complains to me that Byron's and Neva's room looks
like a rat's nest a good deal of the time and Pearl grows very
indignant because "Byron was always used to having things
neat and tidy."

OCTOBER 12, 1933. I got a letter from Mother today which contained a clipping from the *Buffalo Morning Journal*. That clipping has nearly unseated my reason. It is from the issue of October 2 and it reads:

"Funeral services for Mrs. Frances Harbach Kittrege, 138 Vestry Street, will be held from the Church of Sts. Peter and Paul tomorrow at 10 a. m., the Rev. Max Schubert officiating. Mrs. Kittrege was born in Buffalo in 1884 and had lived here all her life. She died at her home yesterday after a long illness. Mrs. Kittrege is survived by her husband, Kenneth J. Kittrege, who is in the insurance business; a son, Homer; a daughter, Jeannette; her mother, Mrs. Florence Harbach, and a sister, Mrs. Paul Clark, all of Buffalo."

Since February 14, 1926, I have been mourning Frances as dead. Yet she died only Sunday. It all seems unreal—much more unreal than the long series of dreams which I had come to regard as telepathic visions of Frances.

I cannot believe it yet. Frances was never Paul Clark's wife. Instead, the obituary reads that she is survived by a sister, Mrs. Paul Clark. That can mean only that Fran's younger sister, Ruth, married Clark.

Instead of marrying Clark as I dreamed it, Frances was the wife of a man I never heard of before—Kenneth J. Kittrege. Kittrege undoubtedly worked in the insurance office with her. She never moved to Raleigh, Utah. She never, apparently, had the child Carol who was killed by the dog. And Fran's death from pneumonia as I saw it was like the rest—a fraud perpetrated by my own subconscious mind.

I can't describe how disconcerting this all is to me. It is as if I were told there never was a Frances Harbach in the first place. It is as if I were told I created her and our early association and love from my imagination too. I couldn't believe that. And I can't believe this. Yet I must believe it.

I remember reading a long time ago about a Chinese philosopher who said he once dreamed he was a butterfly

and now he wondered if he then was a man dreaming he
was a butterfly or whether he now is a butterfly dreaming he
is a man.

His confusion, I imagine, was more or less academic. My
confusion is torturingly real. But when I look back I can
see the shock now is less poignant than if I had gone to
Raleigh, Utah, as I planned so many times. Suppose I had
been able to go. I now can see what an emotional state I
should have been in by the time I approached the cottage
of the Raleigh Paul Clark. And I should have been met by
Paul Clark's slattern wife, a woman I never had seen before,
a woman who never had heard of me, when I expected to see
Fran's sweet face.

After all, how much of life is a dream? What is real and
what is dream? If some dreams are more real than wood and
stone and flesh, who can say they are nothing?

I suffered so much over the dream death of Fran nearly
eight years ago there is no room for suffering now. To me
that was her real death out in Utah. This is merely an echo
of the tragedy. And my sorrow today is only the echo of my
major sorrow.

Even in this sorrow there is an odd and perhaps a perverted
sense of satisfaction in knowledge that Fran named her son
Homer. In that I see proof she loved me. I wish I could see
young Homer. I wonder if he is a child or perhaps nearly
grown. I think young Homer is my spiritual child—mine and
Fran's.

MARCH 11, 1934. Byron has been working for some time as
a home relief investigator. The money he makes is a welcome
addition to the family budget and he is paying off the doctor
for little June, who will be two years old this June 17.

He finds the work very interesting and is learning a lot
about life—especially the seamy side. He has uncovered a
number of "chiselers" and grows fighting mad about them.

If he had his way—being a hotheaded boy—he would execute all persons found guilty of chiseling. I have tried to preach tolerance to him. For, after all, conditions have been so bad that people lose all sense of perspective. They really are not accountable for their actions.

The paper has been having a hard time, also. Advertising has fallen off to an alarming degree. We have had no more pay cuts, for which I can be thankful, but they have reduced the staff almost a fourth in the last two years.

Now we don't even have a make-up editor. I have to give dummy sheets to the printers and then dash back and forth between my desk and the composing room all night. I imagine I make 25 trips back and forth some nights. And after about the twentieth trip up and down the stairs I realize my legs aren't as young as they once were.

On Syra's advice I have been reading "Anthony Adverse" by Hervey Allen. It is a monumental work and an epic of romance.

Syra has been urging me to start writing my novel. "If you don't start it soon you never will," she says.

She points out that I have reached the age of calm judgment. She declares the fact that my dreams of Frances were not telepathy but the work of my own imagination is added proof of my creative ability and that realization of these dreams being only dreams has conquered a streak of sentimentality in me which might have injured my novel.

There is much truth in what she says. I now am able to weigh things carefully rather than be influenced by emotion. I wish I could start writing. But how? If it weren't for Syra I believe I should have given up all hope of ever laying pen to paper. She keeps urging me on, but at present there seems no way. I am working practically seven days a week and under this present system I am absolutely exhausted when I have finished work. More often than not I go to sleep on the owl car going home. I'm afraid I should have written some popular type book and made some money when I was younger. I wasn't so tired after work 10 or 12 years ago. Of course, when I was telegraph editor and head of the copy desk I thought I was too busy. I thought it was sufficient to be observing, to read, and to make notes of my experiences and thoughts.

Then I thought I should be ready to retire in my early fifties. I thought I should have been managing editor or publisher of some paper by the time I was 45. But this I did not take into consideration: one cannot become a managing editor, even when one is in line, until there is a vacancy.

Here there is Fred Gotchell, not much older than I. His arteries perhaps are younger than mine, because he has not been forced to work as hard. He is healthy and competent. If I must wait for him to die or be fired or take another job, I probably will be too old to hold down a managing editor's desk. And even as managing editor I should find it difficult to write. I had planned on retiring after I had been managing editor five or six years and my savings could support me.

My savings! Right now I am trying desperately to pay off a Morris Plan loan.

APRIL 5, 1936. The *Denver Call* has been sold to a Chicago millionaire by the name of Mathewson, who is acquiring a string of newspapers. He is taking Fred Gotchell to Chicago to work in an undetermined capacity. And from Chicago has come our new managing editor, Walter Rassman. Rassman has the reputation of being a bang-up newspaperman and a go-getter. He is only 34 years old, short, dapper and crammed with nervous energy.

The ten days he has been here have been the most hectic in my career—excepting, of course, those times of extreme emergency such as major disasters, national elections, and part of the World War period.

He seems to like me and to be pleased with my work, which naturally pleases me. But he has changed the old order, the old routine entirely.

I was very much worried when it was announced Mathewson had bought the paper and that Rassman was coming to take charge of the editorial department. I heard how young he is and I know how intolerant youth can be of middle age. When I confided my fears to Syra she laughed at me. "Homer, you old foolish," she said, "you talk of being old. Why, you've only reached the years of judgment. If this Rassman is a good executive he'll know that it would be the death of the *Call* to let you go. You've *been* that paper for years."

Then she looked at me long and smiled. "Would you," she asked, "pardon me if I gave you a lesson in psychology?"

I told her any lesson from her would be a pleasure.

"All right," she said. "Not being a woman, you probably don't appreciate just how valuable first impressions are. And, while you really are just the opposite, this young man might get a first impression that you are stodgy and old and not on your toes. It might take him a long time to get over that first impression and he might be unalterably prejudiced against you before you had a chance to prove yourself."

"That's exactly what I'm afraid of," I admitted.

"Let's not allow him to get that first impression, then," said Syra.

"How do you mean?"

Syra put a cigarette in a long ivory holder and I lit it for her. She was wearing a silk tunic affair with Chinese figuring which zips up the front. Then there were green satin trousers and a green tasseled silk cord tied around her slim waist and green slippers. The whole effect was wonderful.

"You don't think clothes are very important, do you?" Syra asked.

"For a woman, yes," I said. "But not for a workingman."

"And that's just where you make a mistake, Homer. You buy those shapeless old dark gray suits that never look well, even when they're new."

"I can't afford fine clothes."

"Good clothes," she said, "are an economy in the long run. They last longer and they give you a personality. Now what I want you to do is to go buy a new suit with a cut and flash —something light-colored and even loud. And I want you to buy some shirts with collars attached—some colored shirts. Don't you know people don't wear linen collars any more— except perhaps bankers? And get a new bright necktie and throw away that old mother-of-pearl tie pin. Tie pins have been passé for ten years. And ditch that old black hat of yours —wherever *did* you find that thing, anyway?"

"I guess," I said, "that I've seemed pretty much of a mess to you."

"You have not."

"But everything about me is wrong, you say."

"Oh, Homer. *I* know you. I know what a darling you are, what a remarkable man you are. I know what you can do. But when you get yourself up the way you do it would take a stranger a long time even to notice you."

"Well," I said, "all this college kid stuff that you recommend isn't going to make me look like a young fellow. Look at my hair."

"Yes, I know," she said. "You're fifty-three, aren't you? Well, I'm fifty, but do I look it?"

"You look," I said, seriously, "about thirty."

She smiled. "And I owe that largely to a perfectly marvelous hair dresser named Jules. I'm going to have you go to Jules and when you leave his shop and when you get these new clothes I'll promise you won't look any older than this new managing editor. Some of the old-timers around the office may rib you a little over your rejuvenation. But Rassman won't have known the old Homer."

I objected I didn't have the money to spend and she finally insisted on lending me $75—as an investment.

So I went up on Sixteenth Street and bought a light-gray suit with just a touch of brown here and there. The coat is cut in sharply at the waist with pleats at the shoulders. I bought a "deep tone" dark-blue shirt and a dark-maroon shirt and a maroon tie and a gray Homburg hat. Then I went to Jules.

Jules was a nervous, Frenchy little fellow who complimented me on the thickness of my gray shock of hair and went to work, first with scissors and then with a bottle and comb. When he had finished my hair no longer was gray. It was a very dark brown, but I had the feeling it looked lusterless and artificial. Jules, however, assured me that was only because I was accustomed to seeing it gray and it would appear most natural and beautiful to anyone else.

Pearl and Mrs. Hawkins were hilarious over my hair and new clothes, Pearl more than half seriously accusing me of having a sweetheart and wanting to know how I could afford to spend all that money. I told her I bought them on time, which will explain anything to Pearl, and Byron convinced her I was right in shedding my sober feathers.

I went to town early in my snappy array and got a shave and facial massage at the barber shop. The pummeling made my face look quite pink and healthy-looking, although it did seem that it loosened the flesh a little on my jaw next to the chin.

It was a scarcely recognizable Homer Zigler who stepped jauntily, if somewhat self-consciously, into the office shortly after noon. The first person I saw was Fred Gotchell standing in the middle of the floor with a neat, broad-shouldered young man. Gotchell looked startled as he caught sight of me. He pushed a thumb and forefinger up under his glasses and rubbed his eyes. But he didn't smile.

"Oh, Zig," he called.

I stepped up with a spring in my legs, carrying my topcoat and gloves in my left hand.

"Mr. Zigler," Gotchell said, "meet Mr. Rassman, the *Call's* new managing editor. Mr. Zigler is our news editor."

Mr. Rassman was wearing a maroon shirt much like mine. I shook hands with him vigorously. "I hope, Mr. Rassman," I said, "that you'll like us here. I know you'll like Denver."

"I know we'll get along fine," he said.

Then I excused myself and went over to my desk, hung up my coat and new hat and went to work. All afternoon and night I was conscious of whispers around at my transformation, but no one presumed to offer comment except Red McCoy, the fresh office boy. When Red came to my desk with some proofs about 8 o'clock he said, "Say, Zig, how about a game of marbles, huh?"

The first thing Rassman did was to shift desks around, altering the position of the city desk in relation to the news desk and having all the reporters' desks moved together into one battery near the phone booths. He had my desk moved away from the wall nearer to the copy desk and got himself a desk next to mine where he could sit and supervise the conferences over Page One.

Then he began to spend money, enlarging the paper one-fourth, filling it up with women's features, stories about Wallis Simpson, former Baltimore woman who is a friend of King Edward VIII, stories about Katharine Hepburn and Joan Crawford and Sally Rand and about the 1936 styles in bathing suits and playing up divorce suits and running 3- and 4-column "leg art" and most of the week printing almost nothing else but the execution of Bruno Hauptmann, murderer of the Lindbergh baby. And he told me to leave out of the paper entirely the agreement of Germany not to increase her military force on the Rhineland provided France agreed not to increase her military strength on the French side. Also left out of the paper was the fact that Mexican women voted for the first time.

I can't say I approve of Rassman's type of paper. But he is managing editor and I daresay our circulation will go up. The *Post* has a big circulation, so I suppose sensationalism is what the public wants. It does seem, however, that a newspaper has a certain responsibility which we may be overlooking now.

One good thing, however, is the fact that Rassman will have the *Call* making money before long and then he should restore our two 10 per cent cuts. I need more money badly.

JULY 26, 1936. Alfred M. Landon accepted the nomination of the Republican Party to run against President Roosevelt. I really feel sorry for Landon. He seems like a nice fellow and probably will be very serious in his campaigning.

I used a little journalistic influence a couple of months ago and got Byron a good WPA job in the office at Fort Collins. He and Neva and little June moved up there about six weeks ago.

It was just as well for them to have a home by themselves. Pearl and Neva have been at sword's points for six months. When they were leaving Neva, who gives the impression of being very timid and soft-spoken, issued a most bitter valedictory.

She stood on the porch holding June's hand and said, "This is one day I'll remember until I die—the happiest day of my life. And if I ever come through your door again I hope somebody has my head examined."

"That suits me fine," said Pearl.

"Oh, now," I said, "I know things have been tough, but I don't want you to feel that way, Neva."

"Oh, you *don't*," she drawled. "You don't want me to *feel* that way."

Byron had just been loading some suitcases and boxes into

the rumble seat of the old Chev. He came up the steps and said, "Well, come on, Neva, let's go."

I said, "Byron, you don't feel so bitter toward us, do you? You know—"

He interrupted, looking me in the eye. "You don't realize," he said, "just how bad it's been here for Neva—for us."

"It's been bad for all of us. But I don't know what *I* could have done."

"Oh," put in Neva, sarcastically, "you don't know what you could have done. That's *you* all over. You don't know. You don't *know*. You should be proud of yourself as a parent."

"I don't know just what you're talking about, Neva," I said.

"Oh, come on," blurted Byron. "Haven't you had enough bickering while you were living here?" He took Neva by the arm and they walked out toward the car. Pearl was crying.

"Well, good-bye and good luck," I called.

"Good-*bye!*" cried Neva.

Byron didn't say anything. He opened the car door and helped Neva in. He didn't look back as he walked around the car and got in the other side. He raked gears as he drove off.

He hasn't written or anything since he left. I'll wait a month or so and then go up to Fort Collins on the bus. I'll be able to straighten things out then.

DECEMBER 5, 1937. A week ago today Mr. Rassman came from his office with a smiling and dapper young man in tow. He introduced him to me as LeRoy Wheeler from Chicago, an old friend.

"In Denver on a visit?" I asked.

"Well—no," said Wheeler.

"That's fine," I said. "I hope you're going to be with us."

Rassman smiled oddly. "Homer," he said, "can you come into my office for a minute?"

I looked at the clock. "Certainly," I said. "There's time before the South Mail."

We went into the managing editor's office. "Sit down," said Rassman, motioning to a chair on the far side of the desk. I sat down, vaguely apprehensive. "Have a cigarette," he said, passing over a bronze box from his desk. He was looking at me intently as I scratched a match and lit the cigarette.

Rassman pursed his lips, "Homer," he said, "I hate like hell to have to do this, but Wheeler is going to be news editor."

For a moment I could not trust my voice. I drew deep on the cigarette.

"You mean," I said, "that I'm fired?"

He shook his head. "You're too good a newspaperman to fire. I've looked up your record and find you've been on the *Call* since nineteen-sixteen. Is that right?"

I nodded. "Why relieve me as news editor, then?" I asked. "I've been news editor for fourteen years and always felt I was giving satisfaction."

"Homer," he said, "you were fine as news editor under the old management. But we're putting out a different type paper now. Frankly, I need a news editor who's a younger man and—"

"Have you got the idea that I'm an old man?" I blurted.

He laughed—a forced laugh. "Not at all, Homer," he said. "Of course you're not old. But you're no longer young. And I need someone who has the fresh viewpoint of youth on the news desk. It's my job to inject new vitality into the *Call.*"

"You need somebody with mature judgment on the news desk," I said.

He ignored me. "What I need is someone who has worked with me and knows my own particular brand of newspapering. I have thought this all out and lay awake many an hour

worrying over it, Homer. It hasn't been easy at all for me,
I want you to know. But I finally decided on bringing
Wheeler here as the best thing for the paper. After all, your
health is none too good and that news job is a nervous strain
on anyone."

I believe I had gone at least ten years without missing a
single day because of illness. But in the last year I *had* been
out four or five days because of stomach trouble, and two
of those days, unfortunately, had come this month.

"Now, Homer," he went on, "I don't want you to worry
about a job. I appreciate your long and faithful service to
this paper and you'll always have a job as long as I am here."

"What job are you putting me on?"

"The copy desk."

"What are you doing with Thorpe?" I asked. "He's been
here longer than I and he's a war veteran."

"Oh, Thorpe will stay in the slot, Homer."

"Then you're putting me on the rim?"

"That's all there is now, Homer. I'm sorry. Perhaps later—"

"At what pay?" I asked.

He hesitated. "I'm afraid," he said, "that forty a week is
the best we can do right now."

"I can do better than that elsewhere," I told him.

"I don't doubt it, Homer. And I wouldn't blame you if
you quit and took another place. But that's the best I can
do at present. You'll never know how sorry I am. My advice
is to stay here now, Homer, and try to get your health back.
Really, you don't look well. I'd go to a good doctor and have
a thorough examination."

"I'll think it over," I said. "I'll let you know next week."

So I went back to my desk and got out the South Mail.
Then I showed Wheeler the file of our features and mats
which I look after and my futures book with the addresses
of the various syndicates we subscribe to and gave him a list

of edition times. He is an avid youngster and treated me with deference.

For two days I did a lot of thinking. I was staying on the news desk for the rest of the week, breaking Wheeler into the routine. I let him do the work while I thought things over.

Byron and Neva and June had been down over Sunday and Neva is to have another baby next month. Byron is expecting some financial assistance from me, but if I can't help him I can't. Pearl, Mrs. Hawkins and I can get along very well on $40 a week. Of course we shall have to move to a cheaper house, but that won't kill us. Most families don't have that much to live on.

The boys have been organizing a Newspaper Guild and have obtained a 40-hour week in many places. They are about ready to open negotiations with Rassman. And, as Mathewson has granted a contract in other cities, there is every reason to believe they will be successful on the *Call.* As a copyreader instead of an executive I should be subject to the 5-day week. That would give me two days a week in which to write on my novel—the opportunity I have been seeking all my life.

I talked over the situation with Syra and she is enthusiastic. She sees my demotion, not as the major calamity it is in Pearl's eyes, but as the best thing that could have happened. She has faith that I shall write something which, if not the Great American Novel, at least will be the nearest approach to it so far.

So I went to good old Dr. Valentine, to whom I have paid hundreds of dollars in the past, but still owe plenty and he gave me a thorough going-over wherein I had to stand in a dark room drinking a substance called barium which tasted like buttermilk charged with chalk dust while X-ray machines buzzed and photographed my insides from every angle.

As usual, Dr. Valentine was reticent about giving me specific information, but his verdict was that I must have an operation at once. He says there is something in my stomach—probably a gastric ulcer—which must come out, and I'm willing to take his word for it. I have faith in him. And I'm going to St. Luke's Hospital tomorrow for the operation.

Dr. Valentine says I can count on about ten days in the hospital, which will get me home in plenty of time for Christmas. Remembering the rush I had raising money to get Pearl "out of hock" when she had her appendix removed, I have borrowed $100 on my life insurance to pay the hospital bill. Doc Valentine can wait. He's used to it.

Mr. Rassman has assured me my pay as a copyreader will go on while I am in the hospital, so I have no worry in that regard. And following the operation I shall have more time to think than I ever have had. Then I shall get my novel mapped out completely in my mind. When I am convalescing at home I shall actually start writing.

The book will start with a young man named Jeremiah Williams who has learned the wagon-building trade in Ohio soon after the Civil War. He has lived a very circumspect life, but when his sweetheart, Genevieve Eberhardt, marries another man, Jeremiah is embittered. He answers the call of vaster horizons to the West.

In the Colorado mountains he prospects a while. He trades an old rifle to an Arapahoe Indian for the Indian's 15-year-old daughter, Sally Beaver. Jeremiah lives with Sally off and on for a year or so, when he isn't too busy prospecting or playing around with the girls on the Cripple Creek "line," but one night he has bad luck at poker and he puts up Sally Beaver, who is a pretty cute little squaw, for $10 and he loses her.

The next morning Jeremiah and Hoke Watrous, who now owns Sally, start out on snowshoes for Jeremiah's cabin. They find Sally dying alone in childbirth, Jeremiah having entirely forgotten the detail that Sally was going to have a baby.

The baby is born alive, however, and is a husky little half-breed whom Jeremiah wraps in a blanket and carries down to Cripple Creek to turn over to an old woman for rearing.

Soon after this Jeremiah makes a small stake and, being tired of mining, opens a general store. He prospers as a merchant. But he makes more "grubstaking" other prospectors, several of whom strike it rich. Jeremiah, of course, gets half of their strikes.

About this time a fancy dancing girl comes to town. Her name is Fawn de Lainer. Fawn isn't exactly a prostitute. She's what they call a gold digger now and she's so coy and blond and pretty that about every man in the district is wild about her.

Jeremiah showers her with gifts, but makes little headway in his conquest until in desperation he asks her to marry him. Then Fawn, who knows well that Jeremiah is a millionaire, says she'll become his wife if he'll move to Denver and build her a mansion. He agrees.

But Fawn is horrified when Jeremiah suggests they take Sally Beaver's baby with them. She is so horrified that Jeremiah is glad to drop the subject. He does, however, have a sense of responsibility for the child and, inasmuch as he and Sally never were married, he takes out adoption papers, naming the little half-breed Jeremiah Jr., and making provisions for old Widow Miller to take care of him until the boy is big enough to send to boarding school.

In Denver Jeremiah branches out. He buys thousands of acres of arid land, puts through an irrigation project and makes the desert literally to bloom. He splits up his land into small irrigated farms and rents them to farmers on a share basis. He builds sugar factories. He buys coal mines and develops them. He is more than a money baron. He is a money monarch.

Meanwhile Jeremiah Jr. is growing up at boarding school. He is a handsome, dark youth with his mother's flashing aboriginal eyes. He goes to Harvard and becomes a football star. And he is about 19 or 20 before Fawn, his stepmother, ever sees him. That is, after she has seen the boy's picture in the newspapers and is so impressed she says to Jeremiah Sr., "Dahling, why don't you ahsk young Jerry to come home for the holidays?"

And Williams, surprised and delighted at his wife's change of heart, wires Jeremiah Jr. to come home for his first visit.

Despite the Williams millions, Fawn finds her former dance hall career a distinct handicap. She experiences difficulty in being taken up by society and life is a bit boresome. In her late thirties, Fawn retains much of her youthful beauty, but she has had little opportunity to make use of it. Now, when young Jeremiah comes home she sets out deliberately to make love to him and the father finds them in a compromising position.

In a murderous rage Jeremiah Sr. seizes a gun and attempts to kill both his wife and son, but athletic young Jeremiah grapples with his father and attempts to disarm him. The gun is discharged during the struggle and old Jeremiah is killed.

For a few moments the situation appears most serious for young Jeremiah. But so great is the political influence of the Williams fortune that the police and newspapers accept without question the statement that Jeremiah Sr. was preparing for a hunting trip to Mexico and that a rifle was discharged accidentally while he was cleaning it.

The will leaves most of the great fortune to Jeremiah Jr., half-breed son born without benefit of clergy.

Jeremiah Jr. carries on where his father left off. He buys iron mines and copper mines and he builds steel mills and manufacturing plants and he acquires two railroads. He also buys himself a seat in the United States Senate as sort of a hobby while he lives in Oriental splendor with one legal wife and a score of beautiful concubines scattered around in convenient apartments.

His son, Jeremiah III, is a spoiled child. From babyhood he has lived the life of a royal prince. His playmates are carefully selected children of the Williams serfs and are required to jump when Jeremiah III speaks. Thus he becomes almost a complete rotter at a very early age.

I shall describe in detail his first sexual experience—with the young daughter of a Williams lieutenant—how she gives in to his importunities because of young Jeremiah's declaration that if she continues to refuse he will have her father discharged and black-listed so her father and mother and younger brother will starve.

Thus Jeremiah III grows into a modern Casanova capable of using dire threats as well as blandishments to gain his end.

When he is 21 a marriage of convenience is arranged for him with Betty Van Cleve of Newport, to join two of the largest fortunes in America. Betty is a small, birdlike girl who has a muddy complexion and who wears octagonal glasses. Jeremiah III doesn't love Betty, but he doesn't worry about that for she offers small handicap to his amorous adventures.

By the time Jeremiah II takes his son into the business they have acquired a huge automobile plant and an airplane factory and the younger Williams becomes ambitious to make the dynasty world-wide. He becomes so interested in his work that he forgets about women for a few months.

One day, however, Jeremiah III notices a beautiful young stenographer working in the general offices. She has gorgeous yellow hair, black eyebrows and long black eyelashes shielding her turquoise eyes. She has a trim, athletic figure. She has everything.

Now of late years Jeremiah III has made it a point not to make passes at women employees. There is no morality in that. It is only that women employees have proved too easy to be much fun. And Jeremiah III has grown to love the chase.

But this girl, whose name is Marcia Morrison, is so extraordinarily attractive that Jeremiah III decides to have business with her, chase or no chase. He makes a pass at her. And to his utter amazement he is scornfully repulsed.

This makes Jeremiah III interested indeed. He has the girl promoted and then offers to make her his private secretary at $125 a week. She refuses the position—for obvious reasons.

Finally young Williams can think of nothing else but Marcia. He sends her flowers. Then he sends her precious jewels which she returns, saying she cannot accept valuable gifts from a married man.

Jeremiah has never seen anything like this. He sits for hours at his desk brooding. Then he disappears.

In six weeks he is back at the office, patently very happy. He calls Marcia into his private office. "Marcia," he says, "I am happier than ever before in my life. I am a free man."

"What do you mean, free?" she asks.

"I mean I've been to Reno. I have divorced my wife whom I never have loved."

"Oh," says Marcia.

"Now," says Jeremiah III, "I am prepared to make you queen of my domain. You are the only girl I ever loved. You are the only girl I ever could love. Marcia, will you marry me?"

"I'm sorry," said Marcia, shaking her head, "but I can't marry you."

Now Jeremiah III really is astounded. It never has occurred to him that *any* woman would need coaxing to become his wife, let alone a stenographer for the great Williams corporation.

He collects his thoughts for a moment and then says, "If you're refusing because you think I'm a rake, that's all over.

I haven't even looked at another woman since I first saw you."

Marcia smiles slightly. She admits she never could marry a man whose habits were as notorious as Jeremiah's, but she admits also she believes a man might reform from his youthful wildness.

Then in a very dramatic scene Marcia tells Jeremiah III the real reason why she will not marry him. She admits she likes him personally more than a little. But she tells him his whole system is reprehensible and her conscience never would allow her to become a part of a money kingdom which oppressed millions of poor people.

Soon after this Jeremiah II dies of arteriosclerosis, leaving Jeremiah III king absolute of the money empire and Marcia resigns her job in disgust when Jeremiah III displays glee at crushing a smaller competitor. She tells him she can see him no more.

That brings Jeremiah to his senses. He asks Marcia what she wants him to do and she tells him. He asks her if she will marry him if he carries out her wishes and she says she believes she would.

Then he looks at her a long moment and says softly, "Marcia, sweetheart, you have opened my eyes. You have shown me the light in the clearing. I will do as you ask."

Next comes the thrilling part where Jeremiah III turns over all his manufacturing plants to the employees to run as co-operatives. All of the chain farms are deeded to the tenants and the Williams money empire is dissolved.

Jeremiah III, standing with his arm around Marcia, makes a speech to the assembled employees of the general offices, telling them he still has a million or so left in cash and that he is going to buy an island in the South Pacific and form a real socialistic colony where every man and woman will be equal and all will share alike in the work and in the pleasure.

He invites all to come along at his expense and 50 or so volunteer.

The last chapter will show them all living happily on Paradise Island where Jeremiah III and Marcia have a son they have named Jeremiah IV. The title of the book will be "Brutal Dynasty."

Pearl has never been very sympathetic about my writing, feeling it took my mind off my job, so I have not outlined "Brutal Dynasty" to her. Syra, on the other hand, is enthusiastic. She feels "Brutal Dynasty" actually may become the Great American Novel she and her fellow critics have been looking for so long. She feels also that the book may well move some money barons to abdicate even as did Jeremiah III.

I owe a great deal to Syra. Had it not been for her encouragement I might easily have lost sight of my old ambition to write.

When I get back to work after my operation I shall have the 6 p. m. to 2:30 a. m. shift on the copy desk. That should give me several hours a day in which to write. And a couple of days a week I can call on Syra, read her what I have written and get her reactions on the development.

This afternoon I shall take over to Syra this old ledger in which I have been writing for more than thirty years. Pearl might go through my personal things while I am in the hospital and I know there are things written here which would make her unhappy. Syra will keep the book safe for me.

It isn't that I am afraid of dying, but I must admit, of course, there always is danger in a serious operation of this sort. I really am not worrying over my operation at all. I know I shan't die because I am only beginning to live. I am now only starting my life's work.